W9-CSE-978

This is an authorized facsimile
printed by microfilm/xerography on acid-free paper
in 1984 by
UNIVERSITY MICROFILMS INTERNATIONAL
Ann Arbor, Michigan, U.S.A.

Macomber, James D., 1939-
    The dynamics of spectroscopic
transitions : illustrated by magnetic
resonance and laser effects / James D.
Macomber. -- New York : Wiley, c1976.
    xxiv, 332 p. : ill. -- (Wiley-
Interscience monographs in chemical
physics)
    "Wiley-Interscience publication."
    Includes bibliographical references
and index.
    Photocopy. Ann Arbor, Mich. :
University Microfilms International,
1980.
    1. Nuclear spectroscopy. 2. Magnetic
resonance. 3   . Quantum optics.
I. Title

The Dynamics of
Spectroscopic Transitions

WILEY-INTERSCIENCE MONOGRAPHS IN CHEMICAL PHYSICS

Editors

John B. Birks, *Reader in Physics, University of Manchester*

Sean P. McGlynn, *Professor of Chemistry, Louisiana State University*

Photophysics of Aromatic Molecules:
*J. B. Birks, Department of Physics,
University of Manchester*

**Atomic and Molecular Radiation
Physics:** *L. G. Christophorou,
Oak Ridge National Laboratory,
Tennessee*

**The Jahn–Teller Effect in
Molecules and Crystals:**
*R. Englman, Soreq Nuclear
Research Centre, Yavne*

Organic Molecular Photophysics:
Volumes 1 and 2: *edited by J. B. Birks,
Department of Physics, University
of Manchester*

Internal Rotation in Molecules:
*edited by W. J. Orville-Thomas,
Department of Chemistry and Applied Chemistry,
University of Salford*

**The Dynamics of Spectroscopic Transitions: Illustrated by
Magnetic Resonance and Laser Effects:**
*James D. Macomber, Department of
Chemistry, Louisiana State University*

The Dynamics of
Spectroscopic Transitions

Illustrated by Magnetic Resonance
and Laser Effects

James D. Macomber

Department of Chemistry
Louisiana State University

A Wiley-Interscience Publication

JOHN WILEY & SONS

New York · London · Sydney · Toronto

Library of Congress Cataloging in Publication Data:

Macomber, James D.   1939–
    The dynamics of spectroscopic transitions.

    (Wiley-Interscience monographs in chemical physics)
    "A Wiley-Interscience publication."
    Includes bibliographical references and index.
    1. Nuclear spectroscopy.   2. Magnetic resonance.
3. Quantum optics.   I. Title.

QC454.N8M3   538'.3   75-25852
ISBN 0-471-56300-5

Printed in the United States of America

10 9 8 7 6 5 4 3 2 1

To my family

Cindy
Heidi
Heather
Marcia
and
Benjamin

Preface

"Even for the physicist [a] description in plain language will be a criterion of the degree of understanding that has been reached."

Werner Heisenberg,
Physics and Philosophy
(Harper & Bros., New York, 1958, p. 168).

"How does a photon get into an atom?" This question, or one similar to it is asked by every student of freshman chemistry or physics the first time he is shown a pair of horizontal lines connected by a vertical arrow, and is told that this picture represents a quantum transition. In particular, the student wants to know what mechanism the photon uses to cause the atom to accept the energy, how long the process takes, and what the atom "looks like" while it is going on. When the answer is not immediately forthcoming, the student is likely to assume that these matters will be explained later in a more advanced course.

If so, he is likely to be disappointed. Indeed, the subject may never be brought up at all. But after four years or more of exposure to energy level diagrams and arrows, and the introduction of terms like "interaction," "uncertainty principle," "quantum jumps," and "selection rules," the student comes to accept his ignorance. If he later becomes a teacher, his students will not hear a discussion of these matters from his lips, and the cycle will repeat.

Of course, there was a time when some of the leading scientific minds of the western world (e.g., Schrödinger and Heisenberg) were also asking how quantum transitions occurred. Not all of the questions proved to be answerable but, for those that were, answers were found. Later, experimental methods were devised to study systems during the absorption and emission processes, first in magnetic resonance and then in other kinds of spectroscopy in which masers and lasers were employed as light sources. Although the results are interesting and exciting, for some reason they are apparently not widely known. Hence, there is evidently a need for some way to bridge the gap between scientists and engineers with a conventional training in quantum mechanics to whom this material may be unfamiliar, and those who use these ideas daily while engaged in the study of coherent transient effects. This book is an attempt to fill this need.

The intended audience is advanced undergraduates, beginning graduate students, and practicing research scientists who use spectroscopy as a tool. Anyone who has had the first physics or chemistry course in quantum mechanics at the college junior or senior level should be able to read the book without difficulty. It is rather short, and heavy emphasis has been placed on very simple physical explanations, using the absolute minimum of mathematics. I hope that this book will improve the teaching of quantum mechanics, by providing a model for the transition process that can be more easily grasped by the student's physical intuition than the one based on energy level diagrams with arrows. Perhaps some readers will even develop research interests in coherent spectroscopy (nuclear magnetic resonance, electron paramagnetic resonance, lasers). If any of these things come to pass, I shall be very pleased.

Thanks are due to Dr. Theodore Hoffman, chemistry editor at Wiley-Interscience, and Boyd Professor Sean McGlynn of the Louisiana State University Chemistry Department for their encouragement from the time when this book was just an idea. In addition, Professor McGlynn, in his capacity as consulting editor, did a marvelous and thorough job of criticizing the manuscript; whatever clarity and quality are present in the writing are due largely to his helpful and detailed suggestions. Several other distinguished scientists also very kindly consented to read the text: I. D. Abella (University of Chicago), D. K. Carpenter (LSU, Baton Rouge), R. H. Dicke (Princeton), R. W. Hellwarth (UCLA), D. E. Kaplan (Lockheed), N. R. Kestner (LSU, Baton Rouge), N. A. Kurnit (MIT), J. P. Wittke (RCA), N. S. Bhacca (LSU, Baton Rouge), and F. T. Arecchi (CISE). Graduate students Bill Thomason and Don Elbers, members of two quantum mechanics classes, Wilhemina Mack, and John Brown helped with proofreading and suggestions as the manuscript neared final form. My daughter Heidi helped with the index.

I am indebted to all those who took the trouble to send me their photographs (see Chapter 1) and illustrations from their publications, and to John Waugh of the Massachusetts Institute of Technology for calling my attention to the work of N. F. Ramsey (Harvard) and Myer Bloom (University of British Columbia). Professor Bloom then helped me understand beam experiments. The graciousness of the many eminent men whose work is described on these pages has been no less inspiring to me than the beauty and elegance of their scientific contributions.

I should like to thank the LSU administration for granting me a sabbatical leave during the spring of 1972 (during which the bulk of the writing was done), and Professor George Pimentel of the University of California at Berkeley, who was my host during this period, for his hospitality.

The superb work of the production and illustration staff at Wiley-Interscience, especially that of Monica Salerno and George Flohn, is gratefully acknowledged.

My deepest gratitude, however, is reserved for my wife. She had the monumental task (with some assistance from Judy Hill and Donna Noble) of typing each draft of this manuscript with its many equations, and she also helped with the proofreading.

JAMES D. MACOMBER

Baton Rouge, Louisiana
July 1975

Contents

Key to Symbols

A	area of "pillbox" portion of sample
A_E	Einstein coefficient for spontaneous emission
A_1	first amplitude parameter in solution of Bloch equation for M_z or Δ
A_1', A_1''	real and imaginary parts of A_1
A_2	second amplitude parameter in solution of Bloch equation for M_z or Δ
$\|A\rangle$	a superposition ket
$[A]$	matrix of A
$[A]_T$	transpose of A matrix
$[A]^\dagger$	Hermitian adjoint of A matrix
$\mathbf{A}$	arbitrary vector in three-dimensional space
$\mathbf{A} \cdot \mathbf{B}$	scalar product of the vectors $\mathbf{A}$ and $\mathbf{B}$
A_x, A_y, A_z	components of the vector $\mathbf{A}$
$\mathbf{a}$	acceleration of a dipole in an inhomogeneous field
a_G	distance between $1/e$ point and center of Gaussian beam
a_j	jth expansion coefficient of the ket $\|a\rangle$
a_j^*	complex conjugate of a_j
$\|a_j\|^2$	complex square of scalar a_j
$a_j(t)$	jth superposition coefficient times jth time-dependent factor in eigenfunctions
$a_j^{(n)}$	$a_j(t)$ for the nth system in the ensemble
a_0	Bohr radius
$\|a\rangle$	ket a, representing a state of the system
$\langle a\|$	bra a, dual to $\|a\rangle$
$\|a\rangle \cdot \|b\rangle$	unsatisfactory scalar product in Hilbert space
$\langle a\|b\rangle$	satisfactory scalar product in Hilbert space
Δa	difference between successive expansion coefficients
α	eigenket of spin-$\frac{1}{2}$ particle with $m = \pm\frac{1}{2}$
(α, β)	scalar product of α and β

α_{jk}	phase of expansion coefficient c_{jk}
α_0	propagator in complex wave phase
α_1, α_2	orientation of the first and second pulses in the rotating frame
B_x, B_y, B_z	components of the vector $\mathbf{B}$
B_1	first amplitude parameter in solution of Bloch equation for v or Ξ
B_1', B_1''	real and imaginary parts of B_1
B_2	second amplitude parameter in solution of Bloch equation for v or Ξ
$|B\rangle$	a superposition ket, orthogonal to $|A\rangle$
$\mathbf{B}$	arbitrary vector in three-dimensional space
	magnetic induction vector
b_j	jth expansion coefficient of the ket $|b\rangle$
b_{jk}	kth coefficient in the expansion of $\mathbf{D}\Phi_j$
$|b\rangle$	ket b, representing a state of the system
$\langle b|$	bra b, dual to $|b\rangle$
β	eigenket of spin-$\frac{1}{2}$ particle with $m = -\frac{1}{2}$
β_0	absorption coefficient
(β, α)	scalar product of β and α
C	in-phase component of polarization wave
c	speed of electromagnetic wave
$c_{A\pm}$	superposition coefficient for expansion of $|A\rangle$ on measurement axis
c_j	jth superposition coefficient of the total wavefunction
c_{jk}	expansion coefficient of the jth perturbed wavefunction in terms of the kth unperturbed wavefunction
$|c_{jk}|$	magnitude of expansion coefficient, c_{jk}
c_{nj}	jth expansion coefficient in the superposition function of the nth system
c_0	speed of electromagnetic wave in vacuum
$c_{\pm j}$	expansion coefficient of $|\pm\rangle$ in basis $\{|j\rangle\}$
χ	magnetic susceptibility
χ', χ''	real and imaginary parts of magnetic susceptibility
$\chi_{xx}, \chi_{xy}, \chi_{yx}, \chi_{yy}$	elements of magnetic susceptibility tensor
χ_2	first nonlinear term in magnetic susceptibility
D	population difference between initial and final states
D_e	population difference between initial and final states at equilibrium
D_{jk}	jkth element of the $\mathbf{D}$ matrix
$D_{jk}^{(n)}$	jkth element of the $\mathbf{D}$ matrix of the nth system in the ensemble

D	electric displacement vector
D$_n$	D operator for the nth system in the ensemble
d	number density of photons
d_M	number density of photons absorbed by matter
d_R	number density of photons in the radiation field
Δ	ratio of actual population difference to that at equilibrium
δ	rate of change of phase with time, z constant
δ'	phase constant for interference beat of superposition wavefunction
δ_{jk}	Kronecker delta
δ_0	normalized off-resonance parameter
$\$$	sine of $U/2$, equal to sine of $\theta/2$
$E1, E2, \ldots$	electric monopole, dipole, etc.
E_1^0	maximum electric field amplitude
E_1	magnitude of electric field vector
$|E|$	real magnitude of complex field E
E_{atom}	magnitude of electric field felt by electron due to nucleus
E	electric field vector
E$_S$	Stark pulse
E$_1$	electric field vector in oscillating wave
e	base of natural logarithms
$\mathscr{E}$	energy
$\{|\mathscr{E}\rangle\}$	set of eigenvalues of the energy
$\mathscr{E}_{\text{atom}}$	total energy of the atom
$|\mathscr{E}_j\rangle$	jth eigenket of the energy
$\mathscr{E}_{\text{photon}}$	energy per photon
$\mathscr{E}_1', \mathscr{E}_2'$	perturbed energy eigenvalues
$\Delta\mathscr{E}$	uncertainty in energy difference between two states
$\Delta\mathscr{E}_{\text{atom}}$	change in energy of the atom produced by transition
ϵ	electric permittivity
ϵ_0	electric permittivity of field-free space
η	electric susceptibility
η', η''	real and imaginary parts of electric susceptibility
η_j	phase constant for jth eigenfunction plus jth superposition coefficient
η_2	first nonlinear term in electric susceptibility
F_x, F_y	complex amplitudes of applied field
$|F_x|, |F_y|$	magnitudes of field amplitudes
F	applied field (electric or magnetic)
F$_0$	force

$f(u)$	normalized line shape function
$f(z)$	an arbitrary state function
G	frequency-dependent gain
G_M	magnitude of magnetic field gradient
g	ratio of relaxation times, T_2/T_1
Γ	phase parameter in solution to Bloch equations
Γ', Γ''	real and imaginary parts of Γ
γ	magnetogyric (or electrogyric) ratio
H_{jk}	matrix element of the Hamiltonian operator
H_1^0	maximum magnetic amplitude of rf field
H_x, H_y, H_z	components of uniform induction field (laboratory coordinates)
H_0	magnitude of uniform induction field
$\overline{H}_0$	average magnitude of uniform induction field
H_1	magnitude of oscillating magnetic field, first three chapters; same for magnetic induction thereafter
$\mathbf{H}$	magnetic field vector, first three chapters; magnetic induction thereafter
$\mathbf{H}_A, \mathbf{H}_B$	inhomogenous magnetic fields in beam selectors
$\mathbf{H}_1$	magnetic field vector in oscillating wave, first three chapters; same for magnetic induction thereafter
H	Hamiltonian operator
H'	Hamiltonian term for a static perturbation
H_R	relaxation term in Hamiltonian operator
H_0	dominant static term in Hamiltonian operator
H_1	time-dependent perturbation term in Hamiltonian operator
h	Planck's constant
$\hbar$	Planck's constant divided by 2π
$\mathrm{Im}\,(a_j)$	imaginary part of a_j
i	square root of -1
ι	damping limit parameter
J	magnitude of irradiance vector
J_{rms}	root-mean-squared magnitude of irradiance vector
$J(x,y)$	beam profile
J_{12}	irradiance from two interfering sources
$\mathbf{J}$	irradiance vector
j	arbitrary integer
$|j\rangle$	jth simultaneous eigenket of S^2 and S_x
k	arbitrary integer
	(in Chapters 3 and 8) the magnitude of $\mathbf{k}$
k_0	Boltzmann's constant

$\hat{k}$	unit vector in propagation direction
$\mathbf{k}$	propagation vector of electromagnetic wave
κ	absorption cross section
L	length of beam chamber
L_0	broad-band loss
L_x, L_y, L_z	components of angular momentum vector
$\mathbf{L}$	orbital angular momentum vector
L	angular momentum vector operator
$\mathsf{L}_x, \mathsf{L}_y, \mathsf{L}_z$	components of angular momentum vector operator
l	length of interaction region
l_C	length of beam path subject to C magnet
l_1	length of transition region
Δl	length of segment in interaction region
$|\Lambda, m\rangle$	simultaneous eigenket of S^2 and S_z
Λ_j	jth eigenvalue of S^2, divided by $\hbar^2$
λ	wavelength
M	number of eigenkets in a complete set (number of eigenstates)
M_0	magnitude of equilibrium magnetization
M_x, M_y, M_z	components of the magnetization of the sample
$M1, M2, \ldots$	magnetic monopole, dipole, etc.
$\mathbf{M}$	magnetization (magnetic polarization) vector.
$\mathbf{M}_0$	spontaneous magnetic polarization
m	general eigenvalue of S_z, divided by $\hbar$
m_j	jth eigenvalue of S_z, divided by $\hbar$
m_0	mass of particle
$|-\rangle$	ket with lower eigenvalue
μ	magnetic permeability
μ_0	magnetic permeability of field-free space
μ_x, μ_y, μ_z	components of linear momentum vector
$\boldsymbol{\mu}$	linear momentum vector
$\boldsymbol{\mu}_j$	linear momentum vector of jth volume element
$\underline{\mu}$	linear momentum vector operator
$\underline{\mu}_x, \underline{\mu}_y, \underline{\mu}_z$	components of linear momentum vector operator
N	number of quantum systems in the ensemble (sample) number of measurements made on a system
N'	number of quantum systems per unit volume
N_s	number of segments in interaction region
n	arbitrary integer
n_R	refractive index
n_0	number of nodes in wavefunction (principal quantum number)

ν	normalized distance into sample
Ω	instantaneous phase of the precession of the magnetic dipole at time t
$\Omega_{jk}^{(n)}$	instantaneous phase of the off-diagonal element of the nth D matrix
$\Delta\Omega$	uncertainty in phase
ω	angular frequency of light wave
ω_0	natural frequency of a quantum system $\equiv$ beat frequency of superposition state
ω_1	precession frequency in field H_1 (twice the nutation frequency)
ω_0^0	center frequency of an inhomogeneously broadened line
ω_0^S	Stark-shifted absorption frequency
ω'	effective frequency of irradiation, due to fringing field
$\Delta\omega$	width of spectral line
$\Delta\omega_j^0$	difference between center frequency of jth isochromat and ω_0^0
o	polarization parameter in susceptibility tensor
o_E	polarization parameter in electric susceptibility tensor
o_M	polarization parameter in magnetic susceptibility tensor
P_0	equilibrium polarization of dipoles in field E_z
$\mathbf{P}$	electric polarization vector
$\mathbf{P}_0$	spontaneous polarization vector
p	magnitude of transition dipole moment (electric or magnetic)
p_E	certain component of electric dipole moment vector
p_M	certain component of magnetic dipole moment vector magnitude of dipole moment vector
$p_{u_1}, p_{u_2}, p_{u_3}$	components of dipole moment vector in particle coordinates
p_x, p_y, p_z	components of magnetic dipole moment vector in laboratory coordinates
$\mathbf{p}_E$	electric dipole moment vector
$\mathbf{p}_M$	magnetic dipole moment vector
P_E	electric dipole moment vector operator
P_M	magnetic dipole moment vector operator
$\P$	saturation/resonance denominator of susceptibility tensor
$\P_E$	saturation/resonance denominator of electric susceptibility tensor
$\P_M$	saturation/resonance denominator of magnetic susceptibility tensor
Φ	time-independent part of wavefunction

Φ'	time-independent part of perturbed wavefunction
ϕ	real phase constant of wave
ϕ'	azimuthal angle in laboratory space
ϕ_y, ϕ_z	phases of y and z components of wave
φ	laboratory angle between directions of propagation of pulses in photon echo experiments
Π	normalized amplitude of in-phase component of polarization wave
π	circumference-to-diameter ratio for circle
Ψ	total (superposition) wavefunction
Ψ_n	total (superposition) wavefunction for nth quantum system
ψ	wavefunction (eigenfunction)
ψ^*	complex conjugate of wavefunction
ψ_1, ψ_2	superposed eigenfunctions
ψ'_1, ψ'_2	perturbed eigenfunctions
$|+\rangle$	ket with higher eigenvalue
Q	partition function
Q	operator that does not commute with R
q	independent variables other than time (e.g., x, y, and z)
q_j	jth eigenvalue of Q
q_0	charge on the proton
R	the physical property represented by R
$\bar{R}$	classical weighted average of R
R_{jk}	matrix element of R
R_1	twice the imaginary part of the off-diagonal elements of the density matrix
R_2	twice the real part of the off-diagonal elements of the density matrix
R_3	difference between the diagonal elements of the density matrix
R_3^e	difference between the diagonal elements of the density matrix at thermal equilibrium
$\langle R \rangle$	expectation value of R
$\langle \bar{R} \rangle$	ensemble average of the expectation value of R
$\langle R \rangle_n$	ensemble average of R for the nth system
R	operator representing some arbitrary physical property of the system
	operator of which a non-stationary state is an eigenstate
$\{R\}_t$	set of operators of which the superposition state is an eigenstate
$\mathrm{Re}(a_j)$	real part of a_j

r	radial distance
	general eigenvalue of R
$r(k)$	result of the kth measurement
$\{\lvert r \rangle\}$	set of eigenkets of R
r_j	jth eigenvalue of R
$\lvert r_j \rangle$	jth eigenket of R
r	three-dimensional position vector
$\mathbf{r}_j$	distance from spin axis to jth volume element
r	three-dimensional position vector operator
$\underline{\rho}$	density operator
ρ_{jk}	element of the density matrix in the laboratory coordinate system
$\rho_{jk}^\dagger$	element of the density matrix in a rotating coordinate system
S	in-quadrature components of polarization wave
S	total spin angular momentum vector
S	operator that commutes with R
	total spin angular momentum vector operator
$[\mathbf{S}, \mathbf{R}]$	commutator of S and R
$\mathbf{S}_x, \mathbf{S}_y, \mathbf{S}_z$	components of the spin angular momentum vector operator in the laboratory coordinate system
$\mathbf{S}_1, \mathbf{S}_2, \mathbf{S}_3$	components of the spin angular momentum vector operator in an arbitrary coordinate system
$\mathbf{S}_\pm$	raising and lowering operators for spin angular momentum
s	spin quantum number (maximum value of m)
$\{\lvert s \rangle\}$	set of eigenkets of S
s_j	jth eigenvalue of S
§	total phase constant for oscillating expectation values
Σ	sum of diagonal elements of density matrix
Σ^e	sum of diagonal elements of density matrix at thermal equilibrium
σ	electrical conductivity
σ_m	magnetic conductivity
T	absolute temperature
$T(t)$	time-dependent part of the wavefunction
$T(0)$	time-dependent part of the wavefunction at $t=0$
T_m	reciprocal half-width of a line that is both homogeneously and inhomogeneously broadened
T_s	spin temperature

T_{jk}	relaxation time of the jkth element of the density matrix
T_1	relaxation time of the diagonal elements of the density matrix for a two-level system
T_2	relaxation time of the off-diagonal elements of the density matrix for a two-level system
T_2'	reciprocal half-width of saturated line
T_2^*	reciprocal half-width of inhomogeneously broadened line
T	torque vector
t	time
t'	interval between pulses in a pulse sequence
t_A	Beer's law absorption time
Δt	duration of radiated wave train
τ	normalized retarded time
Θ	normalized field intensity
Θ_0	normalized field intensity at entrance face
θ	angle between energy axis and axis of certainty
	parameter characterizing amplitudes of superposition coefficients
θ'	polar angle in laboratory space
$d\boldsymbol{\theta}$	vector angular displacement
U	used in Chapter 8 instead of θ to avoid confusion with Θ
u	in-phase mode of bulk-resonance signal
$\hat{u}_1, \hat{u}_2, \hat{u}_3$	unit vectors in particle coordinates
Υ	pulse duration
υ	velocity of propagation of self-induced transparency pulse
V	amplitude of perturbation
	potential difference
$V^\dagger$	maximum amplitude of perturbation
v	in-quadrature mode of bulk resonance signal
	speed of particle in beam
$\hat{v}_1, \hat{v}_2, \hat{v}_3$	unit vectors in measurement coordinate direction
$\Delta v_y, \Delta v_z$	uncertainty in velocity due to beam spreading
v	velocity of particle in beam
W	total probability of absorption
W'	probability of absorption per absorber
$W(q, t)$	distribution function

W_j	statistical weight of jth result
w	work
X	operator representing the coordinate x
x	position coordinate along x axis
	direction of beam of particles
x'	x coordinate in rotating frame
x_j	jth eigenvalue of operator X
$[x_{jk}]$	matrix with elements x_{jk}
Δx	difference between successive eigenvalues of X
$\hat{x}$	unit vector in the x direction of the laboratory coordinate system
Ξ	normalized amplitude of in-quadrature component of polarization wave
ξ_j	phase of the jth superposition coefficient
Y	operator representing the coordinate y
y	position coordinate along y axis
y'	y coordinate in rotating frame
y_0	argument of hyperbolic cosecant function
$\hat{y}$	unit vector in y direction
Z	impedance
Z_0	impedance of a vacuum
Z	operator representing the coordinate z
z	position coordinate along z axis
	direction of propagation of electromagnetic wave
Δz	thickness of "pillbox" section of sample
$\hat{z}$	unit vector in z direction
dz	vector linear displacement
ζ_j	phase constant for time-dependent part of jth wave-function

The Dynamics of
Spectroscopic Transitions

1 Introduction

1.1. Electric fields in atoms and waves

This book is about the interaction of light with matter. Nearly all of the phenomena that are produced by means of this interaction can be called *spectroscopic*, in the broadest sense of the term. Included are the ordinary processes of absorption and emission of radio waves, microwaves, and infrared, visible, and ultraviolet light which leave the associated atoms, ions, or molecules chemically intact. Such phenomena are used by synthetic and analytic chemists in the identification and characterization of substances, and by physical chemists in elucidating molecular structure, determining bond strengths, and studying relaxation processes. When light in the optical region of the spectrum is employed, such effects provide the microscopic basis for theories of color and vision. The explanation of absorption and emission is the purpose of subsequent chapters.

However, there are also several types of interactions between light and matter that are more dramatic or exotic than ordinary absorption or emission and are therefore beyond the scope of this work. In the first part of the present chapter, the boundaries between what is and what is not to be considered will be established. A brief historical summary of the scientific developments upon which the present state of knowledge about absorption and emission is based will be presented in the second part of the chapter.

First, what is meant by *light* and *matter*? Every student of elementary physics learns that a light beam is composed of electric and magnetic fields, E_1 and H_1, situated at right angles to one another, and oscillating sinusoidally in space and time. These oscillating fields may be decomposed mathematically into electromagnetic waves propagating in a direction k perpendicular to the $E_1 H_1$ plane. At a given time for any given wave, the distance between successive peaks in the amplitude of either field (measured in the k direction) is called the *wavelength*, λ. Figure 1.1 is a schematic representation of an electromagnetic wave. The number of peaks that pass by a given point in space during a unit time interval is called the *frequency* of the wave, $\omega/2\pi$. (The symbol ω represents the

1

angular frequency in radians per second.) The distance traveled by a given peak in unit time (also measured in the k direction) is called the *speed* of the wave, c. As in all wave phenomena, the wavelength, frequency, and speed are related by the formula

$$\lambda\left(\frac{\omega}{2\pi}\right) = c. \tag{1.1}$$

Electromagnetic waves differ from one another in both frequency and wavelength. When traveling in a vacuum, they all have the same speed, c_0:

$$c_0 = 2.99 \times 10^8 \text{ m s}^{-1} \text{ (meters per second).} \tag{1.2}$$

The scalar magnitudes, H_1 and E_1, of the *magnetic* and *electric fields* of the waves are also related:

$$E_1 = ZH_1. \tag{1.3}$$

Again, in a vacuum, the value of Z is the same for all waves, namely, Z_0:

$$Z_0 = 377 \text{ ohms.} \tag{1.4}$$

The constant Z_0 is called the *impedance* of free space. Although it is somewhat less familiar than c_0, its significance as a fundamental constant is comparable.

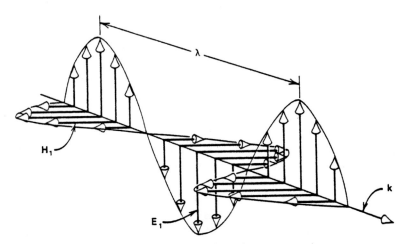

Figure 1.1 Schematic representation of an electromagnetic wave.

Because of the interrelationships described in Eqs. 1.1 and 1.3, two vector quantities suffice to describe most of the interesting properties of each light wave. First, the *propagation vector*, **k**, gives the wavelength and direction of travel:

$$\mathbf{k} = \frac{2\pi\hat{k}}{\lambda} \tag{1.5}$$

($\hat{k}$ is a unit vector in the direction of **k**). Second, the electric field vector gives the amplitude and direction of polarization of the wave. The wave amplitude is important because it is directly related to the *irradiance*, **J**, associated with the wave:

$$\mathbf{J} = \frac{E_1^2\hat{k}}{Z} . \tag{1.6}$$

The dimensions of **J** are energy per unit time per unit area (in a plane perpendicular to $\hat{k}$). The quantity tabulated for most light sources is the root-mean-squared irradiance, J_{rms}:

$$J_{rms} \equiv \left[\frac{\omega}{2\pi} \int_0^{2\pi/\omega} J^2(t)\,dt \right]^{1/2}$$

$$= \frac{\left(E_1^0\right)^2}{2Z} . \tag{1.7}$$

The peak value of E_1 is E_1^0.

Matter, on the other hand, consists of particles. Physicists have discovered a large menagerie of these, including such exotic beasts as neutrinos, mesons, and hyperons. Ordinary matter, however, consists of electrons, protons, and neutrons, and it will be sufficient to describe the interactions of electromagnetic radiation with these particles. In particular, it will be assumed that the protons and neutrons have been organized into one or more nuclei. The nuclei, in turn, have been surrounded by electrons to form atoms, molecules, or ions upon which the light waves impinge.

Since electrons and nuclei are charged, magnetic particles, it is not surprising that they interact with light. Indeed, the electrons and nuclei in atoms, molecules, and ions are held together by electric (and, to a lesser extent, by magnetic) fields. The static electric field intensity E_{atom} felt by an electron of charge $-q_0$ located a distance a_0 away from a nucleus of charge $+q_0$ is given by

$$E_{atom} = \frac{c_0 Z_0 q_0}{4\pi a_0^2}$$

$$\sim 5 \times 10^{11} \text{ V m}^{-1} \text{ (volts per meter)}. \tag{1.8}$$

It is instructive to compare E_{atom} with E_1^0, the electric field associated with a light wave. At a distance of 1 m from a 60 W (watt) light bulb (assumed for simplicity to produce waves of uniform frequency),

$$J_{rms} < \frac{60}{4\pi} \text{ W m}^{-2}. \tag{1.9}$$

The inequality is due to the fact that the efficiency of the bulb is less than 100%. Using Eqs. 1.7 and 1.9, one finds

$$E_1^0 = \sqrt{(2)(377)(60)/4\pi} = 60 \text{ V m}^{-1}. \tag{1.10}$$

(The value of Z for air is very close to that of Z_0.) By way of contrast, a modestly sized high-peak-power ruby laser may produce a flux as great as

$$J_{rms} \sim 10^{12} \text{ W m}^{-2}. \tag{1.11}$$

The corresponding peak electric field intensity is

$$E_1^0 \sim \sqrt{(2)(377)(10^{12})}$$

$$= 3 \times 10^7 \text{ V m}^{-1}. \tag{1.12}$$

Firing the laser beam through a converging lens with a focal length of ~ 0.2 m may reduce the beam diameter from 10 mm to 1 μm. This will bring the peak electric field intensity, E_1^0, into the same range as E_{atom}. Therefore atoms and molecules (e.g., air) at the focal point are ionized by the strong electric fields. The subsequent recombination of electrons with their ions produces a flash and a loud noise analogous to lightning and thunder. In some recent experiments, very powerful lasers have been fired at small solid targets containing lithium and deuterium. The electrons produced are so energetic that they heat and compress the target to the point where nuclear fusion takes place therein.

No such drastic processes will be considered in this book. Mathematically, this restriction can be expressed by the formula

$$E_1^0 \leqslant E_{\text{atom}}. \tag{1.13}$$

Moreover, there are some nondestructive processes that can take place at moderately high power,

$$E_1^0 \cong E_{\text{atom}}, \tag{1.14}$$

which will also be excluded. These are the interactions that produce changes in the frequency of the wave by nonlinear optical processes. They include frequency doubling (harmonic generation) and stimulated Raman and Brillouin scattering. The condition which remains after that in Eq. 1.14 is removed from the one in Eq. 1.13 is

$$E_1^0 \ll E_{\text{atom}}. \tag{1.15}$$

1.2 Photoionization and nonresonant scattering

Some photodestructive optical processes that can be produced at low power will also be eliminated from consideration. To see how these interactions occur, it is necessary to replace the wave picture of light with the photon picture, in which the light beam consists of a stream of photons with number density d moving with velocity $c\hat{k}$. (The dimensions of d are reciprocal volume.) Each photon carries an amount of electromagnetic energy $\mathcal{E}$, which can be calculated from the frequency of the associated wave:

$$\mathcal{E}_{\text{photon}} = \frac{h\omega}{2\pi}. \tag{1.16}$$

The constant h, called Planck's constant, is the same for all photons:

$$h = 6.62 \times 10^{-34} \text{ J Hz}^{-1} \text{ (joules per cycles per second)}. \tag{1.17}$$

Therefore, from Eqs. 1.17 and 1.16 and the definition of d,

$$\mathbf{J}_{\text{rms}} = cdh\left(\frac{\omega}{2\pi}\right)\hat{k}. \tag{1.18}$$

The physical meaning of Eq. 1.18 is that even a rather feeble light beam (small J) can contain particles of high energy (large ω), albeit at low density (very small d).

Consider again the binding of an electron with charge $-q_0$ to a proton with charge $+q_0$. At a separation distance of a_0, the energy will be $\mathcal{E}_{atom}$:

$$\mathcal{E}_{atom} = -\frac{1}{2}\frac{c_0 Z_0 q_0^2}{4\pi a_0}$$

$$\sim -2\times 10^{-18} \text{ J.} \tag{1.19}$$

Whenever the energy of the photon exceeds that calculated in Eq. 1.19, it is possible for the photon to ionize the atom (ion or molecule) that contains the electron in question. The corresponding frequency is seen to be

$$\frac{\omega}{2\pi} > \frac{-\mathcal{E}_{atom}}{h}$$

$$\sim 3\times 10^{15} \text{ Hz.} \tag{1.20}$$

In the case of molecules, light of about this frequency can produce dissociation of bonds or other kinds of photochemical reactions. These processes are also too drastic to be discussed in this book.

There are two ways for light to interact with matter that have not yet been considered. Atoms, ions, and molecules that are illuminated with electromagnetic radiation will necessarily receive energy from the beam. In the absence of the light, each electron (and, to a lesser extent, each nucleus) will circulate within the atom, ion, or molecule of which it is a part, because of the presence of the electric and magnetic fields of all of the other constituents. When the radiation arrives, the electrons will be pushed to and fro by the oscillating electric (and, to a lesser extent, the magnetic) fields in the waves. These pushes, together with the additional motion induced by them, constitute kinetic and potential energy for the atom, over and above that which it had in the absence of light. The quantum system may dispose of this excess energy either by reradiating it or by turning it into other forms.

Which method of dissipation is employed depends on whether or not the frequency of the light wave, ω, is close to one of the characteristic natural (quantum) frequencies of the atomic (molecular, ionic) system, ω_0. If the frequencies ω and ω_0 do not match, the interaction may be termed "nonresonant." If the frequencies do match, the interaction is "resonant." The relationships between the characteristic energies of the atom and the energy of the photon for ionization, and for resonant and nonresonant interactions that do not result in ionization, are presented in Figure 1.2. The amount of excess energy received by an atom, ion, or molecule when it interacts nonresonantly with an electromagnetic wave is ordinarily quite small, and it is usually disposed of with great efficiency by reradiation. The direction of reradiation by an individual atomic system need not be the same as the direction of the incident beam. For this reason, nonresonant interactions are frequently called *light scattering*. If a very large number of scatterers are present, there will in general be interference (constructive and destructive) between the waves reradiated by any pair of them. If there were such a thing as a scattering medium that was perfectly homogeneous within a volume $\sim \lambda^3$, the only scattered waves that would survive are those which propagated in the same direction as that of the incident beam. This scattering process (dominant in many real substances in spite of small inhomogeneities) is called *transmission*.

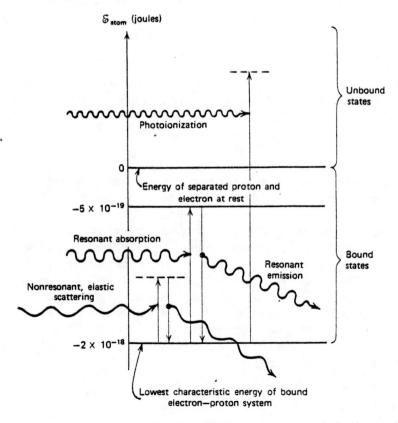

Figure 1.2 Characteristic energies for a hydrogen atom, and the interactions between that atom and photons of various frequencies.

At the boundary between two different homogeneous media, scattering can occur in directions other than the forward one. If the boundary is smooth (all irregularities $\ll \lambda$), constructive interference of the scattered light occurs in only two directions (reverse and forward) from the boundary; the resultant scattering processes are called *specular reflection* and *refraction*. If the boundary is rough on a wavelength scale, many different scattering directions are possible, and *diffuse transmission* and *reflection* result.

If the medium is inhomogeneous (particles of one kind embedded in a medium composed of a different substance), several different kinds of scattering processes may occur, depending on what the shapes of the embedded particles are, whether they are transparent or opaque, and whether they are larger or smaller than a wavelength. A continuum of scattering directions is possible. For example, spherical transparent particles with radii $> \lambda$ can produce rainbows (*Mie scattering*). If the inhomogeneities are periodically spaced at intervals $\sim \lambda$, the scattering occurs in discrete directions and the process is called *diffraction*. Diffraction also occurs around opaque objects and through holes in opaque objects, but the effects are not very dramatic unless the objects or the holes are of size λ. Randomly distributed density fluctuations (wherein the inhomogeneities are small) produce various kinds of weak scattering processes. If the density fluctuations do not move, *Rayleigh scattering* results. If weak density fluctuations propagate through the medium, the scattered light will be shifted in frequency because of the Doppler effect. This process is termed *Brillouin scattering*.

The degree of response of the electrons to the nonresonant electromagnetic wave is called the *polarizability*. If the polarizability oscillates because of rotation and vibration of the molecules to which the electrons are bound, the scattered light will be amplitude modulated. The frequency of the scattered light will therefore be less or greater than that of the incident beam by the modulation frequency (sideband generation). This process is called *Raman scattering*. Although investigations of some of these phenomena, especially Brillouin and Raman scattering, can provide spectroscopic information (and are therefore sometimes called *Brillouin* and *Raman spectroscopy*), such studies are not spectroscopic in the sense intended here. (Garbuny's[1] book is a useful source of information about a wide range of optical phenomena.)

1.3   Resonant interactions and spectroscopy

In this book the word *spectroscopic* is used only to describe resonant interactions between electromagnetic waves and matter. As stated previously, processes that lead directly to ionization and/or chemical reactions are excepted, as well as those that change the frequency of the wave. It is not intended, however, that processes which lead indirectly to chemical reactions (e.g., by subsequent decomposition of an excited molecule) be excluded. Similarly, resonant interactions will be termed "spectroscopic" even if some of the energy that was transferred from the electromagnetic wave to the atom, ion, or molecule eventually ends up as light of a different frequency (e.g., by phosphorescence or by Stokes-shifted fluorescence). It should be obvious that there cannot be a single hard and fast rule which will adequately classify every case that may arise. The intent of the definition, however, is to limit the discussion to interactions that are intrinsically reversible (elastic).

Resonant interactions are ordinarily much stronger than nonresonant ones. (A notable exception is the interaction of visible light with a metallic surface; nearly 100% nonresonant reflection can result.) Each characteristic frequency is actually a band of frequencies of width $\Delta\omega$ more or less symmetrically distributed about some center, ω_0. In many cases, the difference between two successive characteristic frequencies in a particular atomic system exceeds the band width of either of them. If one illuminates such a system by means of a light source of adjustable frequency, a gradual increase in ω will produce first one strong resonant interaction and then another. Between those two strong resonances, only weak nonresonant scattering processes will occur.

A graphical representation of such an experiment, with the magnitude of the response of the atomic system as the ordinate and the frequency of the illuminating light as the abscissa, is called a *spectrogram*. In the case just described, the spectrogram will consist of a series of well-spaced peaks, with the curve returning to the base line (parallel to the abscissa) in between. The peaks are called *spectral lines*. The process of obtaining (and interpreting) a spectrogram is known as *spectroscopy*, and the apparatus used to obtain the information presented on a spectrogram (and in some cases even to draw the curve) is a *spectrometer*. Typical components of a spectrometer are a source of light that produces many frequencies simultaneously, a dispersing element such as a prism or diffraction grating to separate the various frequencies produced by the source, a sample chamber, and a detector to measure the magnitude of the response of the sample to the source (see Figure 1.3).

The resonant transfer of energy from a radiation field to matter (atoms, ions, or molecules) is called *spectroscopic absorption*; the resonant transfer of energy from matter to the radiation field is termed *spectroscopic emission*. If no nonradiative transfer of energy occurs in the time interval between absorption and subsequent emission, the overall process could

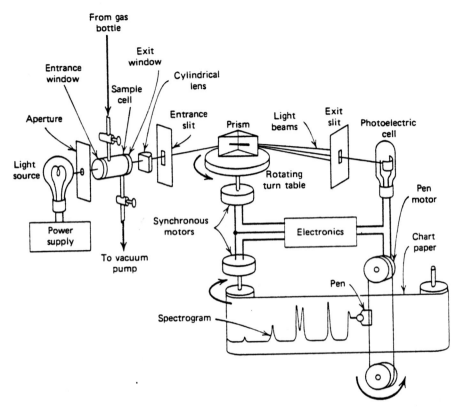

Figure 1.3 Schematic diagram of a continuously recording absorption spectro-photometer.

properly be called *scattering*. Unlike the case of nonresonant scattering, however, a very large fraction of the incident electromagnetic energy participates. For this reason, other names are ordinarily used to describe the interaction (e.g., *resonance trapping*).

These two processes, absorption and emission, give their names to the two main types of spectroscopy. In absorption spectroscopy, the light source produces a well- defined pencil of parallel rays (the beam) which is incident upon a sample in thermal equilibrium at some preselected temperature. The atoms, ions, or molecules in the sample absorb photons from the beam, and either reradiate them in some other direction by emission or turn the energy they represent irreversibly into heat. In either case, the intensity of the beam is much reduced by passage through the sample if its frequency satisfies the resonance condition with any of the atomic frequencies.

1.4   The Bouguer-Lambert-Beer law

Consider a light beam of irradiance $J\hat{k}$ normally incident upon a circular region of the sample of area A. The number of photons removed from the beam in unit time, $-A\,\Delta J/h(\omega/2\pi)$, is equal to the number of photons which have struck the sample in that time, $AJ/h(\omega/2\pi)$, multiplied by the probability, W, that one photon striking A will be absorbed. Canceling $h(\omega/2\pi)$, one has

$$-A\,\Delta J = -WAJ. \tag{1.21}$$

The probability of absorption per photon will be equal to the number of atomic systems in the region of the sample illuminated by the beam, N, times the probability that the photon in question will be intercepted by a given atom, W':

$$W = NW'. \tag{1.22}$$

If the number of absorbers per unit volume is N',

$$N = A\,\Delta z\,N', \tag{1.23}$$

where Δz is the thickness of the sample, and $\hat{z}||\hat{k}$. The parameter W' can be used to define an effective *cross section* for absorption by one atom, κ:

$$W' \equiv \frac{\kappa}{A}. \tag{1.24}$$

In other words, a model for the absorption process is adopted which consists of N spheres, each with cross-sectional area κ, embedded in a transparent matrix of area A and thickness Δz (see Figure 1.4). If Δz is sufficiently small, the probability that one sphere will shadow or obscure another will be negligibly small. Therefore the probability of absorption per photon is equal to the fraction of the total area A blocked by the N atoms:

$$W = \frac{A\,\Delta z\,\kappa N'}{A} \tag{1.25}$$

By inserting the expression for W on the right-hand side of Eq. 1.25 into the formula in Eq. 1.21 and canceling the A's, one obtains

$$-\Delta J = J\kappa\,\Delta z\,N'. \tag{1.26}$$

In the limit as Δz goes to zero, Eq. 1.26 can be written as a differential

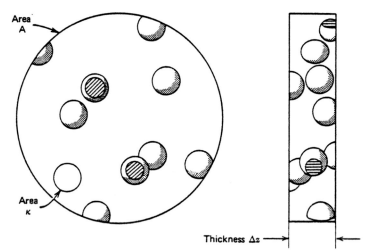

Figure 1.4 Model for the absorption process used to derive the Bouguer-Lambert-Beer law.

equation. This may be integrated to find the diminution in irradiance suffered by a light beam traveling through a thick sample composed of many such lamina stacked together:

$$J(z) = J(0) \exp(-\kappa N'z). \qquad (1.27)$$

Equation 1.27 is commonly known as *Beer's law*. Historically, the discovery that a beam of light is attenuated exponentially with distance as it passes through an absorbing medium was made by Pierre Bouguer, a French pharmacist, in 1729, and independently by the English physicist J. H. Lambert in 1760. The discovery that the damping constant (the argument of the exponential, called the *absorption coefficient*) is proportional to the concentration of the absorbing species, N', was made in 1851 by the German, A. Beer.

In emission spectroscopy, the sample itself becomes the light source. The atoms, molecules, and ions of which the material is composed are heated in an oven or placed in an electric discharge. In this manner, the atomic systems acquire more energy than they would have if they were at thermal equilibrium with their surroundings. Some of the excess energy is radiated away in the form of light, which is separated into waves of different frequencies by the dispersing element and allowed to strike the detector. In principle, the absorption spectrogram for any substance should be the negative image of the emission spectrogram: dark absorption lines should appear on a bright background at exactly the same frequencies at which bright emission lines appear on a dark background. Whenever nonradiative processes for disposing of excess energy are rapid enough to compete with resonant emission, however, this rule of similarity between the two spectra becomes unreliable.

1.5 The importance of spectroscopic transitions

To the scientist, the principal interest in the spectroscopic interaction between light and matter is that the characteristic resonant frequencies of atoms, molecules, and ions can be discovered thereby. Since each different atomic system has a characteristic pattern of spectral lines, the spectrogram becomes a "fingerprint" of that system: spectroscopy is therefore a vital part of modern analytical chemistry. The physical chemist and chemical physicist use spectroscopic information in the study of atomic and molecular processes that determine the characteristic frequencies and widths of the lines. These processes include transitions between various quantum states of the atoms and molecules representing different amounts of magnetic, rotational, and vibrational energy. Also studied are transitions between energy states corresponding to different spatial distributions of the electrons about the nuclear framework. Analogous information about the inner workings of the nuclei themselves can also be obtained spectroscopically.

Regardless of whether or not we share these scientific interests, spectroscopic transitions play a crucial role in our everyday lives. Our most valuable sense is sight, and almost everything we see is rendered visible by these interactions. There are exceptions, of course. The daytime sky is perceived as blue because of Rayleigh scattering; many white objects (e.g., clouds and milk) are seen because of Tyndall scattering; colorless transparent materials such as glass and water are visible because of the glints of light from their surfaces produced by nonresonant dielectric reflection; silvery surfaces show up because of metallic reflection; and some birds, fishes, and oil films display iridescent colors as a result of interference between the reflectances of closely spaced dielectric surfaces. But almost every other material in our environment is seen because some of the light striking it produces spectroscopic-type transitions therein. Examples are grass, clothing, wine, bricks, and human skin. Light absorbed in these processes is usually turned irreversibly into heat: the balance enters our eyes by reflection or transmission. Because absorption lines are frequently spread over only a relatively small range of frequencies, the transmitted and/or reflected light appears colored. Violet, indigo, blue, green, yellow, orange, and red are seen in turn as the frequency diminishes. If the most intense light striking the retina has a frequency of

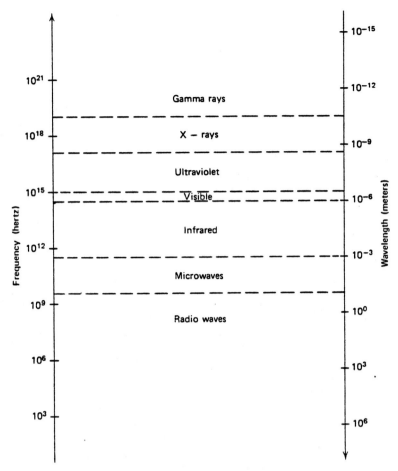

Figure 1.5   The electromagnetic spectrum.

about 9×10^{14} Hz, violet is perceived. At 4×10^{14} Hz, red is seen. Many more spectroscopic transitions occur at higher frequencies and at lower frequencies than those of visible light. See Figure 1.5.

1.6   The question of dynamics

The usual picture of spectroscopic transitions is a "thermodynamic" rather than a "kinetic" one. In other words, the emphasis is usually placed on the coincidence (resonance) between the energy of the photons being absorbed or emitted, $\mathcal{E}_{photon}$, and the difference in energy between the quantum states of the atom undergoing the transition, $\Delta\mathcal{E}_{atom}$:

$$\Delta\mathcal{E}_{atom} = \mathcal{E}_{photon}. \tag{1.28}$$

Seldom is one concerned about the dynamics of the absorption process. An exception, however, should be made: calculations of the overall absorption or emission rate (number of transitions per second, averaged over a large collection of identical quantum systems) produced by weak incoherent light are frequently performed. The parameters produced by means of such calculations (oscillator strengths, extinction coefficients) are used to predict the relative amplitudes and widths of absorption or emission lines that appear on spectrograms. But this is not the same thing as attempting to describe the mechanism by means of which photons are created or destroyed and their energy and momentum transferred to the quantum systems, nor do such calculations provide a description of the state of the quantum systems in the interval between the initiation and the termination of the transition process.

In one branch of spectroscopy, work has not been limited to the study of oscillator strengths and similar factors. Theorists exploring the behavior of magnetic particles (nuclei and electrons) interacting with radio waves and microwaves provided a detailed description of the dynamics of that process. This knowledge had little impact on the rest of spectroscopy, however, because it was generally considered that magnetic resonance was somehow a special case. The discovery that the formulas for nuclear magnetic resonance and electron paramagnetic resonance (nmr and epr) can be generalized to describe any quantum transition is relatively recent; a brief historical account is provided in the next two sections.

1.7 Early history of the quantum theory

In the seventeenth century Newton showed that two massive bodies, whenever attracted to one another by means of a force inversely proportional to the square of the distance between their centers, must necessarily move so that the path of one body is a conic section with the other body located at the principal focus of the conic. Newton further demonstrated that, if gravity is such a force, the observed motions of the planets around the sun correspond with the predictions of his theory with fantastic precision.

In 1785 Charles A. Coulomb showed that the electrostatic force between two charged particles is also an inverse-square force.[‡] Soon after, it became

---

[‡]This fact had previously been discovered, but not published, by Henry Cavendish.

known that matter is composed of atoms and, furthermore, that an atom is in turn composed of negatively charged electrons which can be removed by ionization and of a positively charged residue sufficient to render the atom as a whole electrically neutral.

As soon as Millikan was able to measure the charge on the electron in the early 1900's, the electronic mass could be calculated from the previously known charge-to-mass ratio. It then became clear that most of the mass of the atom is associated with the positively charged residue. In 1911 Rutherford showed that this residue is very small in comparison with the whole size of the atom, and named it the *nucleus*.

In 1913 Bohr reasoned that, since an atom is composed of several relatively light particles attracted to a heavy one by an inverse-square force, the atom must be very similar mechanically to the solar system. The electrons should orbit the nucleus in paths that are conic sections, just as the planets orbit the sun (see Figure 1.6).

Unfortunately, in one important respect, the Bohr model was inconsistent with the observed properties of atoms. In the 1860's James Clerk Maxwell had combined all the known laws of electricity and magnetism into a unified and consistent theory. An important consequence of this development was the prediction that a charged particle (e.g., an electron) undergoing accelerated motion (such as would be produced if the electron indeed moved in a Newtonian orbit about the nucleus) should radiate electromagnetic waves (light). Bohr began his famous paper by showing that the energy of the electron in its orbit must eventually be completely radiated away by this mechanism. The atom should emit a continuous spectrum of electromagnetic waves at higher and higher frequencies as the electrons spiral into the nucleus, ceasing only at the point of complete atomic collapse. Experimentally, of course, atoms do not emit any light spontaneously at normal temperatures. When excited, they do radiate some of their excess energy electromagnetically in a continuum of frequencies. However, as described in the portion of Section 1.1 devoted to emission spectroscopy, a very characteristic discrete spectrum of lines is produced as well. Under no conditions found on earth does a complete collapse of all of the electronic orbits occur.

Bohr was at a loss to explain this apparent contradiction between the laws of mechanics and the laws of electricity and magnetism. Nevertheless, he was able to calculate precisely the frequencies of light absorbed by the hydrogen atom by assuming that (1) the only Newtonian orbits permitted electrons were those with angular momenta equal to integral multiples of $\hbar$ (i.e., $h/2\pi$), (2) the electrons could move from one orbit to another by gaining or losing a quantity of energy equal to the difference in energies of the corresponding orbits, and (3) the necessary energy could be supplied or

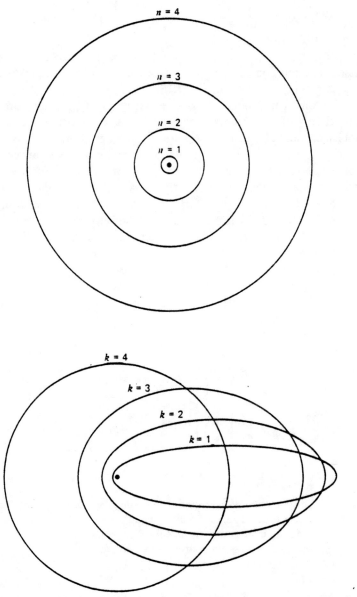

Figure 1.6 Bohr orbits. At the top, orbits with angular momentum $k(\equiv l+1)=n$ are shown. At the bottom, orbits with $n=4$ but differing in k are shown.

removed by the annihilation or creation of bundles of electromagnetic energy called photons (see Eq. 1.28).

In 1905 Einstein showed that light could be assumed to consist of such bundles. The relationship between this description and the wave picture of light was given previously in Eq. 1.16.

In Newtonian mechanics there are two types of planetary orbits. If the initial velocity of the planetary object relative to the sun is greater than the "velocity of escape" for the system (as sometimes is the case for comets), it will move in an open, or hyperbolic, path, make one pass around the sun, and never return. If, on the other hand, the initial velocity is less than the velocity of escape (as is the case for planets), the orbit will close upon itself and become an ellipse. In Bohr's theory, only the closed orbits, corresponding to bound electrons, are supposed to have discrete amounts (quanta) of energy and angular momentum, so that transitions between such orbits give rise to the discrete optical spectrum. A continuum of energies is allowed to the unbound electrons; transitions between their orbits, or between them and bound orbits, produce the continuous optical spectrum. The agreement between the predictions of the Bohr theory and experimental observations of the spectra of one-electron atoms (see Figure 1.7) is extremely good.

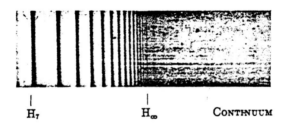

H_7 H_∞ Continuum

Figure 1.7 The spectrum of hydrogen. Higher members of the Balmer series of the H atom in emission (final quantum state having $n=2$), starting from the seventh line and showing the continuum [from *Ann. Phys.* (4) **84**, 565 (1927), Plate 14, Fig. 6, by G. Herzberg]. Spectrogram courtesy of G. Herzberg.

Among the questions left unanswered by the Bohr theory were the following.

1. Why do electrons behave as if they greatly prefer the relatively few quantized orbits of Bohr over all other orbits, when Newton's laws predict an infinite number of permissible bound orbits in any finite energy range?

2. What special feature of the Bohr orbits enables electrons occupying them to be relieved of the necessity of radiation and therefore exempt from

obeying Maxwell's equations? [For excited states (large orbits), the exemption is only temporary, but an electron in the ground state apparently has a permanent dispensation.]

3. What are the dynamics of the absorption and emission processes (see Section 1.6)?

All of these questions, and more, were answered by the *new quantum theory*, developed from 1925 to 1928 by Heisenberg and Schrödinger. The Schrödinger formulation of this theory was based on an idea by De Broglie that matter, like light, has both a wave and a particle nature. Wave mechanics has proved to be an exceptionally useful tool in the development of relatively simple conceptual models for the structures of atoms and molecules. Consequently, it has been historically favored over the earlier Heisenberg formulation by atomic and solid-state physicists, as well as by physical chemists.

In wave mechanics, one describes the position of an electron by calculating a wavefunction $\psi(x,y,z,t)$, the complex square of which is equal to the probability of finding the electron in question at the position specified by the coordinates (x,y,z) at the time t. The Coulombic field set up by the positively charged nucleus creates a "trap" for the electron and localizes its probability wave in the immediate neighborhood. If the initial relative kinetic energy of the electron-nucleus system is sufficiently low, the electron will be caught in this trap. The probability wave will be effectively tied down (localized) by the electrostatic potential in a fashion analogous to the tying down of a sound wave by an organ pipe. It is characteristic of bound oscillators that only discrete frequencies of oscillation (i.e., the fundamental mode and overtones or harmonics) can be sustained by them. The reason for the discrete frequencies is that an integral number of nodes for the wave must be located within the finite geometrical confines of the region in which it is bound.

In this way, wave mechanics answers the first question which the Bohr theory failed to answer: quantization is a natural consequence of the assumption that bound states for electrons in atoms are spatially localized, three- dimensional, standing probability waves with an integral number of nodes, n_0. In particular, the 1s state of hydrogen (K shell) is the fundamental mode of oscillation ($n_0 = 1$) for the probability wave of the electron. There is only one "node," the spherical one at $r = \infty$, in the 1s wave function; therefore there is only one way to construct such a wave (one orbital). For $n_0 = 2$ (L shell), one node is present in addition to the one at $r = \infty$. This mode of oscillation (first overtone) requires more energy to excite than does the fundamental (a fact that can readily be accepted by anyone who has ever played a wind instrument in an orchestra or band!). There are two shapes possible for the extra node, and these are consistent with the symmetry of the Coulombic potential field. First, it can be spherical, like the one at $r = \infty$. The resulting orbital is called $2s$. (All waves with only spherical nodes are defined to be s orbitals.) Next, it can be planar, passing through the nucleus. The resulting orbitals are called, collectively, the $2p$ subshell. (All waves with $n_0 - 1$ spherical nodes, plus one planar node, are called p orbitals.) There are three orbitals in the p subshell because there are three independent directions of orientation for a plane in a three-dimensional space. Similar explanations can be given for the second and higher overtones ($M, N, \ldots$ shells). Some typical orbitals are drawn in Figure 1.8.

1.8 Elucidation of transient phenomena

As mentioned in Section 1.6, the first careful exploration of transient phenomena in quantum mechanics was apparently made by physicists

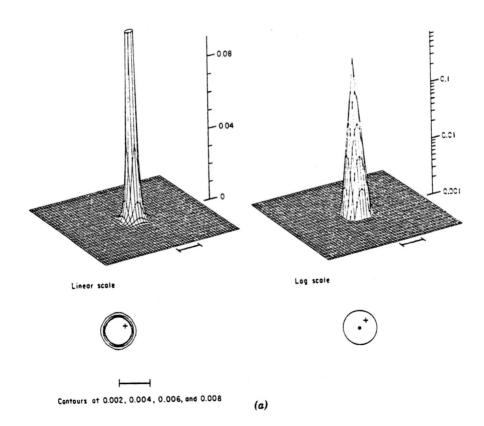

Linear scale

Log scale

Contours at 0.002, 0.004, 0.006, and 0.008

(a)

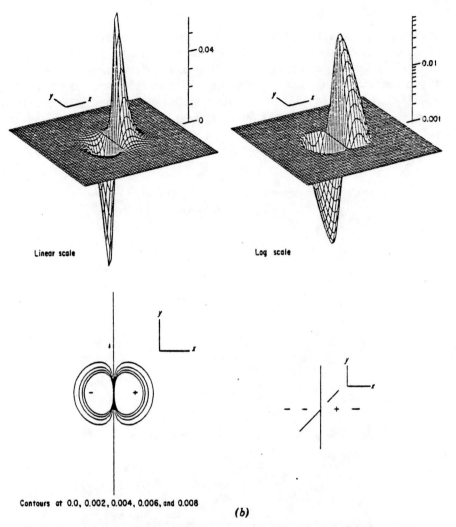

Linear scale   Log scale

Contours at 0.0, 0.002, 0.004, 0.006, and 0.008

(b)

Figure 1.8 Typical atomic orbitals from *Orbital and Electron Density Diagrams* (The Macmillan Co., New York, 1973), by A. Streitweiser, Jr. and P. H. Owens. (*a*) $1s$ (Fig. 1.6 on p. 12 of the book cited). The plot at the upper left is a direct plot of ψ. A plane is clearly defined as a grid 64 atomic units (au) on a side. At the front of this grid a marked line is shown 10 au in length. The grid is the xy plane. For each point in this plane there is a corresponding value for ψ as given by the vertical scale at the right of the grid. For the $1s$ function, ψ has positive values throughout, so the figure plotted is entirely above the plane. The $1s$ orbital is spherically symmetric; Figure 1.8*a* represents the wavefunction in one plane and is not meant to be a "picture" of the entire orbital. (*b*) Same as 1.8*a*, but for $2p_x$ (Fig. 1.10 on p. 18 of the book cited).

studying the magnetic resonance of electrons and nuclei, first in beams (Rabi and his co-workers[2] in the 1930s) and then in bulk matter (Bloch[3] in 1946). The first experimental observation of the dynamic interaction between electromagnetic waves and an absorbing quantum system was made by H. C. Torrey[4] in 1949. The phenomenon he observed is called the transient nutation effect. In the following year, E. L. Hahn[5] devised what is still generally considered to be the most dramatic experimental technique for studying the time evolution of quantum systems, called the method of

Figure 1.9 Recent photograph of Felix Bloch, codiscoverer of nuclear magnetic resonance in bulk matter (for which he received the Nobel Prize in physics) and discoverer of the Bloch equations describing the interaction of coherent radiation and an ensemble of quantum spins. Dr. Bloch is a professor of physics at Stanford University. Photograph by S. U. Photo. Dept., courtesy of Dr. Bloch.

spin echoes. Both of these effects were first observed in nuclear resonance experiments, but it was not long before the techniques were extended to electron spin resonance as well (Blume,[6] 1958).

In 1954 Dicke[7] made an important contribution by discussing the effects of phase coherence among the wave functions of atoms simultaneously undergoing spontaneous emission. Although he did not discuss the time evolution of the atomic ensemble in great detail, he made it clear that ideas previously associated solely with spin systems had a far wider application. The first paper to state explicitly that the quantum-mechanical formalism developed by Bloch to describe the dynamics of the interaction between radio waves and magnetic nuclei could also be used to solve maser problems was written by Feynman, Vernon, and Hellwarth[8] in 1958. In 1960 the first laser was built. Most of the early theoretical treatments of laser phenomena ignored the work of Dicke and Feynman and co-workers, but a few papers, notably those of Yoh-Han Pao[9] (1961) and C. L. Tang[10] (1962), insisted that many problems in this area could not be properly solved unless transient coherent phenomena were taken into account.

Figure 1.10   Henry C. Torrey, discoverer of the transient nutation effect and codiscoverer of nuclear magnetic resonance in bulk matter, at work in his laboratory in June 1948. Dr. Torrey is now a professor of physics and dean of the Graduate School at Rutgers University. Photograph courtesy of Dr. Torrey.

Figure 1.11 Erwin L. Hahn, the first to observe free-induction decay, discoverer of nuclear spin echoes, and codiscoverer of self-induced transparency (SIT). Dr. Hahn was at the University of Illinois during the first two of these accomplishments; SIT was discovered at the University of California at Berkeley, where he is now a professor of physics. The photograph was taken sometime in the mid-1960s and kindly provided by E. L. Hahn.

These workers also extended the formulas of Feynman et al. to incorporate the effects of relaxation. In 1964 the Bloch formalism was applied to the description of pulse propagation in a laser amplifier, first in the case where the electromagnetic wave is in exact resonance with the atomic transitions (Wittke and Warter[11]) and then at any frequency near resonance (Arecchi and Bonifacio[12]).

Little attention was paid to the above work, however, until 1964, when Kurnit, Abella, and Hartmann[13] were able to produce the optical analog to the spin echoes discovered by Hahn. Photon echoes, as these analogs were called, had been predicted previously by Kopvillem and Nagibarov[14] on theoretical grounds, but the independent theoretical work of Kurnit et al., together with their experimental confirmation of the theory, dramatized the importance of the Bloch point of view in laser physics more than any other single event before or since. A flurry of theoretical and experimental papers followed, and "echoes" were observed in a great many spectroscopic experiments: ferromagnetic resonance, antiferromagnetic resonance,

Figure 1.12   Richard J. Blume, discoverer of electron spin echoes, in 1971. Mr. Blume was at the IBM Watson Laboratory, Columbia University, at the time this work was done; he now works for the U. S. Naval Research Laboratories. Photograph by Ray C. Cottingham of Norco, California.

microwave spectroscopy of molecular rotational transitions, and cyclotron resonance. Notable among the workers at that time (1965–1967) was Kaplan.[15] In 1968 Hocker and Tang[16] observed the laser analog to the transient nutations reported by Torrey. Perhaps the most dramatic phenomenon discovered in the past several years has been the self-induced transparency effect (McCall and Hahn,[17] 1967).

It is not the purpose of this book to present a definitive review of this rapidly expanding field. The bibliography given is by no means exhaustive, nor is there even any claim that all of the most important papers have been mentioned. The intent of this chapter has been merely to indicate a few of the historical milestones in the application of quantum mechanics to the problem of elucidating the mechanism by means of which electromagnetic radiation and matter interact in experiments usually described as "spectroscopic." It is now possible to demonstrate conclusively that wave

Figure 1.13 Robert H. Dicke, discoverer of the effect of coherence on spontaneous emission (an essential link between the dynamics of magnetic resonance and those of laser spectroscopy), on Nov. 23, 1966. Dr. Dicke is a professor of physics at Princeton University. Photograph courtesy of R. H. Dicke.

Figure 1.14 Codiscoverers of the applicability of the rotating coordinate treatment of spectroscopic transitions (used in magnetic resonance) to maser problems. (*a*) Richard P. Feynman. Dr. Feynman is a professor of physics at Caltech. Photograph by Floyd Clark, courtesy of R. P. Feynman. (*b*) Frank L. Vernon, Jr., in 1961. Dr. Vernon is now a senior staff scientist at the Aerospace Corporation. Photograph courtesy of F. L. Vernon, Jr. (*c*) Robert W. Hellwarth, in 1958. Dr. Hellwarth is now a professor of physics and electrical engineering at the University of Southern California. Photograph courtesy of R. W. Hellwarth.

Figure 1.15 James P. Wittke, who, with Peter J. Warter, first coupled the Bloch equations to the electromagnetic field to describe the propagation of coherent light through an ensemble of two-level systems at exact resonance. Dr. Wittke works for RCA at the David Sarnoff Research Center in Princeton, N. J. Photograph courtesy of Dr. Wittke.

Figure 1.16 Codiscoverers of the generalization of the work of Wittke and Warter which provides a complete description of the dynamics of spectroscopic transitions. (*a*) F. Tito Arecchi in 1964 or 1965. Dr. Arecchi is the director of quantum optics at CISE (Centro Informazioni Studi Esperienze) in Milan, Italy. (*b*) Rudolfo Bonifacio in 1964 or 1965. Dr. Bonifacio is now employed by IBM in San José, Calif. Both photographs from *IEEE J. Quantum Electron.* **QE-1**, 185 (1965), courtesy of the Institute of Electrical and Electronics Engineers.

Figure 1.17 Codiscoverers of photon echoes. (*a*) Norman A. Kurnit in June, 1961. Dr. Kurnit is currently an assistant professor of physics at MIT. Photograph courtesy of N. A. Kurnit. (*b*) Isaac D. Abella at the echo apparatus, Columbia University Radiation Laboratory, on Apr. 7, 1965. Dr. Abella is currently an associate professor of physics at the University of Chicago. Photograph courtesy of I. D. Abella. (*c*) Sven R. Hartmann in 1963. Dr. Hartmann is a professor of physics at Columbia University and codirector of the Radiation Laboratory. Photograph courtesy of S. R. Hartmann.

mechanics is capable of providing a large amount of information about the dynamics of spectroscopic transitions. Such information has in fact been obtainable from quantum theory since 1928, and much of it involves only the most elementary understanding of this subject.

The rest of this monograph is devoted to an elementary explanation of the essential features of the dynamics of spectroscopic transitions, in the hope that this will enable the reader to understand much of the exciting

Figure 1.18   Villen R. Nagibarov, who, with Uno. Kh. Kopvillem, first predicted echoes, in 1961. Dr. Nagibarov is now a professor of physics at the Physio-Technical Institute of the Kazan Branch of the Academy of Sciences and the Kazan State Pedagogical Institute in the U.S.S.R. Photograph courtesy of V. R. Nagibarov.

work which is being performed today in this field. It can provide a model for the behavior of quantum systems that is more nearly in accord with physical intuition than the one customarily employed. Perhaps, by using this model, the reader may be able to conceive of new experiments to discover heretofore unobserved phenomena in the interaction of radiation and matter!

Figure 1.19 Daniel B. Kaplan, discoverer or codiscoverer of many echo phenomena. Dr. Kaplan is a senior staff scientist at the Lockheed Palo Alto Research Laboratory. Photograph courtesy of Dr. and Mrs. Kaplan.

Figure 1.20 A recent picture of Yoh-Han Pao, who first applied the full Bloch equations (including relaxation terms) to optical transitions. Dr. Pao is a professor of engineering and chairman of the Department at Case Western Reserve University, Cleveland, Ohio. Photograph courtesy of Y. H. Pao.

1.9 References

1. M. Garbuny, *Optical Physics* (Academic Press, New York, 1965).
2. a. I. I. Rabi, "Space quantization in a gyrating magnetic field," *Phys. Rev.* **51**, 652 (1937).
   b. I. I. Rabi, N. F. Ramsey, and J. Schwinger, "Use of rotating coordinates in magnetic resonance problems," *Rev. Mod. Phys.* **26**, 167 (1954).
3. F. Bloch, "Nuclear induction," *Phys. Rev.* **70**, 460 (1946).
4. H. C. Torrey, "Transient nutations in nuclear magnetic resonance," *Phys. Rev.* **76**, 1059 (1949).
5. a. E. L. Hahn, "Nuclear induction due to free Larmor precession," *Phys. Rev.* **77**, 297 (1950).
   b. E. L. Hahn, "Spin echoes," *Phys. Rev.* **80**, 580 (1950).
6. a. R. J. Blume, *Bull. Am. Phys. Soc.*, Ser. II **1**, 397 (1956).
   b. R. J. Blume, "Electron spin relaxation times in sodium-ammonia solutions," *Phys. Rev.* **109**, 1867 (1958).
7. a. R. H. Dicke, "Coherence in spontaneous radiation processes," *Phys. Rev.* **93**, 99 (1954).
   b. R. H. Dicke, "Coherence and the quantum," *J. Opt. Soc. Am.* **47**, 527 (1957).
   c. R. H. Dicke, "The coherence brightened laser," in *Quantum Electronics*, Vol. 1, P. Grivet and N. Bloembergen, Eds. (Columbia University Press, New York, 1964), pp. 35–53.
8. R. P. Feynman, F. L. Vernon, and R. W. Hellwarth, "Geometrical representation of the Schroedinger Equation for solving maser problems," *J. Appl. Phys.* **28**, 49 (1957).
9. Y. H. Pao, "Quantum mechanical description of maser action at optical frequencies," *J. Opt. Soc. Am.* **52**, 871 (1962).
10. a. C. L. Tang, "On maser rate equations and transient oscillations," *J. Appl. Phys.* **34**, 2935 (1963) and **36**, 1797 (1965).
    b. C. L. Tang and B. D. Silverman, "Dynamic effects on the propagation of intense light pulses in optical media," in *Physics of Quantum Electronics*, P. L. Kelley, B. Lax, and P. E. Tannenwald, Eds. (McGraw-Hill Book Company, New York, 1966), pp. 283–293, Fig. 1.
11. J. P. Wittke and P. J. Warter, "Pulse propagation in a laser amplifier," *J. Appl. Phys.* **35**, 1668 (1964).
12. F. T. Arecchi and R. Bonifacio, "Theory of optical maser amplifiers," *IEEE J. Quantum Electron*, **QE-1**, 169 (1965), and **QE-2**, 105 (1966).
13. a. N. A. Kurnit, I. D. Abella, and S. R. Hartmann, "Observation of a photon echo," *Phys. Rev. Lett.* **13**, 567 (1964).
    b. I. D. Abella, N. A. Kurnit, and S. R. Hartmann, "Photon echoes," *Phys. Rev.* **141**, 391 (1966).
    c. S. A. Hartmann, "Photon echoes," *Sci. Am.* **218**, 32 (April 1968).
14. U. Kh. Kopvillem and V. R. Nagibarov, *Fiz. Met. Metalloved.* **15**, 313 (1963), translated: "Light echo on (*sic*) paramagnetic crystals," *Phys. Met. Metallogr.* **15** (2), 136 (1963).

15. a. D. E. Kaplan, "Magnetostatic mode echo in ferromagnetic resonance," *Phys. Rev. Lett.* **14**, 254 (1965).

b. R. M. Hill and D. E. Kaplan, "Cyclotron resonance echo," *Phys. Rev. Lett.* **14**, 1062 (1965).

c. R. M. Hill, D. E. Kaplan, G. F. Herrmann, and S. K. Ichiki, "Emission microwave spectroscopy: OCS," *Phys. Rev. Lett.* **18**, 105 (1967).

16. a. C. L. Tang and H. Statz, "Optical analog of the transient nutation effect," *Appl. Phys. Lett.* **10**, 145 (1967).

b. G. B. Hocker and C. L. Tang, "Observation of the optical transient nutation effect," *Phys. Rev. Lett.* **21**, 591 (1968).

c. G. B. Hocker and C. L. Tang, "Measurement of the transition moment by the optical transient nutation effect," *Phys. Rev.* **184**, 356 (1969).

17. a. S. L. McCall and E. L. Hahn, "Self-induced transparency by pulsed coherent light," *Phys. Rev. Lett.* **18**, 908 (1967).

b. S. L. McCall and E. L. Hahn, "Self-induced transparency," *Phys. Rev.* **183**, 457 (1969).

1.10 Problems

1.1. The vacuum wavelength, λ_0, of the radiation from a typical CO_2 laser is 10.6 μm. Calculate the frequency, $\omega/2\pi$, of these waves in hertz (cycles per second).

1.2. The root-mean-squared power in a CO_2 laser beam is 8.0 W, and the cross-sectional area of the beam is 1.0×10^{-4} m^2.

a. What is the peak electric field amplitude, E_1^0, in volts per meter? Assume that the waves propagate through a vacuum.

b. What is the peak magnetic field amplitude, H_1^0, in amperes per meter under the same conditions?

1.3. An infrared absorption cell 0.10 m long is filled with SF_6 gas at a pressure of 0.20 torr (760 torr $= 1$ atm). A CO_2 laser beam enters the cell with an irradiance of $J_{rms} = 80$ W m^{-2} and leaves the cell with an irradiance of $J_{rms} = 32$ W m^{-2}.

a. Calculate the absorption cross section of SF_6, κ, in square meters per molecule.

b. Calculate the energy difference in joules per molecule between the two levels of the SF_6 molecules responsible for the absorption of 10.6 μm laser radiation.

2 Elementary quantum theory

2.1 States and their properties: operators and kets

In order to understand the dynamics of spectroscopic transitions, it is convenient to review the elementary principles of quantum theory. The treatment that follows differs somewhat in point of view from the one usually presented in a first course in quantum mechanics for chemists. A very straightforward, elegant, and detailed exposition of this material may be found in the book by Fano and Fano.[1]

A quantum system (e.g., an atom, ion, or molecule) behaves at any given time in a characteristic fashion determined by its state. (In a sense, the pattern of behavior *is* the state.) Ordinarily, a large number of different states are possible. The task of quantum mechanics is to enumerate them for each system of interest, and to calculate the physical properties of the system associated with each state. The first step is accomplished by assigning to each state a mathematical entity called a *ket*.

To each observable property of the system is assigned another kind of mathematical entity called an *operator*. The operators transform one ket into another. The transformation process is described algebraically:

$$R|a\rangle = |b\rangle. \tag{2.1}$$

In Eq. 2.1, R is some operator; $|a\rangle$ and $|b\rangle$ are kets. Note that R is written to the left of $|a\rangle$. It is convenient to visualize kets as vectors in an abstract space, called *Hilbert space*. In this case, the operator R rotates and/or stretches $|a\rangle$ in order to turn it into $|b\rangle$ (See Figure 2.1).

Sometimes the result of the operation of R upon a particular ket will be the same ket multiplied by a number, r:

$$R|a\rangle = |b\rangle = r|a\rangle. \tag{2.2}$$

Kets that satisfy Eq. 2.2 are said to be *eigenkets* of R, and the constants r are termed the corresponding *eigenvalues*. It is possible to arrange all of the eigenkets of R into an ordered set, $\{|r\rangle\}$. (Two eigenkets that differ only by

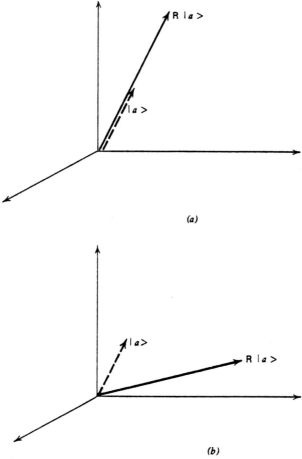

(a)

(b)

Figure 2.1 Effect of operator R on ket $|a\rangle$. At the top, $|a\rangle$ is an eigenket of R; at the bottom, $|a\rangle$ is not an eigenket of R.

a constant multiplicative factor will not be counted as different.) The number of eigenkets in the set, M, may be different for different quantum systems—frequently M is infinity. Eigenkets are of transcendent importance in quantum mechanics for several reasons.

1. If a system is in a state represented by an eigenket of R, the magnitude of the observable physical property represented by R is a constant equal to the corresponding eigenvalue. This is one of the reasons why states represented by eigenkets are sometimes called *stationary states*.[‡]

[‡]Strictly speaking, the adjective "stationary" should be reserved for eigenstates of the Hamiltonian operator. See discussion in Section 2.3.

This term should *not* imply that the constituent parts of the quantum systems are not moving; it means merely that the property represented by R is a constant of the motion. In particular, if $|r_j\rangle$ is the jth member of the set $\{|r\rangle\}$ and R represents the electric dipole moment,

$$R|r_j\rangle = r_j|r_j\rangle, \tag{2.3}$$

and r_j is the electric dipole moment of the system when it is in the jth stationary state (eigenstate). Usually, the r_j's are different from one another; whenever they are the same, the corresponding states (and their kets) are said to be *degenerate*. The label or name of an eigenket (the symbol placed between the | and the $\rangle$) is frequently chosen to be identical with the corresponding eigenvalue, as shown in Eq. 2.3.

2. The eigenkets of one operator, R, may also be eigenkets of another operator, S:

$$S|s_j\rangle = s_j|s_j\rangle \tag{2.4}$$

and

$$\{|r\rangle\} = \{|s\rangle\}. \tag{2.5}$$

The operators R and S are said to have *simultaneous* eigenkets. This means that the observable physical property of the system represented by S is also a constant of the motion in these states. For example, in the states of the hydrogen atom in which energy is conserved, angular momentum is also conserved. There is not necessarily an obvious relationship between the numerical values of r_j and s_j for any j. The product of two operators SR is also an operator, equivalent in its effect on a ket to a transformation first with R and then with S. If R and S have simultaneous eigenkets (e.g., $|r_j\rangle$), the sequence of the operations is immaterial:

$$SR|r_j\rangle = RS|r_j\rangle. \tag{2.6}$$

Sometimes Eq. 2.6 is written without the kets:

$$SR - RS \equiv [S, R] = 0. \tag{2.7}$$

The difference $[S, R]$ is called the *commutator* of S and R. If the commutator is zero, the corresponding operators are said to commute.

3. The eigenkets of one operator R will not usually be satisfactory eigenkets for all of the other operators of interest. Let Q be an operator for which $\{|r\rangle\}$ is not the correct choice of eigenkets:

$$Q|q_j\rangle = q_j|q_j\rangle, \qquad 1 < j < M, \tag{2.8}$$

but

$$\{|r\rangle\} \neq \{|q\rangle\}. \tag{2.9}$$

This means that the observable physical property of the system represented by Q is *not* constant in states in which the property represented by R *is* constant, and vice versa. For example, there are no states of the hydrogen atom in which both energy and linear momentum are conserved. Nevertheless, $\{|q\rangle\}$ and $\{|r\rangle\}$ have the same number of members, M. If the operators R and Q do not have simultaneous eigenkets, they will fail to commute:

$$QR|r_j\rangle \neq RQ|r_j\rangle \tag{2.10}$$

or

$$[Q,R] \neq 0. \tag{2.11}$$

By far the most popular choice of a basis (complete set of eigenkets) to use in solving problems in quantum mechanics is the set of eigenkets of the Hamiltonian operator, H. (The physically observable property represented by the Hamiltonian operator is almost always the energy of the system.) It cannot be emphasized too strongly that this choice of basis is merely a custom, dictated by convenience in attacking the kinds of problems usually discussed in conventional courses in quantum mechanics. It would be an error to assume that quantum systems can exist in no states other than the ones in which the energy is a constant of the motion. If this were assumed, it would then be impossible to explain the rich variety of behavior displayed by quantum systems in nature.

2.2   Stationary states: eigenkets and eigenfunctions

The discussion given in Section 2.1 is the basis for a more precise statement of the two central tasks of quantum theory: (1) to find the ket, $|a\rangle$, that describes the system in the state of interest, and (2) to extract from this ket, by means of the corresponding operators, various physically observable properties of the system.

Suppose, for example, that the system consists of a single electron traveling through space, either freely or under the influence of some attractive or repulsive force. The position of this electron is specified by specifying its coordinates x, y, and z, measured along some convenient set of axes. To each one of these three coordinates corresponds an operator;

let them be called X, Y, and Z. For simplicity, one can concentrate on X. The corresponding eigenvalues will be the possible results of a measurement of the x coordinate of the electron:

$$X|x_j\rangle = x_j|x_j\rangle. \tag{2.12}$$

It is not likely that the system will be in an eigenstate of x; that is, the ket representing the actual state of the system will probably not satisfy Eq. 2.12. But whether or not the correct ket for the system *is* an eigenket of X, it will always be possible to represent that ket as a linear combination of such eigenkets:

$$|a\rangle = a_1|x_1\rangle + a_2|x_2\rangle + \cdots + a_M|x_M\rangle. \tag{2.13}$$

This is so because the eigenkets of any operator representing a physically observable property of the system form what is called a complete set. In Hilbert space, even though the vector $|a\rangle$ may not "point" exactly along any of the axes represented by $\{|x\rangle\}$, the "direction" along which it *does* point can always be specified by giving the "projections" of $|a\rangle$ along each of those axes; these projections are the a_j's (see Figure 2.2).

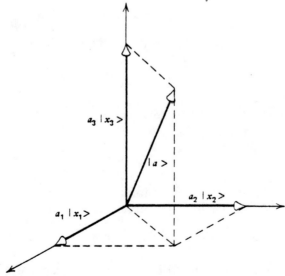

Figure 2.2 Representation of ket $|a\rangle$ as a linear superposition of eigenkets $|x_1\rangle$, $|x_2\rangle$, and $|x_3\rangle$.

It happens that there are an infinite number of possibilities for x_j; that is to say, $M = \infty$. Furthermore, the eigenvalues x_j form a continuum from $-L$ to $+L$, where $2L$ is the length of the portion of the x axis along which motion of the electron is possible. In other words,

$$x_{j+1} - x_j = \Delta x, \tag{2.14}$$

where Δx is a very small number.

It is also usually the case that the a_j's form a continuum:

$$a_{j+1} - a_j = \Delta a. \tag{2.15}$$

Whenever Eqs. 2.14 and 2.15 hold, it is convenient to define a continuous algebraic function, $\psi(x)$, from which all the a_j's can be calculated:

$$\psi_a(x_j) = a_j. \tag{2.16}$$

See Figure 2.3.

The state of the system is completely specified by the a_j's, in accordance with Eq. 2.13. Furthermore, the effect of any operator on $|a\rangle$ will be to transform it into another ket, $|b\rangle$, in accordance with Eq. 2.1. Note that $|b\rangle$ will *also* be expressible in a linear combination of the members of the set of eigenkets of X:

$$|b\rangle = b_1|x_1\rangle + b_2|x_2\rangle + \cdots + b_M|x_M\rangle. \tag{2.17}$$

In general, the coefficients (projections) in the expansion of $|a\rangle$ will differ from those of $|b\rangle$,

$$a_j \neq b_j, \tag{2.18}$$

and will therefore have to be calculated by means of a continuous function different from the one in Eq. 2.16:

$$\psi_b(x_j) = b_j. \tag{2.19}$$

Therefore the operation that transforms $|a\rangle$ into $|b\rangle$, Eq. 2.1, is completely specified by the change in the expansion coefficients:

$$\psi_a(x) \to \psi_b(x). \tag{2.20}$$

It is tempting, therefore, to seek a mathematical method of accomplishing the transformation in Eq. 2.20 directly, rather than indirectly through Eq.

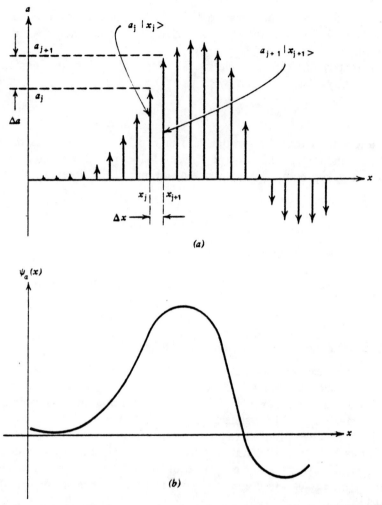

(a)

(b)

Figure 2.3 Relationship between the a's and ψ. At the top, the state of the system is represented by a linear superposition of eigenkets $|x_j\rangle$ with discrete eigenvalues x_j and expansion coefficients a_j. At the bottom, the discrete x_j's have been replaced by a continuum and the a_j's have been replaced by ψ.

2.1. This would have the advantage of replacing operations in the abstract Hilbert space by operations upon relatively more familiar continuous algebraic functions.

Fortunately this can be done in most cases of interest to chemists and chemical physicists. One can write

$$R(x)\psi_a(x) = \psi_b(x), \tag{2.21}$$

and understand that the symbol $R(x)$ in Eq. 2.21 accomplishes the same task in "function space" as the R of Eq. 2.1 does in Hilbert space. In other words, if ψ_a represents an eigenstate of the physically observable property R, then

$$\psi_b = r\psi_a, \tag{2.22}$$

where r is the same eigenvalue that appeared in Eq. 2.2. Equation 2.22 is also called an *eigenvalue equation*, and ψ_a is termed an *eigenfunction* of the operator $R(x)$. These relationships are illustrated schematically in Figure 2.4.

2.3   Schrödinger's equation; time dependence of ψ

It has just been shown that to each ket (associated with motion of an electron) there corresponds a state function $\psi(x)$, which represents the coefficients of the expansion of that ket in terms of a linear combination of the eigenkets of X. More generally, in three dimensions, ψ is a continuous algebraic function of all three coordinate variables, x, y, and z, because the operators X, Y, and Z commute with one another and have simultaneous eigenkets. The calculation of ψ is equivalent to the determination of the corresponding ket and completely specifies the state being represented by that ket.

To accomplish the central tasks of quantum mechanics, as stated in the language of kets at the beginning of Section 2.2, it is necessary to calculate ψ and to find the operators in function space that will extract from it the properties of the system in the state represented by ψ. Recall from Chapter 1 De Broglie's suggestion that particles such as electrons have some of the properties of waves. Schrödinger, following up this suggestion, assumed that the ψ's had the mathematical form of amplitudes for these waves, oscillating in the three spatial dimensions as well as in time. He found the differential equation which must be satisfied by any ψ, in order that it properly represent the state of a quantum system in the way that was just

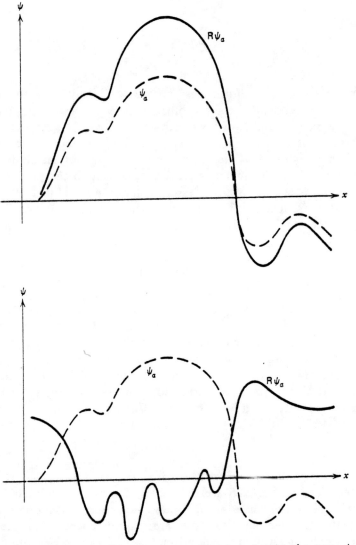

Figure 2.4 Effect of operator R on wavefunction ψ_a. At the top, ψ_a is an eigenfunction of R; at the bottom, ψ_a is not an eigenfunction of R.

described:

$$H\psi = i\hbar\left(\frac{\partial\psi}{\partial t}\right)_q,$$ (2.23)

where $i = \sqrt{-1}$. Henceforth the symbol q will stand for the entire collection of independent variables other than t (in this case the spatial coordinates, x, y, and z, of the electron).

The Hamiltonian operator, H, will in general depend on the variables q and t. In many cases of interest, however, the operator has no explicit time dependence. In such circumstances, it is possible to break Eq. 2.23 into two separate parts. To do this, it is assumed that the wavefunction is expressible as the product of two simpler functions. One function, T, depends only on the time. The other, Φ, depends on all of the other independent variables, q:

$$\psi(q,t) = \Phi(q)T(t).$$ (2.24)

The expression for ψ given in Eq. 2.24 may then be substituted into Schrödinger's equation 2.23. On the left-hand side, T is not affected by H because T and H depend on different variables. It may therefore be removed from the group of symbols to the right of H representing operands and placed to the left of H, becoming merely a scalar multiplier. On the right-hand side, Φ may be permuted with the operator $(\partial/\partial t)_q$ for the same reason. The result is expressed in Eq. 2.25:

$$T(t)H(q)\Phi(q) = i\hbar\Phi(q)\left[\frac{\partial T(t)}{\partial t}\right]_q.$$ (2.25)

If both sides of Eq. 2.25 are divided by $\psi = \Phi T$, the left-hand side will depend only on q, while the right-hand side depends only on the time. If the spatial and temporal variables are truly independent of one another, there is only one way in which a function of q can be equal to a function of t: both must be equal to a scalar constant. By inspection of Eq. 2.25, it can be seen that this constant must have the units of energy. It will therefore be called $\mathcal{E}$. The Schrödinger wave equation has now indeed been broken into two parts as originally intended,

$$\frac{i\hbar}{T(t)}\frac{dT(t)}{dt} = \mathcal{E}$$ (2.26)

and

$$\frac{1}{\Phi(q)} H(q)\Phi(q) = \mathscr{E}.$$ (2.27)

In mathematical language, $\mathscr{E}$ is called the *separation constant*. Equation 2.26 has the solution

$$T(t) = T(0)\exp\left(\frac{-i\mathscr{E}t}{\hbar}\right).$$ (2.28)

After multiplying both sides of Eq. 2.27 by ΦT, it may be seen that ψ is an eigenfunction of H and $\mathscr{E}$ is the corresponding eigenvalue. Physically, then, $\mathscr{E}$ is the total energy of the system whenever it is in the state ψ, and is a constant of the motion.

In conclusion, if H is independent of time, the solutions to Schrödinger's equation 2.23 are the eigenfunctions of H. There are presumably several linearly independent solutions of Eq. 2.27, each of which may correspond to a different value of $\mathscr{E}$, and therefore there is more than one satisfactory ψ. In particular, according to the earlier notation, there are expected to be exactly M possible solutions, the members of the set $\{|\mathscr{E}\rangle\}$:

$$H|\mathscr{E}_j\rangle = \mathscr{E}_j|\mathscr{E}_j\rangle, \quad 1 < j < M.$$ (2.29)

Furthermore, M must be ∞ in this case because (1) there are, by assumption, an infinite number of eigenstates of the position, and (2) the number of eigenstates does not change when one changes from one physically observable property (e.g., position) to another (energy). Since the time-dependent portion of the corresponding eigenfunction (T_j) can be canceled from both sides of Eq. 2.29, the principal emphasis in conventional courses in quantum mechanics is placed on finding the solution to Eq. 2.27. Sometimes sight is lost of the fact that the *complete* eigenfunction must include the time-dependent factor which appears in Eq. 2.26. Indeed, one edition of a respected standard college textbook of physical chemistry[‡] does not even contain the full time-dependent Schrödinger equation 2.23. Only the formula for Φ, Eq. 2.27, is presented! This omission is fatal to an understanding of the process by means of which transitions occur between the eigenstates of H.

[‡]Walter J. Moore, *Physical Chemistry*, 3rd ed. (Prentice-Hall, Englewood Cliffs, N. J., 1962). Fortunately, the full equation does appear in the fourth edition (1972).

From Eqs. 2.24 and 2.28, one finds that

$$\psi_j(q,t) = \Phi_j(q)T_j(0)\exp\left(\frac{-i\mathcal{E}_j t}{\hbar}\right).\qquad(2.30)$$

As stated in Chapter 1, the distribution function (probability density) for finding the system at the coordinates q is given by the complex square of ψ. (It will be shown in the next section why this is so.) Note from Eq. 2.30 that, when this is done, the exponential terms in ψ and ψ^* (the asterisk denotes the complex conjugate) will cancel one another, leaving a function that depends on q alone. Thus the eigenstates of the Hamiltonian operator are stationary in two senses. Not only is the corresponding physically observable property of the system ($\mathcal{E}$) a constant of the motion (as would be true of the eigenstates of any operator), but also the probability density $\psi_j\psi_j^*$ is independent of time. This fact probably contributes to the unfortunate tendency to slight the importance of the $T_j(t)$ functions.

2.4   Kets and bras: orthogonality and normalization

It is always possible to define the scalar product of two ordinary vectors. It is also possible to define the scalar product of two vectors in Hilbert space that represent states of quantum systems. For example, the dot product of two ordinary vectors,

$$\mathbf{A} = A_x\hat{x} + A_y\hat{y} + A_z\hat{z}\qquad(2.31)$$

and

$$\mathbf{B} = B_x\hat{x} + B_y\hat{y} + B_z\hat{z},\qquad(2.32)$$

is simply the scalar

$$\mathbf{A}\cdot\mathbf{B} = A_x B_x + A_y B_y + A_z B_z.\qquad(2.33)$$

To obtain this result, it has been assumed that the vectors in the three different Cartesian directions, $\hat{x}$, $\hat{y}$, and $\hat{z}$, are orthogonal to one another:

$$\hat{x}\cdot\hat{y} = \hat{y}\cdot\hat{z} = \hat{x}\cdot\hat{z} = 0,\qquad(2.34)$$

and normalized to unit length:

$$\hat{x}\cdot\hat{x} = \hat{y}\cdot\hat{y} = \hat{z}\cdot\hat{z} = 1.\qquad(2.35)$$

It is necessary to generalize this procedure so that it will work in Hilbert space. Consider the two kets in Eqs. 2.13 and 2.17. The eigenkets of position, $|x_j\rangle$, are presumably analogous to the unit vectors, $\hat{x}$, $\hat{y}$, and $\hat{z}$. (Recall Figure 2.2.) If they are orthogonal to one another and normalized to unit "length," the scalar product between $|a\rangle$ and $|b\rangle$ may be defined by

$$|a\rangle \cdot |b\rangle = a_1 b_1 + a_2 b_2 + \cdots + a_M b_M. \tag{2.36}$$

But the ket $|a\rangle$ is an eigenket of *some* operator, it matters not which. In that case, it will usually be normalized (e.g., to unity).[‡] If Eq. 2.36 is used,

$$|a\rangle \cdot |a\rangle = a_1^2 + a_2^2 + \cdots + a_M^2 = 1. \tag{2.37}$$

It can be shown that Eq. 2.37 cannot be satisfied in general. In particular, suppose that the scalars a_j are complex numbers (note the i in Schrödinger's Eq. 2.23):

$$a_j = \operatorname{Re}(a_j) + i \operatorname{Im}(a_j). \tag{2.38a}$$

The scalars $\operatorname{Re}(a_j)$ and $\operatorname{Im}(a_j)$ are both real.

[It is also necessary to recall the definition of the complex conjugate of a_j,

$$a_j^* = \operatorname{Re}(a_j) - i \operatorname{Im}(a_j), \tag{2.38b}$$

which will be needed shortly.] The squares of these coefficients are therefore also complex:

$$a_j^2 = \operatorname{Re}^2(a_j) - \operatorname{Im}^2(a_j) + 2i \operatorname{Re}(a_j) \operatorname{Im}(a_j). \tag{2.39}$$

Yet it was decided at the outset (see Eq. 2.37) to define $|a\rangle$ in such a way as to make the sum of the squares be a real number, namely, 1. From Eq. 2.39 it seems that this goal cannot be accomplished by using the definition of the scalar product of two kets given in Eq. 2.36.

This problem is solved by creating a new Hilbert space, called the *dual space*, also of M dimensions. To every ket $|a\rangle$ in the first space there corresponds another kind of vector, called a bra, $\langle a|$, in the dual space:

$$\langle a| = a_1^* \langle x_1| + a_2^* \langle x_2| + \cdots + a_M^* \langle x_M|. \tag{2.40}$$

[‡]In some cases, eigenkets cannot be normalized to unity. An important example is the set of eigenkets of momentum for a free particle. No such problems will be encountered, however, for the quantum systems described in this book.

Note that, in the expansion of $\langle a|$ in terms of the eigenbras of position $\langle x_j|$, the coefficients are the complex conjugates of those used in the expansion of the corresponding ket in Eq. 2.13. When scalar products are formed, a ket from one space is dotted into a bra from the other. This makes a bra(c)ket (the pun is intentional). In particular,

$$\langle a|a \rangle = a_1^* a_1 + a_2^* a_2 + \cdots + a_M^* a_M. \tag{2.41}$$

Note that each term in the sum of the right-hand side of Eq. 2.41 is automatically a real number,

$$a_j^* a_j = \mathrm{Re}^2(a_j) + \mathrm{Im}^2(a_j) \equiv |a_j|^2, \tag{2.42}$$

thereby guaranteeing that the scalar product of $\langle a|$ with $|a\rangle$ is also a real number.

If $|a\rangle$ and $|b\rangle$ are different eigenkets of some operator R with distinct eigenvalues $(r_a \neq r_b)$, it can be shown that they are orthogonal to one another:

$$\langle a|b \rangle = a_1^* b_1 + a_2^* b_2 + \cdots + a_M^* b_M = 0. \tag{2.43}$$

Note that, when M is ∞ and both a and b form a continuum, the sums on the right-hand sides of Eqs. 2.41 and 2.43 become integrals:

$$\lim_{M \to \infty} \sum_{j=1}^{M} a_j^* a_j = \lim_{M \to \infty} \sum_{j=1}^{M} \psi_a^*(q_j)\psi_a(q_j) = \int_{-\infty}^{\infty} |\psi_a|^2 \, dq = 1 \tag{2.44}$$

and

$$\lim_{M \to \infty} \sum_{j=1}^{M} a_j^* b_j = \lim_{M \to \infty} \sum_{j=1}^{M} \psi_a^*(q_j)\psi_b(q_j) = \int_{-\infty}^{\infty} \psi_a^* \psi_b \, dq = 0. \tag{2.45}$$

Equation 2.44 has the following physical interpretation. The value of the integral is the probability of finding the system with the coordinates q, summed over all q. This sum must then correspond to absolute certainty; the system will surely have its q *somewhere* in the range of $-\infty$ to $+\infty$. Since the orthogonality and normalization of state vectors in Hilbert space can be expressed by integrals of products of algebraic functions, it is convenient to say that the state functions themselves are orthogonal and normalized also.

It is also customary to normalize separately the factors Φ_j and T_j which appear in Eq. 2.30. Using Eq. 2.44, one obtains

$$\int_{-\infty}^{\infty} \Phi_j^*(q)\Phi_k(q)\,dq = \delta_{jk},$$ (2.46)

where δ_{jk} is Kronecker's delta,

$$\delta_{jk} = \begin{cases} 1 & \text{if } j = k, \\ 0 & \text{if } j \neq k, \end{cases}$$ (2.47)

and

$$T_j^*(0)T_j(0) = 1.$$ (2.48)

The solution to Eq. 2.48 is

$$T_j(0) = \exp(i\zeta_j),$$ (2.49)

where ζ_j is a real constant.

2.5   Quantum systems "in-between" eigenstates

The eigenstates of the energy by no means exhaust the behavioral repertoire of a quantum system. If $\{\psi\}_R$ is the set of functions representing eigenstates of R, any linear combination of the members of that set ($\psi_1, \psi_2, \ldots$) also represents possible states (see Eq. 2.13). Consider the state Ψ:

$$\Psi = c_1\psi_1 + c_2\psi_2 + \cdots + c_M\psi_M.$$ (2.50)

States such as Ψ may be called *nonstationary* because (1) when the system is in any one of them, the property represented by R will not be a constant of the motion; and (2) if R does not commute with H, the distribution function $\Psi^*\Psi$ will change with time.[‡] The fact that functions of the type given in Eq. 2.50 are necessary and sufficient to represent all possible states of a quantum system is called the *principle of superposition*. Nonstationary states are therefore sometimes called *superposition states*. Equation 2.50 is trivial unless at least two of the c_j's are nonzero. On the other hand, to allow for more than two terms in the sum would greatly complicate the calculations that follow, without introducing any important additional physical insight into the problem. Therefore only the first two terms will henceforth be used.

[‡]This statement is not true if all of the eigenfunctions included in Eq. 2.50 (i.e., those with nonzero coefficients) are degenerate.

Suppose that the superposition function Ψ is substituted into Schrödinger's equation (2.33). Is it true that

$$H(c_1\psi_1 + c_2\psi_2) = i\hbar\left[\frac{\partial}{\partial t}(c_1\psi_1 + c_2\psi_2)\right]_q ? \qquad (2.51)$$

The distributive law may be used on both sides of Eq. 2.51 to achieve

$$Hc_1\psi_1 + Hc_2\psi_2 \overset{?}{=} i\hbar\left[\frac{\partial(c_1\psi_1)}{\partial t}\right]_q + i\hbar\left[\frac{\partial(c_2\psi_2)}{\partial t}\right]_q. \qquad (2.52)$$

Expressions for ψ_1 and ψ_2 may be found by combining Eqs. 2.30 and 2.49:

$$\psi_1 = \Phi_1 \exp\left[i\left(\zeta_1 - \frac{\mathcal{E}_1 t}{\hbar}\right)\right] \qquad (2.53)$$

and

$$\psi_2 = \Phi_2 \exp\left[i\left(\zeta_2 - \frac{\mathcal{E}_2 t}{\hbar}\right)\right]. \qquad (2.54)$$

Remember that the case in which H does not explicitly depend on time is being considered. Furthermore, c_1 and c_2 are assumed to be constants, independent of both q and t.

The first term on the left-hand side of Eq. 2.52 can then be rearranged:

$$Hc_1\psi_1 = c_1 \exp\left[i\left(\zeta_1 - \frac{\mathcal{E}_1 t}{\hbar}\right)\right]H\Phi_1. \qquad (2.55)$$

Next, Eq. 2.27 may be used to find

$$H\Phi_1 = \mathcal{E}_1\Phi_1. \qquad (2.56)$$

On the right-hand side of Eq. 2.52, the first term becomes

$$i\hbar\left[\frac{\partial(c_1\psi_1)}{\partial t}\right]_q = i\hbar c_1\Phi_1\left(\frac{\partial\{\exp[i(\zeta_1 - \mathcal{E}_1 t/\hbar)]\}}{\partial t}\right)_q. \qquad (2.57)$$

Next, the derivative on the right-hand side of Eq. 2.57 may be calculated:

$$\left(\frac{\partial\{\exp[i(\zeta_1 - \mathcal{E}_1 t/\hbar)]\}}{\partial t}\right)_q = \frac{-i\mathcal{E}_1}{\hbar}\exp\left[i\left(\zeta_1 - \frac{\mathcal{E}_1 t}{\hbar}\right)\right]. \qquad (2.58)$$

The corresponding expressions for the second terms on both sides of Eq. 2.52 are identical to Eqs. 2.56 and 2.58 except for the subscripts. These results may be substituted into Eq. 2.52:

$$c_1 \exp\left[i\left(\zeta_1 - \frac{\mathcal{E}_1 t}{\hbar}\right)\right]\mathcal{E}_1\Phi_1 + c_2\exp\left[i\left(\zeta_2 - \frac{\mathcal{E}_2 t}{\hbar}\right)\right]\mathcal{E}_2\Phi_2 \overset{?}{=}$$

$$i\hbar c_1\Phi_1\left(\frac{-i\mathcal{E}_1}{\hbar}\right)\exp\left[i\left(\zeta_1 - \frac{\mathcal{E}_1 t}{\hbar}\right)\right] + i\hbar c_2\Phi_2\left(\frac{-i\mathcal{E}_2}{\hbar}\right)\exp\left[i\left(\zeta_2 - \frac{\mathcal{E}_2 t}{\hbar}\right)\right].$$

$$(2.59)$$

It can be seen from Eq. 2.59 that the equality is satisfied. It has therefore been proved that a wavefunction formed by the linear superposition of two eigenfunctions of the Hamiltonian operator (Eq. 2.50) is as valid a solution to Schrödinger's equation 2.23 as either one of the two constituent eigenfunctions separately. This proof can easily be extended to wavefunctions formed by the linear combination of any number of eigenstates. Therefore superposition states of quantum systems are as "real" (possible) in nature as are eigenstates.

Do wavefunctions representing superposition states (Eq. 2.50) also satisfy the time-independent portion of Schrödinger's equation 2.23,

$$H(c_1\psi_1 + c_2\psi_2) \overset{?}{=} \mathcal{E}(c_1\psi_1 + c_2\psi_2)? \qquad (2.60)$$

The question of how the energy $\mathcal{E}$ should be evaluated in the above expression must be put aside for the moment. Suffice it to say that $\mathcal{E}$ is a nonzero scalar, as it must be in order to be a separation constant. The left-hand side of Eq. 2.60 is identical with the left-hand side of Eq. 2.51, so that it may be replaced by the left-hand side of Eq. 2.59. The right-hand side of Eq. 2.60 may be evaluated immediately from the distributive law. Equation 2.60 therefore becomes

$$c_1\exp\left[i\left(\zeta_1 - \frac{\mathcal{E}_1 t}{\hbar}\right)\right]\mathcal{E}_1\Phi_1 + c_2\exp\left[i\left(\zeta_2 - \frac{\mathcal{E}_2 t}{\hbar}\right)\right]\mathcal{E}_2\Phi_2 \overset{?}{=}$$

$$\mathcal{E}c_1\Phi_1\exp\left[i\left(\zeta_1 - \frac{\mathcal{E}_1 t}{\hbar}\right)\right] + \mathcal{E}c_2\Phi_2\exp\left[i\left(\zeta_2 - \frac{\mathcal{E}_2 t}{\hbar}\right)\right]. \qquad (2.61)$$

It is obvious from inspection of Eq. 2.61 that the equality can be satisfied only if $\mathcal{E} = \mathcal{E}_1 = \mathcal{E}_2$. Therefore, if the superposition states formed by a

linear combination of degenerate eigenstates of the Hamiltonian operator
are excluded from the discussion, the equality expressed in Eq. 2.60 cannot
hold. This means that the time-independent Schrödinger equation 2.56 has
a very limited validity. In particular, if $M = 2$, and these are not energy
degenerate, there are only two possible eigenstates of the system, represented by the wavefunctions that satisfy Eq. 2.29. By way of contrast, there
are an infinite number of possible linear combinations of the form in Eq.
2.50. This is so because there are an infinite number of possible choices of
c_1/c_2, each one of which represents a possible "real" and valid state of the
quantum system. In general, then, Eq. 2.61 may be rewritten as follows:

$$\mathsf{H}\Psi \neq \mathcal{E}\,\Psi. \tag{2.62}$$

Some of the properties of these superposition states will now be explored. In the first place, the distribution functions for positions associated
with these states are not stationary (unless the eigenstates of which they are
composed are degenerate). To prove this, the distribution function can be
calculated:

$$\Psi^*\Psi = c_1^* c_1 \psi_1^* \psi_1 + c_2^* c_2 \psi_2^* \psi_2 + c_1^* c_2 \psi_1^* \psi_2 + c_2^* c_1 \psi_2^* \psi_1. \tag{2.63}$$

Recalling the rules about complex numbers and functions, expressed in
Eqs. 2.38, 2.39, and 2.42, plus the fact that

$$a + a^* = 2\mathrm{Re}(a), \tag{2.64}$$

one may rewrite Eq. 2.63 to obtain

$$|\Psi|^2 = |c_1|^2|\psi_1|^2 + |c_2|^2|\psi_2|^2 + 2\mathrm{Re}(c_1^* c_2 \psi_1^* \psi_2). \tag{2.65}$$

Equations 2.53 and 2.54 supply the necessary expressions for the wavefunctions. Equation 2.65 becomes

$$|\Psi|^2 = |c_1|^2|\Phi_1|^2 + |c_2|^2|\Phi_2|^2 + 2\mathrm{Re}\{c_1^* c_2 \Phi_1^* \Phi_2 \exp[i(\delta' - \omega_0 t)]\} \tag{2.66}$$

In Eq. 2.66,

$$\delta' \equiv \zeta_2 - \zeta_1 \tag{2.67}$$

and

$$\omega_0 \equiv \frac{\mathcal{E}_2 - \mathcal{E}_1}{\hbar}. \tag{2.68}$$

The explicit time dependence of the third term on the right-hand side of Eq. 2.66 proves the assertion that the state represented by the wavefunction in Eq. 2.50 is not stationary. The probability distribution for a system in a stationary state is a "standing wave," $|\psi_j|^2$. Just as is the case in classical mechanics, a standing wave consists of two traveling waves having the same frequency but going in opposite directions (cf. the time dependences of ψ_j^* and ψ_j). Also just as in classical mechanics, whenever a system is excited in such a way that two modes of oscillation of different frequencies are present at the same time, one may expect to "hear" the beat frequency. In this case, $\mathscr{E}_1/\hbar$ and $\mathscr{E}_2/\hbar$ are the different modal frequencies, and ω_0 is the interference beat frequency. The distribution function in Eq. 2.66 then contains two constant terms (the first two on the right-hand side), one for each of the two eigenfunctions of which the total wavefunction is composed. It also contains the third term on the right-hand side; this describes the sinusoidally pulsating interference pattern between wavefunctions for the two eigenstates, which alternate between destructive and constructive interference at the frequency ω_0.

A relationship between the two constants, c_1 and c_2, which appear in Eqs. 2.50 and 2.66 can be discovered, requiring that Ψ be normalized to 1:

$$\int_{-\infty}^{+\infty} |\Psi|^2 \, dq = |c_1|^2 \int_{-\infty}^{+\infty} |\Phi_1|^2 \, dq + |c_2|^2 \int_{-\infty}^{+\infty} |\Phi_2|^2 \, dq$$

$$+ \mathrm{Re}\left\{ c_1^* c_2 \exp[\, i(\delta' - \omega_0 t)] \int_{-\infty}^{+\infty} \Phi_1^* \Phi_2 \, dq \right\} = 1. \quad (2.69)$$

The integrals on the right-hand side of Eq. 2.68 may be evaluated from the orthogonal character of the Φ's—see Eq. 2.46. Equation 2.69 becomes

$$|c_1|^2 + |c_2|^2 = 1. \quad (2.70)$$

The most general solution to Eq. 2.70 is

$$c_1 = \left[\cos\left(\frac{\theta}{2}\right) \right] \exp(i\xi_1) \quad (2.71)$$

and

$$c_2 = \left[\sin\left(\frac{\theta}{2}\right) \right] \exp(i\xi_2). \quad (2.72)$$

The real scalars, θ, ξ_1, and ξ_2, replace the real and imaginary parts of the c's as the parameters that specify the superposition state. A physical interpretation of them will be given in Chapters 4 and 6. The total wavefunction in Eq. 2.50 can then be written as

$$\Psi(q,t) = \left[\cos\left(\frac{\theta}{2}\right)\right]\Phi_1(q)\exp\left[i\left(\eta_1 - \frac{\mathcal{E}_1 t}{\hbar}\right)\right]$$

$$+ \left[\sin\left(\frac{\theta}{2}\right)\right]\Phi_2(q)\exp\left[i\left(\eta_2 - \frac{\mathcal{E}_2 t}{\hbar}\right)\right], \qquad (2.73)$$

where η_j is defined by

$$\eta_j = \zeta_j + \xi_j, \qquad j = 1, 2. \qquad (2.74)$$

2.6   Eigenvalues and expectation values

Bras, kets, and wavefunctions for both stationary and nonstationary (superposition) states have been discussed. Next, a method for extracting information about the physical properties of a system from these entities must be found.

Suppose that the physical property of interest is represented by the operator R. Furthermore, suppose that the system is in a state represented by the ket $|a\rangle$. If the system is not in an eigenstate of R, it must be in a superposition of such states because the eigenstates of any operator constitute a complete set. Then the ket $|a\rangle$ can be written as a linear combination of the eigenkets of R, which shall be labelled by their corresponding eigenvalues, r_j:

$$|a\rangle = a_1|r_1\rangle + a_2|r_2\rangle + \cdots + a_M|r_M\rangle. \qquad (2.75)$$

Equation 2.75 will be suitable for the description of $|a\rangle$ even if the system represented thereby is in an eigenstate (e.g., the 39th eigenstate) of R. In this case, it is simple to set all the a_j's equal to 0 except a_{39}, which can be made equal to 1.

Regardless of the number of nonzero terms in the sum, what will be the outcome of an experiment on the system in which the physical property R is measured? The answer to this question is decided by first operating upon $|a\rangle$ with the operator R and then forming the scalar product of the resultant ket with the bra $\langle a|$.

In the first step, the distributive law is used, plus the fact that operating with R commutes with multiplying by the scalar coefficients a_j:

$$R|a\rangle = a_1 R|r_1\rangle + a_2 R|r_2\rangle + \cdots + a_M R|r_M\rangle. \qquad (2.76)$$

Since, on the right-hand side of Eq. 2.66, the operators R are operating only upon eigenkets, the results are known:

$$R|a\rangle = a_1 r_1 |r_1\rangle + a_2 r_2 |r_2\rangle + \cdots + a_M r_M |r_M\rangle. \tag{2.77}$$

In the next step, the formation of the scalar product with $\langle a|$, the fact that the eigenkets of R are orthogonal to one another and normalized to unity is used:

$$\langle a|R|a\rangle = |a_1|^2 r_1 + |a_2|^2 r_2 + \cdots + |a_M|^2 r_M. \tag{2.78}$$

If the system is in the 39th eigenstate, all of the terms on the right-hand side will be zero except the 39th, which will have the value r_{39}. Experimentally, the measurement process will produce a result equal to r_{39}. Furthermore, the measurement will be reproducible; for example, repeated measurements performed under identical conditions will produce the same result. On the other hand, if the system is in a superposition of eigenstates (two or more a_j's nonzero in Eq. 2.75), measurements of the property represented by R will not be reproducible. Each individual measurement will have, as its result, an eigenvalue corresponding to one of the eigenfunctions included in the superposition wavefunction. There will be no way to predict, in advance of a particular measurement, which of the possible different eigenvalues will be obtained therefrom. This fact is called the *uncertainty principle*. The probability that the result of the measurement will be that expected for the jth state will be $|a_j|^2$. Whenever the jth state shows up, the value of R obtained will be r_j. The expression on the right-hand side of Eq. 2.78 corresponds to the average result of a large number of such measurements. The average value of some physical property of a quantum system is called an *expectation value*. This special term is used to emphasize the distinction between the averaging process in classical mechanics, necessitated by experimental failure to adequately control all of the variables affecting the outcome of the measurement, and quantum-mechanical averaging, necessitated by fundamental laws of nature.

Equation 2.78 is identical with the formula for finding the weighted average of $\bar{R}$ in classical statistics:

$$\bar{R} = \frac{\displaystyle\sum_{j=1}^{M} W_j r_j}{\displaystyle\sum_{j=1}^{M} W_j}. \tag{2.79}$$

The M symbols W_j are the statistical weights to be assigned to each of the independent possibilities for R; it is easily seen that the $|a_j|^2$ terms in Eq 2.78 play the same role as the W_j's in Eq. 2.79. The sum in the denominator on the right-hand side of Eq. 2.79 is usually 1 because the statistical weights are ordinarily normalized before use.

It sometimes happens in both classical and quantum statistics that there is a continuum of possibilities. In such cases, the M statistical weights W_j are replaced by a continuous distribution function:

$$\overline{R(t)} = \frac{\int_{-\infty}^{+\infty} W(q,t)R(q)\,dq}{\int_{-\infty}^{+\infty} W(q,t)\,dq}. \tag{2.80}$$

In Eq. 2.80, R and W are both algebraic functions of the coordinate q. Again, the denominator on the right-hand side is ordinarily 1:

$$\lim_{n \to \infty} \sum_{j=1}^{M} |a_j|^2 r_j = \int_{-\infty}^{+\infty} |\psi_a(q,t)|^2 r(q)\,dq. \tag{2.81}$$

Therefore, from Eqs. 2.21, 2.45, and 2.78,

$$\langle R(t) \rangle \equiv \langle a|R|a \rangle = \frac{\int_{-\infty}^{+\infty} \Psi^*(q,t)R(q)\Psi(q,t)\,dq}{\int_{-\infty}^{+\infty} |\Psi(q,t)|^2\,dq}. \tag{2.82}$$

Just as was the case in classical statistics, the denominator is usually 1. The operator R operates only on Ψ, the function that appears immediately to its right, in accordance with the usual custom. The symbol $\langle R \rangle$ is used to distinguish between the expectation value and the classical weighted average, $\overline{R}$.

It can be easily seen that, if Ψ is an eigenfunction of R, its time dependence will cancel that of Ψ^*. In such a case, $\langle R \rangle$ will depend on the time only if the operator R does as well. On the other hand, if Ψ is a linear combination of nondegenerate eigenfunctions of R (and therefore represents a superposition state for the system), $\langle R \rangle$ will be time dependent even if the operator R and the coefficients c_j are constants. For example, the wavefunction of Eq. 2.73 may be used in Eq. 2.82:

$$\langle R(t) \rangle = R_{11} \cos^2\left(\frac{\theta}{2}\right) + R_{22} \sin^2\left(\frac{\theta}{2}\right)$$

$$+ 2\cos\left(\frac{\theta}{2}\right)\sin\left(\frac{\theta}{2}\right)\text{Re}\{R_{12}\exp[i(\S - \omega_0 t)]\}. \tag{2.83}$$

where

$$\S \equiv \eta_2 - \eta_1 \tag{2.84}$$

and

$$R_{jk} \equiv \int_{-\infty}^{+\infty} \Phi_j^*(q) R(q) \Phi_k(q) \, dq. \tag{2.85}$$

The parameters θ, η, and ω_0 were defined in Eqs. 2.68, 2.71, 2.72, and 2.74. The symbol R_{jk} is sometimes termed the jkth matrix element of R.

Note that the results in Eq. 2.83 are completely general, in that they apply to any physically observable quantity represented by an operator which does not explicitly contain the time. Note also that, if two such operators commute, the expectation values of the physical properties that they represent must have the same kind of time dependence. The facts represented mathematically by Eq. 2.83 can be re-expressed in more physical terms. The averaged properties of a quantum system cannot depend on the time unless the system is in a superposition state.[‡] The time dependence is due to the beating together of the two (or more) probability waves that have been superposed (compare Eqs. 2.66 and 2.83). The coefficients of the eigenfunctions, c_1 and c_2 (see Eqs. 2.71 and 2.72), must be *simultaneously* nonzero. In particular, suppose that $\theta = \pi/2$. Then $|c_1|^2 = |c_2|^2 = \frac{1}{2}$. It is *not* correct (or, at least, it is very misleading) to describe the state represented by

$$\Psi = \frac{\psi_1 + \psi_2}{\sqrt{2}} \tag{2.86}$$

as one in which the system spends half of its time in the eigenstate represented by ψ_1 and the other half in the eigenstate represented by ψ_2. If the system represented by the function in Eq. 2.83 really did "hop back and forth" between the states represented by ψ_1 and ψ_2, there would never be an interval during which both wavefunctions would be present simultaneously, and therefore the beat term would always have zero amplitude. There would never be any time dependence in any physically observable property of the system, in the same way that one does not hear the beat between two notes played on a piano in succession. (The significance of the c's will be discussed in greater detail in Chapter 4.)

[‡]Possible exceptions are provided by cases in which the operators themselves change with time.

2.7 Superposed eigenfunctions and perturbed eigenfunctions

There is a superficial similarity between the defining equation for superposition states (Eq. 2.50) and equations that arise in the branch of
quantum mechanics called "perturbation theory." However, *there is no
similarity between superposition states and the "mixed states" encountered in
perturbation theory*. To prove this, a brief review of the latter is now
presented.

Let ψ_1 and ψ_2 be two eigenfunctions of a Hamiltonian, H, with eigenvalues $\mathscr{E}_1$ and $\mathscr{E}_2$. Suppose, however, that the problem of interest is one
for which the Hamiltonian is

$$H = H_0 + H'. \tag{2.87}$$

It may be difficult or inconvenient to start from scratch and solve the new
problem, finding the new eigenfunctions, ψ'_1 and ψ'_2, and eigenvalues, $\mathscr{E}'_1$
and $\mathscr{E}'_2$, directly. There will be two differences between the set $\{\psi_j\}_{H_0}$ and
the set $\{\psi'_j\}_{H_0+H'}$. The spatial distributions of the electron(s) will be
different, and (because the corresponding eigenvalues are different) the
time-dependent factors will also be different. In particular,

$$\psi_1(q,t) = \Phi_1(q) \exp\left(\frac{-i\mathscr{E}_1 t}{\hbar}\right), \tag{2.88}$$

$$\psi'_1(q,t) = \Phi'_1(q) \exp\left(\frac{-i\mathscr{E}'_1 t}{\hbar}\right), \tag{2.89}$$

$$\Phi_1(q) \neq \Phi'_1(q), \tag{2.90}$$

and

$$\mathscr{E}_1 \neq \mathscr{E}'_1. \tag{2.91}$$

Similar inequalities will hold for ψ_2 and ψ'_2.

On the other hand, if $\Phi_1(q)$ and $\Phi_2(q)$ constitute a complete set for the
first problem, the *location* of the electron in the second problem can be
described by

$$\Phi'_1(q) = c_{11}\Phi_1(q) + c_{12}\Phi_2(q) \tag{2.92}$$

and

$$\Phi'_1(q) = c_{21}\Phi_1(q) + c_{22}\Phi_2(q). \tag{2.93}$$

Note especially that it is *not* true that

$$\psi_1'(q,t) = c_{11}\psi_1(q,t) + c_{12}\psi_2(q,t), \tag{2.94}$$

for example. This is so because the time dependence of ψ_1' is controlled by $\mathcal{E}_1'$, which in general will be different from the time dependence of ψ_1 and ψ_2, the latter being controlled by $\mathcal{E}_1$ and $\mathcal{E}_2$, respectively. In fact, Eqs. 2.92 and 2.93 have no particular quantum-mechanical significance because the problem for which Φ_1' and Φ_2' are appropriate is different from the one for which Φ_1 and Φ_2 are appropriate. The expansion of Φ_1' in terms of Φ_1 and Φ_2 was performed only for mathematical convenience; any other functions that are complete over x,y,z space would, in principle, do as well. In practice, Φ_1 and Φ_2 are convenient because they both happen to be eigenfunctions of H_0. By definition, ψ_1' and ψ_2' are eigenfunctions of H:

$$H\psi_1' = \mathcal{E}_1'\psi_1' \tag{2.95}$$

and

$$H\psi_2' = \mathcal{E}_2'\psi_2'. \tag{2.96}$$

Equation 2.89 and 2.92 may be substituted into Eq. 2.95:

$$(H_0 + H')(c_{11}\Phi_1 + c_{12}\Phi_2)\exp\left(\frac{-i\mathcal{E}_1't}{\hbar}\right) = \mathcal{E}_1'(c_{11}\Phi_1 + c_{12}\Phi_2)\exp\left(\frac{-i\mathcal{E}_1't}{\hbar}\right). \tag{2.97}$$

If neither H_0 nor H' depends on the time, $\exp(-i\mathcal{E}_1't/\hbar)$ will commute with H on the left-hand side of Eq. 2.97 and subsequently be canceled with the same term on the right-hand side. Next, the distributive law and the fact that ψ_1 and ψ_2 are eigenfunctions of H_0 may be used to transform Eq. 2.97 into

$$c_{11}(\mathcal{E}_1\Phi_1 + H'\Phi_1) + c_{12}(\mathcal{E}_2\Phi_2 + H'\Phi_2) = c_{11}\mathcal{E}_1'\Phi_1 + c_{12}\mathcal{E}_1'\Phi_2. \tag{2.98}$$

Equation 2.98 can be transformed into two scalar equations by first multiplying from the left by Φ_1^* and integrating over coordinates, and then repeating the process using Φ_2^* instead. The results are as follows:

$$c_{11}(\mathcal{E}_1 + H_{11}') + c_{12}H_{12}' = c_{11}\mathcal{E}_1' \tag{2.99}$$

and

$$c_{11}H_{21}' + c_{12}(\mathcal{E}_2 + H_{22}') = c_{12}\mathcal{E}_1'. \tag{2.100}$$

The only integrations that must be performed to obtain Eqs. 2.99 and 2.100 are

$$H'_{11} \equiv \int \Phi_1^*(q) H'(q) \Phi_1(q)\, dq, \qquad (2.101)$$

$$H'_{22} \equiv \int \Phi_2^*(q) H'(q) \Phi_2(q)\, dq, \qquad (2.102)$$

and

$$H'_{12} \equiv \int \Phi_1^*(q) H'(q) \Phi_2(q)\, dq. \qquad (2.103)$$

This is so because Φ_1 and Φ_2 are orthogonal functions and because H′, like all other operators in quantum mechanics, is Hermitian:

$$H'_{21} = H'^{*}_{12}. \qquad (2.104)$$

(Equation 2.104 can be taken as the defining equation of a Hermitian operator.) It is also necessary that Φ'_1 and Φ'_2 be normalized. From this fact it follows that

$$|c_{11}|^2 + |c_{12}|^2 = 1 \qquad (2.105)$$

and

$$|c_{21}|^2 + |c_{22}|^2 = 1. \qquad (2.106)$$

Equations 2.99 and 2.100 can be summarized in matrix form:

$$\begin{pmatrix} 0 \\ 0 \end{pmatrix} = \begin{bmatrix} (\mathcal{E}_1 + H'_{11}) - \mathcal{E} & H'_{12} \\ H'_{21} & (\mathcal{E}_2 + H'_{22}) - \mathcal{E} \end{bmatrix} \begin{pmatrix} c_{11} \\ c_{12} \end{pmatrix} \qquad (2.107)$$

The theory of linear equations may be used to show that the determinant of the 2×2 coefficient matrix on the left-hand side of Eq. 2.107 must be zero. This gives rise to what is called the *secular equation*:

$$[(\mathcal{E}_1 + H'_{11}) - \mathcal{E}][(\mathcal{E}_2 + H'_{22}) - \mathcal{E}] - H'_{12} H'_{21} = 0. \qquad (2.108)$$

This equation is quadratic in $\mathcal{E}$, the only unknown, and will therefore have only two solutions. One of these will be the desired $\mathcal{E}'_1$, and the other will be $\mathcal{E}'_2$, the eigenvalue that is appropriate for the other wavefunction. Substitution of $\mathcal{E}'_1$ into Eqs. 2.99 and 2.100 will give two equations with four unknowns, the real and imaginary parts of c_{11} and c_{12}. If these coefficients are written as

$$c_{jk} = |c_{jk}| \exp(i\xi_{jk}),\qquad\qquad(2.109)$$

Eqs. 2.105 and 2.106 may then be used to find $|c_{11}|$, $|c_{12}|$, and $\xi_{11} - \xi_{12}$.

Thus it can be seen that Eqs. 2.92 and 2.93 describe, *not* a superposition of two eigenstates to form a nonstationary state of a system with a Hamiltonian, H_0, but rather the spatially dependent parts of two new eigenfunctions, each appropriate for the new Hamiltonian, $H_0 + H'$ (see Figure 2.5).

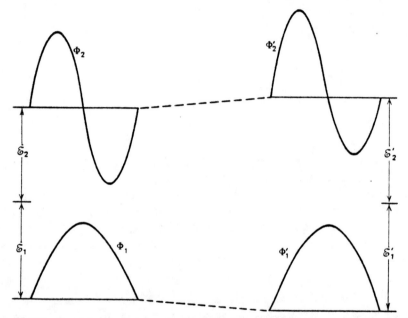

Figure 2.5   Perturbation of the spatial part of the wavefunction by H'. On the left, the wavefunctions are unperturbed; on the right, perturbed.

2.8   References

1.   U. Fano and L. Fano, *Basic Physics of Atoms and Molecules* (John Wiley and Sons, New York, 1959).

2.9   Problems

2.1.   Prove that, if two operators R and S have simultaneous eigenkets, they commute.

2.2   Imagine a particle of mass m_0 constrained to move in one linear dimension, x. Examples are a bead on a taut string and a piston in a cylinder. Furthermore, imagine that the motion of the particle is confined to a small portion of the x axis, $0 < x < L$ (e.g., a bead on a length of string that is knotted at both ends to prevent the bead from slipping off). The description of this system, called the one-dimensional infinite-square-well-potential problem, is discussed in many books on quantum mechanics. The spatial parts of the eigenfunctions of the Hamiltonian operator are

$$\Phi_n(x) = \begin{cases} \sqrt{2/L} \ \sin(n\pi x/L), & 0 < x < L, \\ 0, & 0 > x > L, \end{cases}$$

where n is a positive integer:

$$n = 1, 2, 3, \ldots, \infty.$$

The corresponding eigenvalues are

$$\mathcal{E}_n = \frac{n^2 h^2}{8 m_0 L^2}.$$

a.   Find an expression for the *total* eigenfunctions, $\psi_n(x, t)$, of the Hamiltonian operator for the bead on a string.

b.   Find an expression for the total wavefunction, Ψ, representing the particle in a linear superposition of the nth and pth eigenstates of the energy. Use equal superposition coefficients,

$$c_n = c_p = \frac{1}{\sqrt{2}},$$

in order that the results may describe the "halfway" state.

2.3.   Suppose that the bead in Problem 2.3 has an electric charge of $+q_0$, and the leftmost knot on the string, a charge of $-q_0$. Then the system will have an instantaneous electric dipole moment of $q_0 x \hat{x}$, where x is the instantaneous position of the bead and $\hat{x}$ is a unit vector in the x direction.

a.   Calculate the expectation value of the dipole moment for the bead on the string when the system is in the $n = 1$ eigenstate of the energy. The operator for the x coordinate is x itself:

$$X = x.$$

b.   Calculate the expectation value of the dipole moment for the bead on the string when the system is in the "halfway" superposition of the $n = 1$ and $p = 2$ eigenstates of the energy.

c. Perform the same calculation as in Problem 2.3b, but use as the superposed states the $n=1$ and $p=3$ eigenstates of the energy.

2.4. Define $\mathcal{E}$ by the relation

$$2\mathcal{E} = \frac{(1^2 - 2^2)h^2}{8m_0L^2}.$$

Then, for the bead on the string described in Problem 2.2, set the zero of energy at the midpoint between the first and second eigenvalues:

$$\mathcal{E}_1 = -\mathcal{E}_2 = \mathcal{E}.$$

Suppose that a perturbation is applied to this system:

$$H'_{11} = H'_{22} = 0, \quad \text{and} \quad H'_{12} = H'_{21} = V\mathcal{E},$$

where V is a dimensionless parameter.

a. Show that the perturbed energies are

$$\mathcal{E}'_1 = -\mathcal{E}'_2 = \mathcal{E}\sqrt{1+V^2}.$$

b. Show that the spatial parts of the perturbed eigenfunctions of the new Hamiltonian operator are (aside from an arbitrary phase factor)

$$\Phi'_1 = \Phi_1 \cos\left(\frac{\theta}{2}\right) + \Phi_2 \sin\left(\frac{\theta}{2}\right)$$

and

$$\Phi'_2 = \Phi_1 \sin\left(\frac{\theta}{2}\right) - \Phi_2 \cos\left(\frac{\theta}{2}\right),$$

where

$$\frac{\theta}{2} = \tan^{-1}\left(\frac{V}{1+\sqrt{1+V^2}}\right).$$

c. Assume that $V=0.5$. Then make energy level diagrams for both the perturbed and unperturbed cases, and sketch on each level the corresponding wavefunctions. Compare the results with those presented in Figure 2.5.

3 Elementary electromagnetic theory

3.1 Relationship between classical and quantum-mechanical theories

Spectroscopy is the study of resonant, reversible exchanges of energy between chromophores (atoms, ions, and molecules) and an oscillating electromagnetic field. In Chapter 2, a theoretical description of the chromophores was presented. The purpose of this chapter is to provide a description of the electromagnetic field. The theoretical description of the chromophores, although elementary and incomplete, hewed strictly to the principles of the theory believed to be rigorously correct for such systems —namely, quantum mechanics. By way of contrast, it is proposed to describe the radiation field in accordance with classical electromagnetic theory, which is known to be only an approximation to the correct theory, with a limited range of validity. A thorough exposition of the classical theory may be found in many standard textbooks (e.g., the one by Stratton[1]).

Before beginning the classical treatment, it is appropriate to discuss briefly the rigorously correct theory of the electromagnetic field, quantum electrodynamics.[2] Many features of that theory of interest to spectroscopists are best discussed by contrasting them with corresponding features of the classical treatment. In classical electromagnetic theory, an arbitrary collection of charges and currents can serve as the source of electromagnetic waves. The dependence of the electric and magnetic fields produced by this source on space and time can be very complicated and must be analyzed by means of Maxwell's equations in their full generality. In spectroscopic experiments, however, the sample consists of absorbing quantum systems so situated in relation to the source that the fields of the latter take on a very simple form, namely, sinusoidal electromagnetic waves. Details of calculations based on this fact will be discussed in subsequent chapters. For the present purposes, it is sufficient to remember from Chapter 1 that each wave can be characterized by two parameters, its propagation vector, $\mathbf{k}$, and its electric field vector, $\mathbf{E}_1$. The wavelength may be obtained from the magnitude of $\mathbf{k}$, and the amplitude from the magnitude of $\mathbf{E}_1$. Finally, the velocity of propagation of these waves in a vacuum is c_0, a constant of nature. Ordinarily in spectroscopy, a sample is exposed simultaneously to several waves of differing $\mathbf{k}$ and $\mathbf{E_1}$. It is also usually the case, however, that this complication can be ignored and the interaction of the sample with each wave treated separately.

In the quantum theory of radiation the wave picture is replaced by the photon picture, also introduced in Chapter 1. Each photon is a point particle of zero rest mass, containing electromagnetic energy hck and traveling in a direction parallel to $\mathbf{k}$ with a velocity c. In this chapter it will be convenient to allow the electric field amplitude to be a complex number. The number density of photons associated with a given wave must be proportional to $|E_1|^2$. Therefore

$$|E_1|^2 = \mathbf{E_1^*} \cdot \mathbf{E_1},\tag{3.1}$$

rather than the E_1^2 used in Chapter 1, where E_1 was assumed to be real (Eqs. 1.6 and 1.18). For the rest of this chapter, E_1 will be written E.

3.2 Applicability of classical and quantum theories

The statements made in Section 3.1 can be expressed in more formal language. Associated with each possible value of $\mathbf{k}$ is a mode of the radiation field. The energy in this mode is quantized in accordance with the formula

$$\mathcal{E}_{\mathbf{k},m} = \hbar ck(m + \tfrac{1}{2}), \qquad m = 0, 1, 2, \ldots, \infty,\tag{3.2}$$

where m is the number of photons in the mode characterized by $\mathbf{k}$. (Usually, the zero of energy is defined in such a way that the $\tfrac{1}{2}$ on the right-hand side of Eq. 3.2 does not appear.)

Note that, even in the total absence of photons ($m = 0$), there is still energy in the mode. A similar situation occurs in the quantum-mechanical treatment of matter, although it was not discussed in Chapter 2. An example is provided by the vibrational motions of a molecule. If such motions are adequately described by the harmonic oscillator model, the eigenvalues of the Hamiltonian operator are given by an expression identical in form to Eq. 3.2. In particular, there is an irreducible minimum vibrational energy, $\mathcal{E}_{\min}$, where

$$\mathcal{E}_{\min} = \frac{\hbar\omega}{2}.\tag{3.3}$$

This energy is present at equilibrium even at the absolute zero of temperature and is called the *zero-point energy* of the oscillator. Zero-point energy is required in order to satisfy the requirements of the uncertainty principle.

Similarly, in Eq. 3.2 a zero-point energy is associated with the radiation field even in so-called *field-free* space. It must be included for the same reason that prevailed in the oscillator problem: it is required in order to satisfy the uncertainty principle. The corresponding zero-point electromagnetic fields perturb the motions of electrons in their courses around atomic nuclei. In particular, they thereby remove the degeneracy between the 2s and 2p states of the hydrogen atom, an effect called the *Lamb shift*. The effect of the zero-point fields of greatest general interest to spectroscopists is their power to force excited quantum systems to emit radiation. Such emission is called *spontaneous* emission. By way of contrast, emission forced by the radiation field in states where $m > 0$ is termed *stimulated* emission. No explanation of spontaneous emission on the basis of classical electromagnetic theory is as satisfying as this quantummechanical one.

A number of other electromagnetic phenomena are satisfactorily explained only by means of the quantum theory of radiation. For example, the distribution of energy among the different modes of an optical cavity at thermal equilibrium (Planck's law) implies a quantization of these modes. When this is used to explain spectroscopic transitions, such as those produced by absorption of energy from the kth mode of the radiation field, one imagines the field to be initially in an eigenstate of the energy characterized by the presence of m photons. After the transition has occurred, the field contains $m - 1$ photons.

Unfortunately, the *dynamics* of these changes are not easy to picture from this viewpoint. During the transition process, the radiation field will not have a definite energy, and will therefore be in a superposition of states having definite numbers of photons.[3]

3.3 When the classical theory may be used

A solution to the difficulty described in Section 3.2 is provided by the *correspondence principle*. Roughly speaking, this principle states that, whenever a quantum system is in a state associated with very large quantum numbers, that quantum system behaves in much the same way that it would if classical mechanics and classical electromagnetic theory applied instead. If the quantum system being considered happens to be the kth mode of a radiation field, it will be a good approximation to replace the photon stream by a classical electromagnetic wave if and only if m, the number of photons in that mode, is very large. (A more detailed and accurate statement of the necessary and sufficient conditions can be found in the work of Jaynes and Cummings.[4])

Such intense fields are easily obtained from conventional sources in radio and microwave spectroscopy (nmr and epr), and in other regions of the spectrum wherever masers and lasers are employed. The classical theory can therefore be used without apology whenever such radiators are used. From Eq. 3.2 it can be seen that in such fields stimulated emission will be a more important mechanism for returning a chromophore to its ground state than spontaneous emission. The reason is that, in this case, $m \gg \frac{1}{2}$. Because the wave picture of light will be used throughout this book, spontaneous emission, whenever it has a measurable effect on the dynamics of the transition process, will be treated in an ad hoc fashion as just another relaxation mechanism.

Much of spectroscopy is performed using light sources very much weaker than those for which the correspondence principle permits the use of the semiclassical theory. Fortunately, the values of most of the measurable physical properties of quantum systems obtained by means of spectroscopic experiments performed in feeble light agree with the results obtained from experiments employing intense sources.[4]

3.4 Waves and particles and their "sizes"

The traditional experiment used to demonstrate the wave-particle duality of light is the diffraction experiment. Light from an incandescent source is filtered and collimated until all the waves that remain have very nearly the same **k**. These waves are used to illuminate a small aperture, and the transmitted light then falls upon a screen. If the smallest dimension of the aperture greatly exceeds a wavelength of the incident light, the edges of the aperture cast an apparently sharp shadow. (Even in this case, however, if one looks very closely at the edges of the shadow, they will not appear sharp.) The pattern formed by the transmitted light on the screen is a well-defined image of the aperture and has very nearly the same dimensions. The illumination will be very nearly uniform over the image.

This experiment is analogous to firing a shotgun at a paper target through a knothole in a fence. If there are many pellets in the shell, and if the hole in the fence is smaller than the transverse scatter in pellet trajectories (but much larger than any one pellet), the pattern of pellets will form a reasonably good image of the knothole (see Figure 3.1). For this reason, the large-aperture experiment demonstrates the particle-like properties of light; photons, traveling on straight-line trajectories, form the same kinds of patterns that would be expected of shotgun pellets.

If the large aperture is replaced by one having at least one dimension comparable to λ, the pattern formed by the transmitted light becomes much larger than the aperture and exhibits bands or rings of alternating

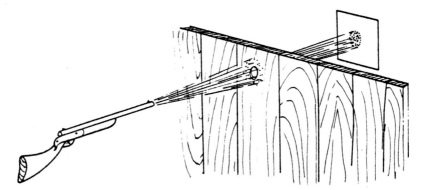

Figure 3.1. Particles passing through an aperture make a fair image of the aperture.

high and low intensity (see Figure 3.2). This diffraction pattern is characteristic of waves and is due to the alternating constructive and destructive interference among them.

A less well-known but historically important equivalent set of experiments may be performed by substituting small disks, balls, and wires for circular and rectangular apertures. The images formed on the screen in these experiments will be identical with those formed in the ones described previously, except that light areas will appear where dark ones were seen before, and vice versa. For example, if a ball is used, the nature of the shadow formed on the screen depends on the ratio of the diameter of the ball to the wavelength of the light used to illuminate it. If the diameter is much greater than λ, the particle picture of light provides an accurate description of the shadow. If the diameter of the ball is less than (or comparable to) λ, the wave picture of light is appropriate instead.

3.5   Electromagnetic waves and quantum systems: size ratios

The subject of this book is the interaction of light with quantum systems. It has already been decided to consider a light beam as a collection of electromagnetic waves rather than as a stream of photons. Is this choice consistent with the facts about light waves presented in Section 3.4? The quantum systems (e.g., atoms, ions, or molecules) are analogous to the balls in the experiment just described. In order to use the wave picture, then, it is necessary that the wavelength of light used to produce spectroscopic transitions exceed the radius of the quantum system being illuminated. Quantum systems found in nature vary greatly in diameter, and there are many kinds of spectroscopy, each of which employs electromag-

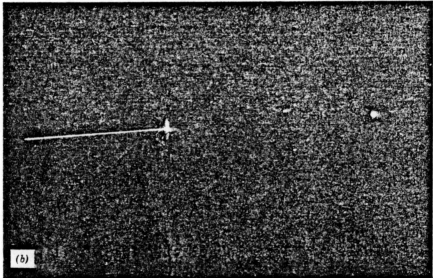

Figure 3.2. Light passing through a small circular aperture. (*a*) A laser (He-Ne, $\lambda = 632.8$ nm) appears on left-hand edge of picture; a pinhole of 102-μm diameter appears near the center, and the spot illuminated by the beam appears on a white card at the right of the picture. All optical components are mounted on an optical bench placed in a Plexiglas trough. (*b*) With the room light out and the Plexiglas trough filled with fog (from dry ice in warm water) to make the beam visible by scattered light, the beam spreads into a Fraunhofer diffraction pattern on the card. This pattern illustrates the wave nature of light; the rings would be bigger but too faint to be seen if the pinhole were smaller. Photographs by Douglas M. Macomber.

netic radiation in a different region of the spectrum. It is not obvious that the necessary condition regarding the size ratio is always met, and for that reason the following discussion is presented.

First, note that very few "quantum systems" have diameters much larger than the diameter of a typical atom ($\cong 0.1$ nm). An obvious exception is provided by the spectroscopy of solids, where transitions between states in various energy bands may involve highly delocalized electrons. In these cases the corresponding wavefunctions may extend over a macroscopic portion of a crystal, and the following analysis will not apply. However, much of the spectroscopy of atoms, molecules, and ions in condensed phases can be adequately described by means of transitions between spatially localized wavefunctions. Here the dimensions of the electronic orbitals are of the same order of size as those that are appropriate for the same atoms, ions, and molecules isolated from one another as they would be in the gas phase. In these cases, therefore, the assumption of a "ball" diameter of less than 1 nm is valid. It may be objected that some macromolecules (molecules containing many atoms) have radii of gyration much larger than 1 nm. However, the spectroscopic properties of such molecules are ordinarily dominated by small, relatively isolated clumps of atoms called *chromophoric groups*. Seldom does the diameter of an individual chromophore exceed 1 nm, so that this assumption holds even in these molecules.

Now it is appropriate to list the various common kinds of spectroscopy, in decreasing order of wavelength of light employed: nuclear magnetic and quadrupole resonance, electron spin resonance and rotational spectroscopy, vibrational spectroscopy, electronic spectroscopy, and nuclear spectroscopy. In the first and last named, the chromophore is the atomic nucleus, with a diameter of the order of 10 femtometers (10^{-15} m). Because of the size ordering in the above list, only nuclear spectroscopy need be considered. The gamma rays used in nuclear spectroscopy ordinarily have a much longer wavelength than 10 fm, so that the wave picture of light is appropriate for nuclear spectroscopy. For the three kinds of spectroscopy employing wavelengths between those of nuclear magnetic resonance and nuclear spectroscopy, the appropriate regions of the spectrum are the microwave, infrared, and visible-ultraviolet. The corresponding wavelengths are 10 mm, 10 μm, and 1 μm to 100 nm, all much larger than the "ball diameter" of 1 nm. According to these arguments, then, the wave picture of light is appropriate for all forms of spectroscopy with the possible exception of that of electronic transitions in the vacuum ultraviolet.

The latter possibility may be disposed of by the following argument. First, in Chapter 1, the scope of the book was limited to the study of transitions between *bound states* of the corresponding quantum systems.

Any more drastic process (e.g., ionization) was called *destruction* rather than *spectroscopy*, at the risk of offending those who might object to such a restricted definition of the latter term. Next, an argument due to Heitler[2] can be used to calculate the shortest wavelength associated with the spectroscopic study of a bound electron in an atom. From Eqs. 1.1 and 1.6,

$$\mathcal{E}_{photon}(\max) = \frac{hc_0}{\lambda(\min)} .$$
(3.4)

From Eq. 1.28,

$$\mathcal{E}_{photon}(\max) = \Delta\mathcal{E}_{atom}(\max)$$
(3.5)

and

$$\Delta\mathcal{E}_{atom}(\max) = \mathcal{E}_{atom}(\max) - \mathcal{E}_{atom}(\min).$$
(3.6)

At the ionization limit for bound electrons,

$$\mathcal{E}_{atom}(\max) = 0.$$
(3.7)

Finally, $\mathcal{E}_{atom}(\min)$ was given in Eq. 1.19, where a_0 is now interpreted as the Bohr radius associated with the orbital in its normal (i.e., ground) state.

Equations 3.4 to 3.7 may be combined with Eq. 1.19 to yield

$$\frac{hc_0}{\lambda(\min)} = \frac{c_0 Z_0 q_0^2}{8\pi a_0} .$$
(3.8)

Therefore,

$$\frac{4\pi a_0}{\lambda(\min)} = \frac{Z_0 q_0^2}{2h} .$$
(3.9)

The particular dimensionless collection of fundamental constants that appears on the right-hand side of Eq. 3.9 is very famous. It is called α, the fine-structure constant, and is very nearly equal to $1/137$.

It may be concluded, therefore, that in any experiment that can be described as spectroscopic the wavelength of electromagnetic radiation employed must exceed the diameter of the quantum system with which it interacts (the chromophore) by at least a factor of 137. Consequently, the description of the interaction of electromagnetic radiation and matter in spectroscopic experiments by means of the wave picture of light is consistent with both the correspondence principle (if the light is intense) and the results of experiments in physical optics.

3.6   Series expansions for electromagnetic fields

Since the wave picture of light for spectroscopic experiments has been adopted, the next step is to recall that the field intensities in such waves vary in both space and time. A quantum system bathed in these fields will sense both of these variations. Because of the spatial modulation of the waves, the field intensity at any one instant of time felt by an atom, ion, or molecule will not be uniform. The nonuniformities, or gradients, in the field intensities from one side of the chromophore to the other will, however, be a small fraction of the rms values of these intensities. In fact, the fraction will be of the order of a_0/λ, which has been shown to be less than 1%. For this reason it is ordinarily a good approximation to neglect the spatial variation of field intensities in the electromagnetic waves that illuminate a quantum system in a spectroscopic experiment. Therefore, from the point of view of an atom, ion, or molecule, light consists of spatially uniform electric and magnetic fields, oscillating sinusoidally in time. In this regard, a quantum system in a light wave is like a cork bobbing up and down on an ocean swell, but not being tipped or longitudinally displaced thereby.

This is very fortunate for anyone who wishes to understand the dynamics of spectroscopic transitions because there are only a limited number of ways in which a quantum system can interact with a spatially uniform field. Suppose that the propagation vector for the wave is parallel to the z axis, and that the atom, ion, or molecule in question is located at the origin. At any instant of time, the spatial dependence of the applied field in the vicinity of the origin may be expressed by a McLaurin series:

$$E(z,t) = E(0,t) + \left[\frac{\partial E(z,t)}{\partial z} \right]_{z=0} z + \frac{1}{2!} \left[\frac{\partial^2 E(z,t)}{\partial z^2} \right]_{z=0} z^2 + \cdots . \quad (3.10)$$

An equation identical in form to Eq. 3.10 describes the magnetic field, $H(z,t)$. These series converge in the case of interest ($z \cong a_0$), and do so uniformly, each term being about $1/137$ of the previous one. The reason for the convergence can be seen by dividing the second term on the right-hand side of Eq. 3.10 by the first, replacing the differentials by finite differences. The result will be $(\Delta E/E) \cdot (z/\Delta z)$. The maximum ΔE occurs when $\Delta z = \lambda/2$; in this case $|\Delta E/E| = 2$. With $z = a_0$, $(z/\Delta z) = 2/137$.

The atom, ion, or molecule, from the point of view of electromagnetic theory, consists in general of an arbitrary collection of charges and currents which interacts with the externally imposed fields. It is possible to describe an arbitrary collection of charges and currents by a power series (of a different kind from the McLaurin expansion of the external field) called the *multipole expansion*. The details of this expansion are described in standard textbooks on electromagnetic theory.[‡] It is sufficient here to give a qualitative description of the various terms that appear therein, and the implications of each to spectroscopy.

The charge distribution in the atom, ion, or molecule gives rise to the electric part of the multipole series. Each term in the electric part describes an asymmetry present in the charge distribution. The grossest asymmetry is described by the first term; successive terms represent increasingly subtle asymmetries, so that from a physical point of view this series also converges uniformly.

The first term, called the *electric monopole*, simply represents the net charge of the system. Therefore only ions have a nonzero electric monopole moment; for neutral atoms and molecules, the largest possible non-vanishing electric term is the electric dipole. Pure dipoles have equal numbers of positive and negative charges, but these are distributed in such a way that the "center of gravity" of the former is displaced from that of the latter. Polar molecules (e.g., HCl, N_2O, and H_2O) are those which, according to classical mechanics, would be expected to have permanent nonzero electric dipole moments. Molecular ions such as HCl^+ are expected to possess both electric monopole and dipole moments, and symmetric neutral molecules (e.g., H_2, CO_2, and CH_4), neither one. Just as a dipole may be formed from two equal and opposite monopoles displaced from one another, so the next term, the electric quadrupole, may be formed by two equal and oppositely directed dipoles with separated

[‡]The mathematical formalism associated with the multipole expansion is as follows. An arbitrary microscopic volume element within the atom, ion, or molecule ($d\tau$) has a charge density ρ. The charge in this element, $\rho\,d\tau$, contributes a term to the electric potential at some point of observation. Let the point of observation be located by r; then the electric potential, V, is given by $(4\pi\epsilon_0)^{-1}\int(\rho\,d\tau/r)$. The vector h connects $d\tau$ with the center of mass of the atom, ion, or molecule of which it is a part, and the vector connecting the center of mass with the point of observation is R; $R = h + r$. If the point of observation is very many atomic diameters away from the center of mass, r will differ only by a small amount from R, and the quantity $1/r$ can be expanded in a Taylor series in terms of $1/R$. The resultant expression for the electric potential is as follows:

$$V = (4\pi\epsilon_0 R)^{-1} \sum_{n=0}^{\infty} R^{-n} \int \rho h^n P_n(\cos\theta)\,d\tau,$$

and the electric field E is the gradient of V. In this expression, θ is the angle between h and R, and the P_n are the Legendre polynomials. The successive terms in the expansion are contributions to the electric potential arising from projections of the successive electric multipole moment vectors upon the R axis. The electric field intensity is the gradient of this potential. A similar expansion for the *current* density (rather than the charge density) yields the magnetic multipoles.

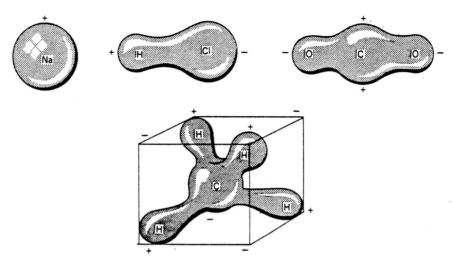

Figure 3.3. Molecules with various electric multipole moments: Na^+, monopole; HCl, dipole; CO_2, quadrupole; CH_4, octupole.

centers. Examples are CO_2 and PF_3Cl_2. These molecules always possess a positive or negative "waist" with head and feet of opposite polarity. The molecule-ion OCS^+ should possess all three of these electric moments. The octupole, hexadecapole, and the remaining 2^n-poles represent charge distributions so subtle[‡] that they ordinarily have little effect on the physical properties of the quantum systems that possess them. Some of the molecules displaying these moments are shown in Figure 3.3.

As the charges in the atom, ion, or molecule circulate in their orbital paths, electric currents are set up that give rise to magnetic phenomena. The corresponding magnetic multipole series differs in two important respects from the electric one. In the first place, magnetic monopoles (e.g., an isolated "north" without a corresponding "south" nearby), unlike electric monopoles, may not exist in nature. Only one observation of a magnetic monopole has ever been reported[5], and the evidence presented in that case was rather indirect. In the second place, the effects that the possession of a magnetic multipole produce on the behavior of a quantum system are usually less important than those produced by the corresponding electric monopole. For example, magnetic dipoles are usually comparable in importance to electric quadrupoles, magnetic quadrupoles to electric octupoles, and so on.

[‡]If the reader is puzzled by the use of the word "subtle," he should consider a bull and an earthworm. The earthworm is the sexual equivalent of a dipole (it functions one way on one end, and the other way on the other end). Surely the question of its sex is a more subtle one than that of the bull (monopole).

Finally, there is a rule that, for quantum systems in their lowest (ground) energy states, alternate multipoles are forbidden. Let the electric ones be designated by E, and the magnetic ones by M, followed by "1" for monopole, "2" for dipole, and so on. The allowed multipoles are $E1$, $M2$, $E4$, $M8$, $E16$, and so forth. Some readers may be surprised at the absence of $E2$, or the electric dipole moment, and ask, "What about the HCl molecule?" The answer is that for HCl in the gas phase "ground state" means "ground" in everything, including the rotational wavefunction. The instantaneous electric dipole moment of the molecule in such a state does exist, of course, but its orientation is completely uncertain. Hence there is a complete vector cancellation of this dipole when the expectation value is calculated. The situation is completely analogous to that of the hydrogen atom (the "protonium electride" molecule, it might be called), which also lacks a permanent electric dipole moment in its $1s$ state, for the same reason (see Figure 3.4).

3.7 Interactions between multipoles and field asymmetries

For the present discussion, the important point is that the behavior of an arbitrary collection of charges and currents in an arbitrary external field can be determined by considering separately the interaction of each one of the multipole moments of the former with each term in the McLaurin expansion of the latter (Eq. 3.10), and adding the results. If this is done, several important general principles immediately come to light.

First, the electric multipole moments will interact only with the electric field, and the magnetic multipole moments will interact only with the magnetic field. Second, within any McLaurin series, each field term will interact with two and only two multipole moments. This can be seen on physical grounds. First, consider the interaction of the first (uniform field) term of Eq. 3.10 with a charged particle (electric monopole). The field will exert a force on the particle, and the latter will thereby be accelerated in the field. The acceleration will be linear, in a direction either parallel or antiparallel to the field, depending on the sign of the charge (see Figure 3.5a). Now imagine two charges, separated by a rigid insulating rod (i.e., an electric dipole) in the same field. One charge will feel a force and be accelerated in one direction, and the other charge, in the other direction. The charges being equal and opposite, the forces will constitute a couple. Because the rod between them is rigid, the couple will produce a torque and there will be no net linear displacement, but merely a rotation of the dipole about its center of mass (see Figure 3.5b.) Next, imagine two electric dipoles rigidly attached to one another (a quadrupole) in the same field. Again, because the net charge is zero, the net linear force, accelera-

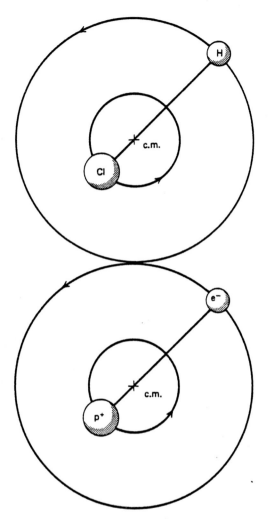

Figure 3.4. Top: HCl in its ground state, with no electric dipole moment. Bottom: H atom in its ground state, with no electric dipole moment.

tion, and displacement will all be zero. Both dipoles will feel equal torques, but, because their moments are oppositely directed, in opposite senses. Because of the rigid connection between them, no net angular acceleration or displacement will be possible (see Figure 3.5c.) This shows that a quadrupole cannot be affected by a uniform field. The same analysis can be given for all higher electric multipole moments; because they represent even subtler asymmetries in the charge distribution, they will not be

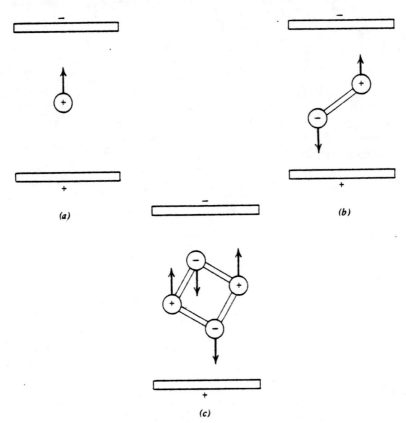

Figure 3.5.   Multipoles in a uniform field: (*a*) monopole, (*b*) dipole, (*c*) quadrupole.

affected either. In summary, the first term in the McLaurin expansion of the electric field will exert a linear force on an electric monopole and an angular force (torque) on an electric dipole, and will have no influence on any higher moments. If the word "electric" were replaced by "magnetic" in the above sentence, it would still be true.

Now the second term in Eq. 3.10—the uniform electric field gradient term, with contribution of zero to E at $z = 0$—will be considered. If a point electric monopole (e.g., the center of charge of an ion) were located at $z = 0$, it would feel no force because the electric field is zero at that point. The equilibrium would be very unstable, of course, because even the slightest perturbation in the position of the monopole along the z axis would move it into a region of nonzero electric field. It would then be accelerated by the field into a region where the force would be stronger

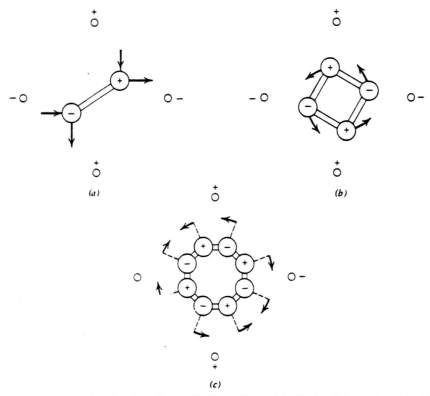

Figure 3.6. Multipoles in a linear field gradient: (a) dipole, (b) quadrupole, (c) octopole.

yet, and so on until the monopole had been completely swept out of its original position.

Next consider a point dipole. It is convenient to imagine that the field gradient is produced by four wires perpendicular to the plane of the paper, and intersecting the paper at the corners of a square (see Figure 3.6a). The wires are labeled as the points of the compass: N, E, S, and W. N and S are raised to a positive electric potential, and E and W are lowered to a negative potential. If the dipole is initially oriented to the northeast (e.g., positive "end" northeast and negative "end" southwest), it is clear that the dipole will feel a force, causing an acceleration toward the southeast. The fields from the S and E wires will pull, and those from the N and W wires will push, producing a linear displacement of the dipole.

A point quadrupole, located in the middle of this same arrangement, may be thought of as a very small arrangement of charges of alternating sign (n, +; e, −; s, +; w, −). When placed at the center of this apparatus, it will feel torque about its center. This torque will produce an angular displacement (rotation) of the quadrupole toward one of two possible equilibrium positions (e.g., Ns, Ew, Sn, We) (see Figure 3.6b). Finally, an octopole, which may be thought of as two quadrupoles with a common center displaced angularly from one another by 90°, will feel no net torque (Figure 3.6c).

Just as was the case for the uniform field, the discussion of the effect of a uniform field gradient may be repeated, substituting the word "magnetic" for "electric," and the conclusion will remain true.

Evidently, it is possible to proceed indefinitely in this fashion for all of the terms in Eq. 3.10; the results anticipated are summarized in Table 3.1.

Table 3.1 Forces felt by a point multipole in an arbitrary field, F
L = linear acceleration, A = angular acceleration, N = no acceleration, U = unstable equilibrium

2^n Pole, Order of n =	$\partial^m F/\partial t^m$, m =				
	0	1	2	3	4 ....
0	L	U	U	U	U
1	A	L	U	U	U
2	N	A	L	U	U
3	N	N	A	L	U
4	N	N	N	A	L
5	N	N	N	N	A
6	N	N	N	N	N

3.8 Electromagnetic waves and quantum systems: interactions

It has been shown that, within an accuracy of at least 136 parts in 137, the electric and magnetic fields produced by a light wave in a spectroscopic experiment are uniform; terms of the kind $(\partial^m/\partial z^m)_0$, with $m \neq 0$, can therefore be neglected. For this case, the results can be summarized in Table 3.2.

Since there are apparently few magnetic monopoles in nature, the corresponding entry in Table 3.2 may be neglected. The electric monopole term applies only to ions; as a practical matter, the interaction of light from the sun with charged particles in the earth's ionosphere by means of this interaction helps shield us from harmful ultraviolet rays. Also, radiowave messages may be bounced between remote points on the earth's surface from the underside of this same layer. Finally, the high reflectivity of metals is a well-known optical phenomenon produced by the interaction of conduction electrons with the uniform electric fields of light waves. Although any of these phenomena may occasionally be of practical im-

Table 3.2   Forces felt by a quantum system interacting
spectroscopically with a light wave
L = linear acceleration, A = angular acceleration,
N = no acceleration

Order of 2^n pole, n =	Kind of Multipole	
	Electric	Magnetic
0	L	L
1	A	A
2	N	N
3	N	N
4	N	N
5	N	N
6	N	N

portance to spectroscopists, none will be considered further in this book. Rather, attention will be concentrated on the spectroscopic interaction of electromagnetic radiation with neutral atoms and molecules, and with charged species (such as nuclei) in which the electric monopole interaction plays no more than a trivial role (e.g., nmr and epr).

Finally, it should be noted that, in Maxwell's equations, the effects of matter on the fields are characterized by only three parameters. The electric conductivity, σ, has to do with the interaction of electric monopoles in the matter with the applied electric field. The electric permittivity, ϵ, is concerned with the interaction of electric dipoles in the matter with the applied electric field. The magnetic permeability, μ, is associated with the interaction of magnetic dipoles in the matter with the applied magnetic field. If magnetic monopoles abounded, one would have to introduce a new parameter, σ_m, magnetic conductivity, to characterize their interaction with the applied magnetic field; in this case, Maxwell's equations would assume an even more symmetric form.

In summary, *there are only three possible mechanisms by means of which electromagnetic radiation can interact with matter in a spectroscopic experiment*; that is to say, there are only three ways in which the matter can exchange energy with the radiation field. Suppose that the matter is to *receive* energy from the radiation field (absorption). The radiation field must do electromechanical *work* upon the matter (i.e., the quantum systems absorbing the energy). There are only two ways in which work can be done. First, a linear force, $\mathbf{F}_0$, may produce linear displacements, $d\mathbf{z}$. In that case, the work, w, is given by the elementary formula

$$w = \int \mathbf{F}_0 \cdot d\mathbf{z}. \tag{3.11}$$

Second, an angular force (torque), $\mathbf{T}$, may produce angular displacements, $d\theta$; in that case, the work is given by

$$w = \int \mathbf{T} \cdot d\theta. \tag{3.12}$$

The only way in which a uniform electric or magnetic field (e.g., the fields associated with a light wave in a spectroscopic experiment) can exert a linear force upon an arbitrary collection of charges and currents (e.g., a quantum chromophore) is through the corresponding monopole moment (σ). This interaction will play no more than a trivial role in the experiments which shall subsequently be described, as was stated previously.

The only way that a uniform electric or magnetic field can exert a torque upon an arbitrary collection of charges and currents is through the corresponding dipole moment (and therefore through the parameter ϵ or μ). For neutral atoms or molecules, then, *spectroscopic transitions are produced whenever the electric or magnetic fields of the light wave exert a torque upon the electric or magnetic dipole moments of the absorbing quantum systems.* These moments are the "handles" by means of which the radiation field "grasps" atoms or molecules with which it interacts. Whenever such a handle exists, the transition in question is called "electric (or magnetic) dipole allowed." Whenever such a handle is absent, the transition is termed "electric (or magnetic) dipole forbidden." To an accuracy of better than 136 parts in 137, *no other types of transitions are possible.*

This general a priori conclusion is not the only one that may be drawn about the interaction mechanism. It must now be remembered that, although the electric and magnetic fields which constitute a light wave may appear *spatially* uniform to a quantum system in a spectroscopic experiment, they by no means appear *temporally* uniform. In fact, these fields completely reverse direction twice during each optical cycle, of duration $2\pi/\omega \equiv \lambda/c$. This fact implies that the dipole moment with which the field interacts must *also* oscillate in time, if the net energy transfer during one complete optical cycle is to be nonzero. The truth of this statement can be demonstrated by the following argument. The energy of a dipole $\mathbf{p}_E$ (or $\mathbf{p}_M$) in a field $\mathbf{E}$ (or $Z_0\mathbf{H}/c_0$) is given by

$$\mathcal{E} = -\mathbf{p}_E \cdot \mathbf{E}. \tag{3.13}$$

If $\mathbf{E}$ oscillates between $-|E|\hat{z}$ and $+|E|\hat{z}$ during each cycle, but $\mathbf{p}_E$ is constant, the time average of $\mathcal{E}$ in Eq. 3.13 will be zero.

In fact, it is easy to see that, for efficient energy transfer, the oscillation frequency of the dipole must be very nearly the same as the oscillation frequency of the field.

The problem of coupling two oscillators by matching their frequencies is well known to anyone who has ever pushed a small child on a swing. To increase the level of excitation of the child-swing oscillating system by drawing energy from the doting-parent oscillating system, two conditions must be satisfied. First, there must be a coupling mechanism (in this case, the contact force between the pusher's hand and the rear surface of the swing seat). Second, the pusher must synchronize his pushes with the natural period of oscillation of the pushee (determined in this case by the classical mechanics of pendulum motion) (see Figure 3.7a). By "synchronization" is meant not only making the frequencies of the two oscillators equal, but also matching their phases. A 180° phase error in the push (pusher going forward while the swing system is moving backward) will result in energy being transferred from the child to the parent (the former ending up motionless, and the latter being knocked head over heels: see Figure 3.7b), rather than vice versa.

If the pusher's hand is replaced by one of the fields of the light wave, the

(a)

Figure 3.7. Energy transfer between oscillators: (a) parent doing work on child-in-swing,

(b)

Figure 3.7. (*b*) Child-in-swing doing work on parent.

rear of the swing seat is replaced by the corresponding quantum-mechanical dipole moment, and the contact force is replaced by the electromagnetic force, the analogy between the two systems is evident. In the case of an atom or molecule undergoing a spectroscopic transition, the natural frequency is determined by quantum mechanics. The frequencies of the two oscillations must match one another in quantum mechanics as well as in classical mechanics, and, depending on the relative phases of the oscillation of the field and of the dipole, either absorption or stimulated emission of radiation is obtained.

3.9 Complex susceptibilities, electric and magnetic

The effects of the microscopic multipole interactions on the bulk electromagnetic properties of the system are discussed in this section. Imagine a substance consisting of charged particles in thermal and mechanical equilibrium. There will be no net flow of current in such a material in the absence of any external forces. If a uniform electric field $\mathbf{E}$

is applied to this substance, however, each of the charged particles will feel a force. Particles that are free to do so will move in response to this force and begin to flow through the material—the external field thus induces an electric current. The parameter σ is a measure of the mobility of charges; if it is zero (as will ordinarily be the case for substances discussed in this book), the electric monopoles in the material will not influence the electromagnetic behavior of the material.

Now imagine instead that the substance is composed of microscopic particles with permanent electric dipole (rather than monopole) moments. At thermal and mechanical equilibrium these dipoles will be oriented at random (provided that they do not interact strongly with one another). Therefore the vector sum of the electric dipole moments in any small (but macroscopic) volume element of the material will be zero, and no net electrical field will be associated with the sample. If an electric field is applied to this substance, each of the electric dipoles will feel a torque. Dipoles that are free to do so will move in response to this torque and will eventually line up with **E**. The vector sum of the dipole moments in small macroscopic volume elements of the material will no longer be zero, and a net electric field will be associated with the sample because of these dipoles. The external field thus induces a net dipole density (number of unit-sized microscopic dipole moments per unit volume) called the *electric polarization* of the sample and given the symbol **P**.

In addition to the orientation of permanent dipoles, other methods exist for producing polarization of the sample. Molecules having a nonuniform charge distribution can be stressed by the electric field, and the bonds of these molecules will stretch and bend in response to this stress. The results of the stretching and bending of the molecular framework will be to create molecular electric dipoles where none were present before, or to modify dipole moments already present. These created and/or modified moments will add up vectorially and contribute to **P**.

Finally, the entire positively charged nuclear framework can be displaced in one direction by the electric field, and the surrounding electrons displaced in the other. This also creates an atomic or molecular dipole moment in the direction of the field and adds to **P**.

All of the above three sources of polarization are important in determining the electromagnetic behavior of matter when the applied field **E** is static. If **E** oscillates in time, the dipoles (both permanent and induced) have some difficulty in keeping up because of the inertia of the particles to which they are attached.

The parameter ϵ is a measure of the ease with which the dipoles are induced by the field. From the argument given in the preceding paragraph, it may be concluded that there should be a relationship between ω (the frequency of the oscillation of E) and the magnitude of ϵ. In particular, ϵ should diminish in size as ω increases because of the diminishing ability of the atomic and molecular motions to respond. This is generally found to be the case, but there are other features of the ϵ versus ω curve that are not explained by the reasoning given above.

Superimposed on the relatively featureless background just described are a number of "spikes"—relatively large changes in ϵ occurring over a rather narrow frequency range. The center frequency of each of these spikes is located near that one of the resonant quantum transitions of the particle of which the sample is composed (ω_0). The molecular, atomic, or ionic dipole moments induced in these regions of the wave arise from the superposition of the quantum states associated with the transition. The oscillating applied field E first produces these dipoles and then interacts with them (in accordance with the mechanism described in Section 3.8) to transfer electromagnetic energy into or out of the sample material.

Regardless of the mechanism that gives rise to P, it is always possible to express this polarization mathematically in terms of the field E:

$$P = P(E). \tag{3.14}$$

The function on the right-hand side of Eq. 3.14 can be expanded in a McLaurin series:

$$P = P_0 + \epsilon_0 \eta E + \epsilon_0 \eta_2 EE + \cdots, \tag{3.15}$$

where η, η_2, and so on are expansion coefficients to be discussed later. The first term on the right-hand side is nonzero only in special materials called *ferroelectrics*; and if conventional sources are used, the electric fields in light waves are much too small for the third and subsequent terms to have any practical importance. If very intense (e.g., laser) sources are used, it is not possible to assume a linear relationship between P and E (nonlinear optics), but for the moment this complication will be disregarded. The product $\epsilon_0 \eta$, which appears in the second term, may, for the present, be considered to be merely the conventional notation for $(dP/dE)_{E=0}$, and is a property of the polarizable material under consideration. The total field is the sum of the applied field and that which arises from the polarized matter. The quantities P and E cannot be added directly, of course, because they have different units; P has the units of dipole moments per unit volume, and E has the units of electric field strength. Conventionally the sum, D, is expressed in the same units as P:

$$D = \epsilon_0 E + P. \tag{3.16}$$

The parameter ϵ_0, called the *electric permittivity of free space*, may be regarded at present as merely a conversion factor that transforms the field **E** into an equivalent electric dipole moment per unit volume. The quantity represented by **D** is termed the *electric displacement*; it is equal to the net effective polarization, which is the sum of the "genuine" polarization, **P**, and the equivalent polarization due to the driving field, **E**. The second term on the right-hand side of Eq. 3.15 may be substituted for **P** in Eq. 3.16 to obtain

$$\mathbf{D} = \epsilon_0 \mathbf{E} + \epsilon_0 \eta \mathbf{E}. \tag{3.17}$$

The terms proportional to **E** may be collected to obtain

$$\mathbf{D} = \epsilon \mathbf{E}, \tag{3.18}$$

with

$$\epsilon = \epsilon_0 (1 + \eta). \tag{3.19}$$

In Eqs. 3.18 and 3.19, ϵ is the total electric permittivity discussed previously; it is the sum of two terms, the first representing the "permittivity of the vacuum," and the second, the effect of the polarizable medium. The quantity represented by the symbol η is called the *electric susceptibility* of the medium.

The equations corresponding to Eqs. 3.14 to 3.19 for magnetic phenomena are as follows:

$$\mathbf{M} = \mathbf{M}(\mathbf{H}), \tag{3.20}$$

$$\mathbf{M} = \mathbf{M}_0 + \chi \mathbf{H} + \chi_2 H \mathbf{H} + \cdots, \tag{3.21}$$

$$\mathbf{B} = \mu_0 (\mathbf{H} + \mathbf{M}), \tag{3.22}$$

$$\mathbf{B} = \mu_0 (1 + \chi) \mathbf{H}, \tag{3.23}$$

$$\mathbf{B} = \mu \mathbf{H}, \tag{3.24}$$

and

$$\mu = \mu_0 (1 + \chi). \tag{3.25}$$

The units of **B** are lines of magnetic force per unit area (flux).

The names of the previously undefined symbols are as follows:

M, magnetic polarization (sometimes "magnetization");
μ_0, magnetic permeability of free space:
B, magnetic induction (in magnetic resonance, the symbol H is used for this);
and
χ, magnetic susceptibility.

The *spontaneous* magnetic polarization, M_0, which is important for ferro-magnetic materials, has obviously been discarded in Eq. 3.23. The units of H and M are both magnetic dipole moments per unit volume. It seems unfortunate that the conventional definitions of P and M necessitate the omission of the factor ϵ_0 on the right hand side of Eq. 3.16 in front of the former, but retention of the factor μ_0 on the right hand side of Eq. 3.22 in front of the latter.

It is convenient to permit η and χ to be complex numbers:

$$\eta \equiv \eta' + i\eta'' \tag{3.26}$$

and

$$\chi \equiv \chi' + i\chi''. \tag{3.27}$$

3.10   Effect of susceptibilities on wave propagation

Next, Maxwell's relations may be used to derive the wave equations,

$$\left(\frac{\partial^2 E}{\partial z^2}\right)_t + \epsilon\mu\left(\frac{\partial^2 E}{\partial t^2}\right)_z = 0, \tag{3.28}$$

and

$$\left(\frac{\partial^2 H}{\partial z^2}\right)_t + \epsilon\mu\left(\frac{\partial^2 H}{\partial t^2}\right)_z = 0. \tag{3.29}$$

In the interest of simplicity, attention will be concentrated on Eq. 3.28. A solution is assumed of the form

$$E = |E|\exp\{i[\phi + \omega(\alpha_0 z - t)]\}, \tag{3.30}$$

where $|E_0|$, ϕ, ω, and α_0 are all constants: all symbols except α_0 on the right-hand side of Eq. 3.30 represent real numbers. Equation 3.30 may be substituted into Eq. 3.28 to yield

$$(i\omega\alpha_0)^2 E + \epsilon\mu(-i\omega)^2 E = 0. \tag{3.31}$$

Equation 3.31 is satisfied if and only if

$$\alpha_0^2 = \epsilon\mu. \tag{3.32}$$

Equations 3.19 and 3.25 to 3.27 may be substituted into Eq. 3.32 to find an expression for α_0^2:

$$\frac{\alpha_0^2}{\epsilon_0 \mu_0} = \left[(1+\eta')(1+\chi') - \eta''(\chi'')\right]$$

$$+ i\left[(1+\eta')(\chi'') + \eta''(1+\chi')\right]. \tag{3.33}$$

To obtain α_0 itself, it is necessary to find the square root of a complex number. The answer is as follows. If

$$\sqrt{\alpha_0^2} \equiv u + iv \tag{3.34}$$

and

$$\alpha_0^2 \equiv U + iV, \tag{3.35}$$

then

$$u = \pm \frac{\left[(U^2 + V^2)^{1/2} + U\right]^{1/2}}{\sqrt{2}} \tag{3.36}$$

and

$$v = \pm \frac{\left[(U^2 + V^2)^{1/2} - U\right]^{1/2}}{\sqrt{2}}. \tag{3.37}$$

These formulas may be verified as follows. Substitute Eqs. 3.36 and 3.37 into Eq. 3.34 and square both sides. The result should be Eq. 3.35.

Returning to Eq. 3.33; one finds

$$\frac{2[\mathrm{Re}(\alpha_0)]^2}{\epsilon_0\,\mu_0} = \left[(1+\eta')^2+(\eta'')^2\right]^{1/2}$$

$$\times \left[(1+\chi')^2+(\chi'')^2\right]^{1/2}$$

$$+ \left[(1+\eta')(1+\chi')-\eta''(\chi'')\right] \qquad (3.38)$$

and

$$\frac{2[\mathrm{Im}(\alpha_0)]^2}{\epsilon_0\,\mu_0} = \left[(1+\eta')^2+(\eta'')^2\right]^{1/2}$$

$$\times \left[(1+\chi')^2+(\chi'')^2\right]^{1/2}$$

$$- \left[(1+\eta')(1+\chi')-\eta''(\chi'')\right]. \qquad (3.39)$$

Exactly the same results may be obtained from the wave equation for H, Eq. 3.29.

If the spectroscopic transition in question is electric dipole allowed, χ' and χ'' may usually be neglected. In this case, Eqs. 3.38 and 3.39 simplify to yield

$$\mathrm{Re}(\alpha_0) = \pm \frac{\sqrt{\epsilon_0\,\mu_0}\;\sqrt{1+\eta'}}{\sqrt{2}}\left\{\left[1+\left(\frac{\eta''}{1+\eta'}\right)^2\right]^{1/2}+1\right\}^{1/2} \qquad (3.40)$$

and

$$\mathrm{Im}(\alpha_0) = \pm \frac{\sqrt{\epsilon_0\,\mu_0}\;\sqrt{1+\eta'}}{\sqrt{2}}\left\{\left[1+\left(\frac{\eta''}{1+\eta'}\right)^2\right]^{1/2}-1\right\}^{1/2}. \qquad (3.41)$$

A further simplification is possible because ordinarily $[\eta''/(1+\eta')]\ll 1$, permitting the use of the series expansion

$$\sqrt{1+x} \cong 1 + \frac{x}{2}, \qquad x \ll 1: \tag{3.42}$$

$$\alpha_0 \cong \pm \sqrt{\epsilon_0 \mu_0} \sqrt{1+\eta'} \left\{ \left[1 + \frac{1}{8}\left(\frac{\eta''}{1+\eta'}\right)^2 \right] + \frac{i\eta''}{2(1+\eta')} \right\}. \tag{3.43}$$

3.11 Absorption coefficient and refractive index

Finally, the physical significance of the parameters that appear in Eq. 3.43 must be discovered. This may be done most easily by substituting Eq. 3.43 into the exponential expression for E in Eq. 3.30. First, let $\eta' = \eta'' = 0$. Since these terms are the only ones that represent the presence of matter, the resulting expression describes the properties of an electromagnetic wave in a vacuum:

$$E = |E| \exp\left[i\left(\phi \pm \omega \sqrt{\epsilon_0 \mu_0}\, z - \omega t\right)\right]. \tag{3.44}$$

Since ω is the angular frequency in radians per second,

$$\omega \alpha_0 \equiv k. \tag{3.45}$$

Therefore, Eqs. 1.1, 1.5, 3.3, and 3.45 may be used to show that

$$\sqrt{\epsilon_0 \mu_0} = \frac{1}{c_0}. \tag{3.46}$$

Equation 3.44 may be rewritten again to yield

$$E = |E| \exp\left\{ i\left[\phi \pm \frac{\omega}{c_0}(z \mp c_0 t)\right]\right\}. \tag{3.47}$$

The choice of algebraic signs in the exponent determines the direction of propagation. For example, set $\phi = 0$ and choose the upper sign. At location $z = 0$, the wave in Eq. 3.47 will have a "crest" ($E = |E|$, $H = |H|$) at $t = 0$. Anyone who wishes to "ride" upon this crest must "move" (change z) in such a way that the argument of the exponent remains zero for all time. The solution is $z = c_0 t$. It is just as easy to see that a wave traveling in the $-z$ direction is represented by the choice of the lower sign in Eq. 3.47.

If the matter is restored ($\eta', \eta'' \neq 0$) in Eq. 3.43, $\sqrt{\epsilon_0 \mu_0}$ is multiplied by the factor $\sqrt{1+\eta'}$. From Eq. 3.46, it can be seen that this has the effect of reducing the velocity of propagation:

$$c_0 \rightarrow \frac{c_0}{n_R} , \tag{3.48}$$

where

$$n_R \equiv \sqrt{1 + \eta'} . \tag{3.49}$$

The property represented by the symbol n_R is of course the *refractive index* of the medium.

Using Eqs. 3.46 and 3.49, one may rewrite Eq. 3.42 as

$$\alpha = \frac{n_R \left[1 + \left(i\eta'' / 2n_R^2 \right) \right]}{c_0} . \tag{3.50}$$

In Eq. 3.50, the upper algebraic sign has been chosen for concreteness, and it is assumed that $(\eta'' / 8n_R^2)^2 \ll 1$. Then Eq. 3.50 may be substituted into Eq. 3.30 to achieve the following expression for the electric field:

$$E = |E| \exp \left\{ i \left[\phi + \omega \left(\frac{n_R}{c_0} \right) z - \omega t \right] \right\} \cdot \exp \left(\frac{-\omega \eta'' z}{2 n_R c_0} \right). \cdot \cdot \tag{3.51}$$

Earlier, it was stated that the intensity of the light is proportional to the complex square of the electric field (Eq. 3.1). Therefore,

$$J \propto |E|^2 \exp \left(\frac{-\omega \eta'' z}{n_R c_0} \right). \tag{3.52}$$

This expression may be compared with Eq. 1.27 to show that Eq. 3.52 is, in fact, the Beer-Lambert law. The physical significance of η'' is now clear; it gives rise to the *absorption coefficient*, β_0 (see Eq. 1.27):

$$\beta_0 \equiv \frac{\omega \eta''}{n_R c_0} = N' \kappa. \tag{3.53}$$

In summary, a relationship has now been found between the real and imaginary parts of the electric susceptibility and the refractive index and absorption coefficient of the medium, respectively.

3.12 Phase relationships: absorption, emission, and dispersion

What is the appropriate relationship between the phase of the driving field, E, and the dipole moment being driven, p_E? It may be remembered that this question motivated the above digression. The mathematics of this problem is most conveniently handled by the use of the complex number notation introduced in Chapter 2. (See Eqs. 2.38, 2.39, 2.42, and 3.1.)

Complex numbers sometimes seem very mysterious to those not accustomed to their use. For the moment, it is sufficient to consider a complex number, a, as merely an ordered pair of real numbers, $\mathrm{Re}(a)$ and $\mathrm{Im}(a)$. In particular, Eq. 3.30 represents

$$\mathrm{Re}(E) = |E| \cos\left[\phi + \omega(\alpha_0 z - t)\right] \tag{3.54}$$

and

$$\mathrm{Im}(E) = |E| \sin\left[\phi + \omega(\alpha_0 z - t)\right]. \tag{3.55}$$

The phase constant, ϕ, may be set equal to zero in Eqs. 3.54 and 3.55 without loss of generality in this case. Because E is a single quantity, in principle measurable in the laboratory, only one of the two expressions in Eqs. 3.54 and 3.55 can have physical significance. Conventionally, $\mathrm{Re}(E)$ is chosen; $\mathrm{Im}(E)$ would serve just as well, provided only that one were consistent throughout the calculation.

If Eqs. 3.26 and 3.20 are substituted into Eq. 3.15, keeping only the second term of the latter, the following expression for the oscillating polarization is obtained:

$$P = \epsilon_0(\eta' + i\eta'')|E| \left\{ \cos\left[\omega(\alpha_0 z - t)\right] + i\sin\left[\omega(\alpha_0 z - t)\right] \right\}. \tag{3.56}$$

To be consistent, $\mathrm{Re}(P)$ must be chosen as the physically observable polarization. Therefore, from Eq. 3.56,

$$\mathrm{Re}(P) = \epsilon_0|E| \left\{ \eta' \cos\left[\omega(\alpha_0 z - t)\right] - \eta'' \sin\left[\omega(\alpha_0 z - t)\right] \right\}. \tag{3.57}$$

From Eqs. 3.54 and 3.57 it can be seen that, whenever matter is polarized by an oscillating electric field, the resultant polarization wave is shifted in phase with respect to the driving field. The phase shift can be described by associating it with the real and imaginary parts of the electric susceptibility. The part of the polarization wave in phase with the driving field is proportional to η'; the part of the polarization wave in quadrature (90° out of phase) with the driving field is proportional to $\eta''[\cos(\theta + \pi/2) = -\sin\theta]$. The use of complex numbers is then merely a device to enable one to describe two properties of the polarizable medium, η' and η'', by a single symbol, η.

   All of the above considerations are summarized in Figure 3.8. First, let the oscillations of the dipole moments of the atoms or molecules in the

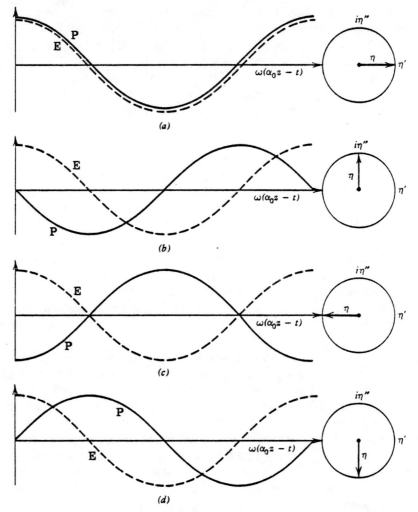

Figure 3.8.   Phase relationships between driving field and polarization waves for the following: (a) dispersion, (b) absorption, (c) anomalous dispersion, (d) stimulated emission.

spectroscopic sample be 90° out of phase (in quadrature) with the oscillations of the fields of the light wave. This corresponds to the choice $\eta'=0$,
$\eta''>0$, and will, as has been shown, result in absorption of energy from the
wave (see Eq. 3.52). The velocity of light through the medium will be the
same as if no transitions were occurring in the medium (see Eqs. 3.48 and
3.49). The absorption coefficient will be largest whenever the frequencies
of the two oscillating systems are equal (Figure 3.8*b*).

Next, let the oscillations of the dipole moment be 0° out of phase (in
phase) with the field oscillations. This corresponds to the choice $\eta'>0$,
$\eta''=0$. There will be no absorption (see Eq. 3.52), but there will be a
marked reduction in the phase velocity of the light wave (see Eqs. 3.48 and
3.49). The index of refraction is frequency dependent because ϵ is
frequency dependent, as stated in Section 3.10. When a light ray crosses
the boundary between two substances having different refractive indices, it
is bent (refracted) by an amount depending on the angle between the ray
and the normal to the boundary, and also on the ratio of the n_R's. This is
why a beam of white light (a mixture of waves with different frequencies)
obliquely incident upon a prism is dispersed (separated) into rays of
different colors (the constituent frequencies). For this reason, the dependence of the refractive index on frequency is sometimes called *dispersion*
(Figure 3.8*a*).

Next, let the dipoles oscillate 270° out of phase with the fields. This
corresponds to $\eta'=0$, $\eta''<0$. Inspection of Eq. 3.52 shows that, whenever
this condition occurs, light will be amplified by the medium; the process is
called *stimulated emission*. Just as was the case for absorption, the phase
velocity of the wave is unaffected by the transition in question, and the
magnitude of η'' depends on the frequency differences between the oscillators (Figure 3.8*d*).

Finally, consider the case in which the dipoles are 180° out of phase
with the driving fields. This corresponds to $\eta'<0$, $\eta''=0$. Again, no energy
will be transferred to or from the quantum system. The phase velocity of
the wave will increase (see Eqs. 3.48 and 3.49) beyond the vacuum value,
c_0. This does not violate the relativistic requirement concerning the velocity
of light, which restricts only the group velocity (velocity of the center of
the wave packet). The frequency dependence of the magnitude of η'
reverses the order of the colors dispersed by a prism made of such a
material. For this reason, this phenomenon is called *anomalous dispersion*
(Figure 3.8*c*).

It should be noted that "frequency difference," as used in the above
paragraphs, refers to the difference between the *actual* frequency of the
wave, ω, and the *natural* frequency of the dipole oscillators, ω_0. The actual
frequency of the dipole oscillators is the same as that of the driving field, ω

(see Eq. 3.57). This will be true whenever the assumption of a linear relationship between E and P is valid (linear optics), save only for a small "pulling" effect due to absorption (see the second term in square brackets on the right-hand side of Eq. 3.43).

It may occur to the reader that, insofar as the *total* magnitude of the dipole moment of an atom or molecule is fixed by quantum mechanics, the vector sum of the components of that dipole moment in phase and in quadrature should be constant. This implies that there ought to be a relationship between η' and η'' analogous to the Pythagorean theorem. Such a relationship, in fact, exists; it is called the *Kramers-Kronig relation*.

The reader may also ask, "Why does the most efficient energy transfer in spectroscopy occur when the oscillators are in quadrature, rather than in phase, the latter being the case for the swing and its pusher?" It will be seen later that this is so because the torque developed is proportional to the vector (cross) product of the dipole moment and field vectors. It is well known that the cross product of two vectors is a maximum when the vectors are perpendicular.

The discussion of electromagnetic theory in this chapter is by no means exhaustive. It was intended merely to provide a review of the elementary ideas from that subject which will be required in subsequent chapters. A much fuller understanding can be gained by reading a good textbook on the subject.[1]

3.13   References

1. J. A. Stratton, *Electromagnetic Theory* (McGraw-Hill Book Company, New York, 1941).
2. W. Heitler, *The Quantum Theory of Radiation*, 3rd ed. (Clarendon Press, Oxford, 1954), p. 177.
3. R. J. Glauber, "Coherent and incoherent states of the radiation field," *Phys. Rev.* **131**, 2766 (1963).
4. E. T. Jaynes and F. W. Cummings, "Comparison of quantum and semiclassical radiation theories with application to the beam maser," *Proc. IEEE* **51**, 89 (1963).
5. P. B. Price, E. K. Shirk, W. Z. Osborne, and L. S. Pinsky, "Evidence for detection of a moving magnetic monopole," *Phys. Rev. Lett.* **35**, 487 (1975).

3.14   Problems

3.1.   At a pressure of 1.0 torr, the unsaturated absorption coefficient, β_0, for SF_6 gas is 46 per meter for irradiation at a wavelength $\lambda = 10.6 \ \mu m$. The index of refraction is $n_R = 1.00$, and the transition responsible for the absorption is electric dipole allowed.

a.   Calculate the real part of the electric susceptibility of SF_6.

b.   Calculate the imaginary part of the electric susceptibility of SF_6.

3.2. The electric field associated with a CO_2 laser beam ($\lambda = 10.6 \ \mu m$)
depends on distance and time in accordance with the expression

$$\mathbf{E} = \hat{x}|E|\operatorname{Re}\{\exp[i\omega(\alpha_0 z - t)]\}$$
$$= \hat{x}|E|\cos[\omega(\alpha_0 z - t)].$$

When this beam propagates through a sample characterized by an electric
susceptibility

$$\eta = \eta' + i\eta'',$$

it produces a polarization wave, $\mathbf{P}$:

$$\mathbf{P} = \hat{x}\epsilon_0|E|\operatorname{Re}\{\eta \exp[i\omega(\alpha_0 z - t)]\}$$
$$= \hat{x}\epsilon_0|E|\cos[\phi + \omega(\alpha_0 z - t)].$$

a. Write an expression for the phase shift of the polarization wave, ϕ, in
    terms of η' and η''.
b. Using the numerical values of η' and η'' calculated for SF_6 in Problem
    3.1, calculate the numerical value of ϕ.

4 Interaction of radiation and matter

4.1 Dipoles and waves: the semiclassical theory

In Chapter 1 it was stated that atoms, ions, molecules and other quantum systems can absorb and emit electromagnetic radiation. Quantum-mechanical methods for calculating the properties of quantum systems were described in Chapter 2. In Chapter 3 it was explained that the most important method for the exchange of energy between radiation and matter is the exertion of torques by the uniform fields of the former upon the dipole moments of the latter. The purpose of this chapter is to link together the material presented in the first three chapters to produce a unified picture of spectroscopic transitions. Because the dipole moments will be calculated by means of quantum mechanics and the radiation fields by means of classical electromagnetic theory, the resultant description of the interaction process is called the *semiclassical* (or sometimes *neoclassical*) *theory of quantum transitions*.[1]

It has been shown that the *sine qua non* of a spectroscopic transition is the existence of an electric or magnetic dipole moment, nonzero in magnitude, oscillating sinusoidally in time at a frequency very nearly equal to that of the electromagnetic wave. The question that arises is, "What dipole moment?"

Consider, for example, the hydrogen atom. In the Bohr theory, described in Chapter 1, the electron was supposed to move in an elliptical orbit around the nucleus. At each instant of time, the electron and the nucleus form an electric dipole of magnitude $q_0 r$, where r is the vector joining the two particles. As time passes, the dipole changes direction and magnitude periodically because the ellipse is a closed curve. Thus orbital motion of the electron generates an oscillating dipole moment. Furthermore, the frequencies of oscillation calculated from the Bohr theory are in the right range to explain the observed spectrum whenever $r \cong a_0$ (see Eq. 3.8). But it was also explained in Chapter 1 how the acceleration of the charged electron as the dipole oscillates would necessarily produce the complete collapse of the hydrogen atom (and, by extension, all other atoms and molecules as well).

How is this problem resolved by the new quantum theory of Heisenberg and Schrödinger? In this theory, the energy and the electric dipole moment of the hydrogen atom are incompatible variables, in the sense described in Chapter 2; that is to say, the Hamiltonian operator H and the position operator r do not commute with one another in Hilbert space. At the beginning and the end of the transition process, the system is in an eigenstate of the energy (represented by H), and therefore is in a superposition state of the dipole moment (represented by $q_0 r$). If any attempt is made to measure the dipole moment of the atom in either the initial or the final state, the measurement will produce a definite result—the electron will be found *some*where. But *where* it will be found is unpredictable because of the uncertainty principle. Dipoles measured in this way are sometimes called "instantaneous" dipoles.

The best that can be done, then, is to calculate the average dipole moment obtained if one were to perform a large number of measurements upon the atom. Between each measurement of the dipole, it will be necessary to return the quantum system to the same initial state (i.e., an eigenstate of the energy). This average was named the "expectation value" in Chapter 2.

4.2   The transition dipole moment of a hydrogen atom

Consider, for example, the first line in the Lyman series of the hydrogen spectrum (during which the atom undergoes a transition from the $1s$ to the $2p$ state). Is the expectation value of the electric dipole moment of a hydrogen atom in the $1s$ state nonzero? If so, will it oscillate at the correct frequency to explain the observed spectrum? The dipole moment operator is a vector quantity with three components (see Eq. 2.12):

$$\mathbf{p}_E = q_0 \mathbf{r} = q_0 (X\hat{x} + Y\hat{y} + Z\hat{z}). \tag{4.1}$$

The expectation value of the x component may be calculated by means of Eq. 2.82:

$$\langle q_0 x \rangle_{11} \equiv q_0 \int d\mathbf{r}\, \psi_{1s}^*(\mathbf{r}, t)\, X \psi_{1s}(\mathbf{r}, t), \tag{4.2}$$

where

$$X = r \sin\theta' \cos\phi' \tag{4.3}$$

and

$$d\mathbf{r} = r^2\, dr \sin\theta'\, d\theta'\, d\phi'. \tag{4.4}$$

(Primed symbols are used because the corresponding unprimed ones have been reserved for different quantities.) Any standard textbook on elementary quantum mechanics can supply the eigenfunctions of the Hamiltonian operator for hydrogen:

$$\psi_{1s}(\mathbf{r}, t) = (\pi a_0^3)^{-1/2} \exp\left(\frac{-i\mathcal{E}_1 t}{\hbar}\right) \exp\left(\frac{-r}{a_0}\right), \qquad (4.5)$$

where

$$a_0 = \frac{4\pi\epsilon_0\hbar^2}{m_0 q_0^2}. \qquad (4.6)$$

The eigenvalue of the energy, $\mathcal{E}_1$, was given in Eq. 1.19:

$$\mathcal{E}_1 \equiv \mathcal{E}_{\text{atom}}. \qquad (4.7)$$

When Eqs. 4.2 to 4.7 are combined, the resultant integration shows that

$$\langle q_0 x \rangle_{11} = 0. \qquad (4.8)$$

The same result would have been obtained for $\langle q_0 y \rangle$ and $\langle q_0 z \rangle$. This explains why no energy is radiated by the hydrogen atom while it is in the $1s$ state, and therefore the electron does not spiral into the nucleus as described in Chapter 1. The collection of "instantaneous dipoles" associated with the $1s$ eigenfunction has a net vector sum of zero.

Similarly, it may be shown that the expectation value of the electric dipole moment of a hydrogen atom in its $2p_x$ state is zero. For example,

$$\langle q_0 x \rangle_{22} \equiv q_0 \int d\mathbf{r}\, \psi_{2p_x}^*(\mathbf{r}, t) \times \psi_{2p_x}(\mathbf{r}, t) = 0, \qquad (4.9)$$

where

$$\psi_{2p_x}(\mathbf{r}, t) = (32\pi a_0^5)^{-1/2} \exp\left(\frac{-i\mathcal{E}_2 t}{\hbar}\right) \exp\left(\frac{-r}{2a_0}\right) r \sin\theta' \cos\phi' \qquad (4.10)$$

and

$$\mathcal{E}_2 = \frac{\mathcal{E}_1}{2^2}. \qquad (4.11)$$

Equation 4.9 explains why the $2p_x$ state of hydrogen is also one of the stationary states: like the $1s$ state, it lacks a persistent electric dipole moment and therefore cannot generate or interact with electromagnetic waves. ("Persistent" is used here to mean only a nonzero expectation value; a persistent dipole is to be contrasted with an instantaneous one. The term "static" is reserved for a quantity that does not oscillate in time.)

The only thing that has not yet been calculated is the expectation value of the electric dipole moment of the hydrogen atom in a nonstationary state formed by the linear combination of $1s$ and $2p_x$ states (the $1s$ and $2p_x$ superposition state):

$$\Psi(\mathbf{r}, t) = c_{1s}\psi_{1s}(\mathbf{r}, t) + c_{2p_x}\psi_{2p_x}(\mathbf{r}, t). \tag{4.12}$$

In accordance with Eq. 2.83,

$$\langle q_0 x \rangle_{\Psi\Psi} = \langle q_0 x \rangle_{11}\cos^2\left(\frac{\theta}{2}\right) + \langle q_0 x \rangle_{22}\sin^2\left(\frac{\theta}{2}\right)$$

$$+ 2\cos\left(\frac{\theta}{2}\right)\sin\left(\frac{\theta}{2}\right)\mathrm{Re}\{\langle q_0 x \rangle_{12}\exp[i(\S - \omega_0 t)]\}. \tag{4.13}$$

From Eqs. 4.8 and 4.9, Eq. 4.13 reduces to

$$\langle q_0 x \rangle_{\Psi\Psi} = q_0\sin\theta\cos(\S - \omega_0 t)\langle x \rangle_{12}, \tag{4.14}$$

where

$$\omega_0 = \frac{3 m_0 q_0^4}{8(4\pi\epsilon_0)\hbar^2}. \tag{4.15}$$

Also, from Eqs. 4.5 and 4.10,

$$\langle x \rangle_{12} = \frac{256}{243}\frac{a_0}{\sqrt{2}}. \tag{4.16}$$

It just so happens that the angular frequency of the electromagnetic wave radiated by hydrogen atoms in producing the first spectral line of the Lyman series in emission or absorption is correctly given by Eq. 4.15. Furthermore, the maximum magnitude of the dipole moment, which occurs when $\theta = 90°$ ($c_{1s} = c_{2p} = 1/\sqrt{2}$), implies a certain intensity for the resultant emission or absorption. The predicted and observed intensities also agree, within the limits of experimental uncertainties.

The nonzero expectation value of the electric moment of hydrogen in this superposition state is therefore precisely the oscillating dipole that is called for in the semiclassical theory of quantum transitions. It may be termed the *transition dipole moment*.

Finally, it should also be noted that, as the emissive transition proceeds, c_{2p} decreases from 1 to 0. As soon as c_{2p} equals 0, the product $c_{1s}^{*}c_{2p}$ $= \frac{1}{2}\sin\theta\exp[i(\xi_{2p}-\xi_{1s})]$ in Eq. 4.14 becomes 0 and the radiating dipole disappears. When two oscillators at different frequencies (such as adjacent piano strings) are excited simultaneously, one hears, in addition to the frequencies of the oscillators themselves, an interference "beat" note. The oscillation of the dipole moment of the superposition state is just such a beat. In an atomic emitter that has ceased radiating, one of the two oscillators has died out, leaving only the other (the fundamental)— consequently, the beat note disappears. Throughout this process, the frequency of the beat note is constant, although its amplitude is continually changing, because the frequencies of the fundamental and harmonic that have interfered to produce it are constant. The electronic "motion," initially described by one standing wave pattern, has been converted into another standing wave pattern of a lower frequency. When standing wave oscillations of two different frequencies are simultaneously present in the same oscillator (as they are in the radiating atom), the interference beat note appears as a multiply reflected traveling wave. The traveling wave provides the mechanism by means of which the excess energy is transferred to the surroundings. A drawing of the hydrogen atom in the superposition state is presented in Figure 4.1.

The Bohr frequency condition

$$\omega = \frac{(\mathcal{E}_2 - \mathcal{E}_1)_{\text{atom}}}{\hbar}, \tag{4.17}$$

was rationalized (in Chapter 1) in terms of thermodynamic necessity: the energy of the created (or annihilated) photon, in accordance with the Law of Conservation of Energy, must equal the amount of energy lost (or acquired) by the atom in the process. A kinetic interpretation of this, promised in Chapter 1, has just been presented. The frequency of electromagnetic radiation emitted by a dipole antenna must be precisely the frequency with which electric charges oscillate in that antenna. In absorption, the necessity of doing work by means of fields that exert a torque upon an oscillating dipole requires that the fields in question oscillate at the same frequency as the dipole being driven. It was pointed out in Chapter 3 that the driving field must "chase after" the driven dipole, so that the torque will always be exerted in the same sense. If there is a frequency difference between the two oscillators, the phase relationship

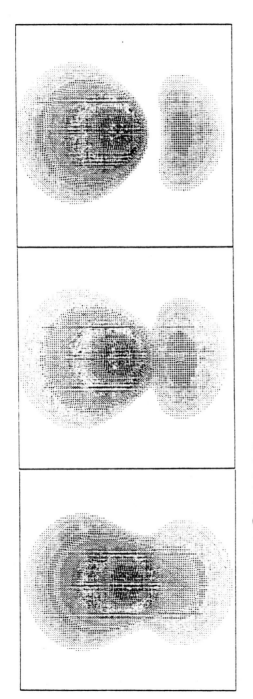

Figure 4.1. The hydrogen atom in a superposition of the $1s$ and $2p_x$ states, radiating about one-half cycle of the first Lyman line in the vacuum -uv spectrum. Each diagram is plotted inside a square $13\frac{1}{3}\,a_0$ (Bohr radii) on a side. The probability density, $|\psi|^2$ (unit volume $= a_0^3$), in the xy plane is represented by dot density, d (unit area $= a_0^2$), according to

$$|\psi|^2 = |\psi_{1s}(t) + \psi_{2p_x}(t)|^2$$

$$= \frac{\exp\left[(15/4)^2 d\right]}{\pi \exp(13/2)}$$

$$= 0.000479 \exp(14.1d).$$

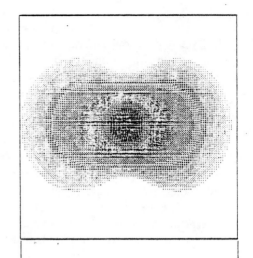

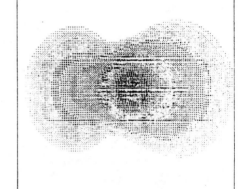

The time intervals, Δt, between successive diagrams are chosen so that

$$\frac{[\mathcal{E}(2p_x) - \mathcal{E}(1s)]\Delta t}{\hbar} = \pi/6,$$

where

$$\Delta t = 3.38 \times 10^{-17}\,\text{sec}.$$

This figure was prepared with the assistance of Henry Streiffer using the facilities of the LSU computer center.

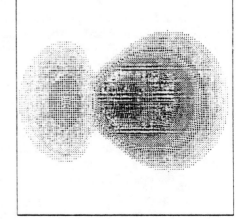

that exists between them at any one time will reverse after a time interval of $(2\pi \Delta\omega)^{-1}$ seconds. Then the work done during one portion of the optical cycle will be undone in the subsequent portion (see Eq. 3.13).

The material of the preceding paragraphs constitutes a physical model for the dynamic interaction between radiation and matter in spectroscopic transitions; it may be summarized as follows. During the act of radiation or absorption of light by matter, electromagnetic waves constitute fields that are uniform in space but oscillating in time. These fields exert torques upon the oscillatory dipole moments (more precisely, upon the oscillatory expectation values of dipole moments) of quantum systems (e.g., atoms and molecules, or chromophoric portions of the latter). These dipole moments arise only if the systems are in states represented by a linear superposition of the nondegenerate eigenfunctions associated with the initial and final states. Net transfer of energy from one oscillating system to another (e.g., from the field to the matter) depends on the magnitudes of the corresponding fields and dipoles, the differences in their phases, and the departures of their frequencies from the natural (i.e., quantum) beat frequency of the superposed eigenstates.

4.3 Conceptual problems with the theory

The model of spectroscopic transitions just presented has some features that are easily grasped by physical intuition, and it yields results in accord with experiments. The explanation does not rely on words such as *interaction*, *annihilation*, and *creation*. In subsequent chapters, it will be shown that this model also provides explanations in satisfactory agreement with experiment for even finer details of the absorption spectrum (e.g., linewidths), as well as for recently discovered "exotic" phenomena (e.g., photon echoes and self-induced transparency).

It should be noted, however, that in the present status of the discussion several very important matters remain unexplained. For example, how does the transition process get started? Reconsider the problem of the Lyman spectrum of hydrogen. The initial state in emission will be $2p$; c_{1s} will be zero. From Eq. 4.13 it can be seen that there will be no oscillating dipole moment to generate the initial radiation field. The coefficient c_{2p} will be zero in the same formula in the case of absorption. There will therefore be no electromagnetic "handle" for the radiation fields to "grab" at the beginning of the absorption process. This difficulty could be resolved if every quantum system possessed a static dipole moment in the $\hat{z}$ direction while in an eigenstate. It would have to be static for the state to be stationary and to satisfy the requirement that oscillating portions of $\mathbf{P}$ lie solely in the xy plane. This $\hat{z}$ component could be an initial "handle" on the quantum system with which the **E** field could interact. In magnetic resonance spectroscopy, such a component of a dipole moment actually exists. It is, of course, magnetic rather than electric; for spin-$\frac{1}{2}$ particles it points in the z direction in one eigenstate (spin up) and in the $-z$ direction in the other (spin down).

In the case of electronic transitions, there is seldom a static $\hat{z}$ component of a dipole moment (cf. the case of hydrogen). In Chapter 7, it will be shown that a generalized transition dipole moment can be defined by analogy with the actual magnetic moment of an electron or a proton. The x' components of these moments give rise to the genuine "in-phase" oscillating component of **P** (dispersion); the y' components, to the genuine "in-quadrature" oscillating component of **P** (absorption); and the static z components, to a fictitous moment proportional to the difference between the squares of superposition coefficients, $|c_2|^2 - |c_1|^2$. It will be shown in Chapter 7 that the sum of these three moments moves like a vector under the influence of the electromagnetic wave with which it interacts, the entire formalism developed for allowing use of magnetic resonance spectroscopy (where all three components are genuine dipoles). One serious conceptual difficulty with this model can and should be addressed immediately—that of the relationship between the uncertainty principle and superposition states. As was noted in Chapter 2, people are sometimes confused about superposition states. Measurements performed on quantum systems yield only eigenvalues as results. This fact leads some persons to conclude that atoms, ions, molecules, and so forth can exist only in the eigenstates which correspond to these eigenvalues. If this view is held, it is very difficult to explain the dynamics of spectroscopic transitions. Frequently it is asserted that systems change from one eigenstate of the energy to another by means of discontinuous processes called *quantum jumps*. Furthermore, the details of the jumping process are supposed to be fundamentally unknowable because of the uncertainty principle.

The point of view heretofore expressed in this book seems to be very different from the one that produced the idea of quantum jumps. Superposition states have been taken very seriously—indeed, they have been considered every bit as genuine as eigenstates. The dynamics of the transition process have been explained by means of a model in which the electromagnetic waves operate upon the quantum system in a continuous fashion. The fields do work upon dipole moments that have nonzero expectation values only for superposition states. Indeed, there apparently have been no jumps at all in this picture.

How are these two points of view to be reconciled? What is the meaning of the superposition coefficients? How is the notion of a continuous process compatible with the discontinuities in the eigenvalues? *Are* there quantum jumps? How does the uncertainty principle affect the results of measurements performed on systems in superposition states? It is the purpose of subsequent sections of this chapter to answer as many of these questions as possible.

4.4 Quantum jumps and the uncertainty principle

The first step in discussing these problems is to describe the transition of a quantum system from one eigenstate of the energy to another in a very careful way. The initial state will be numbered "1," and the final state, "2":

$$H_0|1\rangle = \mathcal{E}_1|1\rangle, \tag{4.18}$$

$$H_0|2\rangle = \mathcal{E}_2|2\rangle. \tag{4.19}$$

In accordance with the usual notation, $|1\rangle$ and $|2\rangle$ are orthogonal eigenkets of the Hamiltonian operator, H_0, with corresponding eigenvalues $\mathcal{E}_1$ and $\mathcal{E}_2$. The system will be prepared in such a way that it is definitely in state 1 at times $t < 0$ (something that can always be done).

At $t = 0$, a perturbation of constant "strength" V will be applied to the quantum system. The precise meaning of V will be discussed later. For the moment it will be sufficient to note that V has the dimensions of energy and is associated with the process of producing a transition of the system from state 1 to state 2 in a time Υ. In other words, the perturbation represented by V is switched off at $t = \Upsilon$, and for all $t > \Upsilon$ the system is definitely in state 2. Not all perturbations have this nice property of being able to complete their mission in a definite time interval, of course. (The ones described as "coherent," however, generally have this property.)

In the interval $0 \leqslant t \leqslant \Upsilon$, the state of the system is represented by a ket that will be labeled as $|A\rangle$, a linear superposition of the two relevant eigenkets of H_0:

$$|A\rangle = c_{A1}|1\rangle + c_{A2}|2\rangle. \tag{4.20}$$

The coefficients c_{A1} and c_{A2} are continuous functions of the time. The coefficient c_{A1} goes from 1 to 0 in the interval $0 \leqslant t \leqslant \Upsilon$, and the coefficient c_{A2} goes from 0 to 1 in the same interval. At all times,

$$|c_{A1}|^2 + |c_{A2}|^2 = 1. \tag{4.21}$$

Equation 4.21 is required so that the superposition ket $|A\rangle$ will be properly normalized (see Eq. 2.70). As was shown in Chapter 2, Eq. 4.21 will be satisfied automatically by the choices

$$c_{A1} = \cos\left(\frac{\theta}{2}\right) \exp\left(i\xi_1\right) \tag{4.22}$$

and

$$c_{A2} = \sin\left(\frac{\theta}{2}\right) \exp\left(i\xi_2\right). \tag{4.23}$$

See Eqs. 2.71 and 2.72. It will be shown in Chapter 6 that

$$\theta = \frac{Vt}{\hbar}. \tag{4.24}$$

Perturbations which satisfy all of the above conditions are usually called 180° or π pulses (note what happens when $\theta = 180°$ in Eqs. 4.22 and 4.23). In addition to the previous assumption that relaxation can be neglected, it will also be assumed that the perturbation is "small":

$$|V| \ll |\mathcal{E}_2 - \mathcal{E}_1|. \tag{4.25}$$

It was noted earlier that a measurement of the energy of the system in the interval $0 < t < T$ will give either the result $\mathcal{E}_1$ or $\mathcal{E}_2$. In particular, no value of the energy intermediate between $\mathcal{E}_1$ and $\mathcal{E}_2$ will ever be observed. Furthermore, the probability that $\mathcal{E}_1$ will be observed is $|c_{A1}|^2$, and the probability of finding $\mathcal{E}_2$ instead is $|c_{A2}|^2$. It was also mentioned that two conclusions are sometimes drawn from these facts. First, the quantum system proceeds from state 1 to state 2 by means of a quantum jump at some time in the interval $0 \leqslant t \leqslant T$. Second, the uncertainty principle prevents an accurate prediction of the time at which the jump will occur. One may only state that $|c_{A1}(t)|^2$ is the probability that it will have already occurred before the time in question. Quantum jumps of this kind will henceforth be called *Schrödinger jumps*, due to Schrödinger's criticism[2] of pictures of the transition process based upon them.

It is easy to see from this discussion why believers in Schrödinger jumps are likely to consider that the only genuine states of a quantum system are the eigenstates of the energy (in this case those represented by $|1\rangle$ and $|2\rangle$). In this view the superposition state has only a formal validity, in that it is a solution to Schrödinger's equation and identifies the initial and final states. Therefore c_1 and c_2 in Eq. 4.20 are viewed as "information variables." The actual state of the system is either 1 or 2, and there is no way of telling which; all that can be done is to measure the energy of the system and, in this way, remove the ambiguity.

The alternative interpretation of the facts about quantum transitions (i.e., the failure to observe any energy between $\mathcal{E}_1$ and $\mathcal{E}_2$ experimentally) begins with the assumption that the superposition state is a genuine state of the system. More precisely, in the process of undergoing the transition from state 1 to state 2, the system passes through a continuum of superposition states, designated collectively by $|A\rangle$. Each one of these is different from all the others and, in particular, different from the eigenstates represented by $|1\rangle$ and $|2\rangle$. Each of these A states is supposed to be every bit as "real" as states 1 and 2. One of the properties shared by all the superposition states is that the eigenkets $|A\rangle$ which represent them are not eigenkets of the energy. This is the reason why no definite value between $\mathcal{E}_1$ and $\mathcal{E}_2$ is ever obtained when that property is measured in the interval $0 < t < \Upsilon$. Instead, *the act of measurement itself* precipitates a jump into either state 1 or state 2. This type of quantum jump was described by Heisenberg[3] in a reply to Schrödinger and will therefore henceforth be designated as a *Heisenberg jump*. The probability that a system in a superposition state will jump to stationary state 1 at time t is $|c_{A1}(t)|^2$; the probability that it will jump to state 2 instead is $|c_{A2}(t)|^2$.

Since both of these models, portrayed schematically in Figure 4.2, predict results in complete accordance with the experiments described thus far, it might be thought that the distinction between Schrödinger and Heisenberg jumps is a meaningless one. It is possible, however, to imagine an experiment that would distinguish between these two kinds of quantum jumps. At the same time, the properties of the superposition states would be elucidated.

Suppose that $|A\rangle$ in Eq. 4.20 is an eigenket of an operator R representing some physical property of the system *other than the energy*, with corresponding eigenvalue r_A:

$$R|A\rangle = r_A|A\rangle. \tag{4.26}$$

Furthermore, it will be supposed that there exists another eigenstate of R, represented by $|B\rangle$ with corresponding eigenvalue $r_B \neq r_A$:

$$R|B\rangle = r_B|B\rangle. \tag{4.27}$$

Finally, it will be supposed that $|B\rangle$, like $|A\rangle$, can be represented as a linear combination of $|1\rangle$ and $|2\rangle$. In particular, suppose that

$$|B\rangle = -c_{A2}^*|1\rangle + c_{A1}^*|2\rangle, \tag{4.28}$$

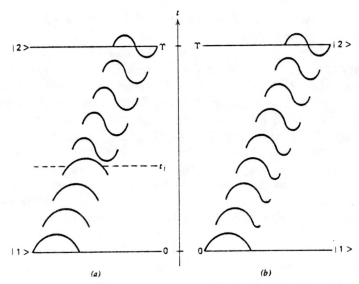

Figure 4.2. Two different models for the change of a wavefunction with time during a quantum transition. (*a*) System hops abruptly from state 1 to state 2 at time t_j (Schrödinger jump); the time t_j cannot be predicted with certainty. (*b*) System evolves gradually from state 1 to state 2, as reflected by the continuous deformation of its wavefunction. No quantum jumps occur unless the transition process is interrupted by an energy measurement (Heisenberg jump).

where the coefficients c_{A1}^* and c_{A2}^* are the complex conjugates of those that appear in Eq. 4.20. It is easy to show that $|B\rangle$ is orthogonal to $|A\rangle$ and normalized to unity (see Eq. 4.21):

$$\langle B|A\rangle = 0 \tag{4.29}$$

and

$$\langle B|B\rangle = 1. \tag{4.30}$$

The coefficients for $|B\rangle$ in Eq. 4.28 have been chosen so that

$$|1\rangle = c_{A1}^*|A\rangle - c_{A2}|B\rangle \tag{4.31}$$

and

$$|2\rangle = c_{A2}^*|A\rangle + c_{A1}|B\rangle. \tag{4.32}$$

If a physical property represented by such an operator as R can be found (and if a device can be constructed in the laboratory to measure it), measurement of that property at time t will decide between Schrödinger and Heisenberg jumps. Suppose that the quantum model implied by Heisenberg jumps is the correct one. At time t, the system will be in the legitimate state A. Measurements of the property represented by R will therefore yield the result r_A, and never r_B. Now suppose that the quantum model implied by Schrödinger jumps is correct instead. At the time of measurement, t, the system will be in either state 1 or state 2, according to whether or not it has already undergone its jump. But neither state 1 nor state 2 is an eigenstate of R. Instead, both of these states are linear combinations of two different eigenstates of R with distinct eigenvalues (see Eqs. 4.31 and 4.32). Therefore the measurement of the property represented by R will yield a result that cannot be predicted with certainty. If the system were really in state 1, the result would be r_A (with probability $|c_{A1}|^2$) or r_B (with probability $|c_{A2}|^2$) (see Eq. 4.31). If the system were really in state 2, the result would be r_A (with probability $|c_{A2}|^2$) or r_B (with probability $|c_{A1}|^2$) (see Eq. 4.32).

In fact, the superposition state is real and there are no Schrödinger jumps in nature, just as Schrödinger expected. There are Heisenberg quantum jumps instead, just as Heisenberg stated, but only if the system is forced to jump by the wrong kind of measurement. A "wrong" measurement is one of some physical property represented by an operator that fails to commute with R. Conversely, if the appropriate kind of physical property can be found for a "right" measurement (e.g., one represented by R), it will be possible to measure a property of a system "in between" eigenstates of the Hamiltonian without being subject to the limitations of the uncertainty principle. The wavefunction is changing continuously with time because the coefficients c_1 and c_2 are changing, as a result of the influence of the perturbation represented by V. Therefore the operator R will be "right" only at a particular time t. At any other t, a different operator will be the right one. In this way, an infinite number of operators $\{R\}_t$ (not one of which commutes with any other or with the Hamiltonian) may be defined; these could be used to map out the progress of the system throughout the course of the quantum transition. In the next section, the foundations will be laid for a thought (*Gedanken*) experiment to perform just such measurements.

4.5   The spin-$\frac{1}{2}$ system

The quantum system selected for study in the *Gedanken* experiment is the electrically neutral, spin $s = \frac{1}{2}$ particle. This system has been mentioned before in this book and will be discussed again, in great detail, in Chapter

6. For the purposes of the present discussion, it will be sufficient to anticipate a few of the results of Chapter 6.

Spin-$\frac{1}{2}$ particles behave as if they had magnetic dipole moments of magnitude $\sqrt{3}\,\gamma\hbar/2$, where the constant γ is characteristic of the kind of system considered (e.g., silver atom, proton, or neutron). Since a magnetic dipole moment is a vector quantity, it has a direction as well as a magnitude. The most convenient method for the experimental determination of both the magnitude and the direction of a vector is to measure the projection of the vector on each of three mutually perpendicular Cartesian axes. The orientation of the unit vectors in these directions, $\hat{x}, \hat{y}$, and $\hat{z}$, will be considered fixed (laboratory reference frame). In Chapter 3, the magnetic moment vector was labeled by the symbol $\mathbf{p}_M$. Therefore,

$$\mathbf{p}_M = p_x\hat{x} + p_y\hat{y} + p_z\hat{z}. \tag{4.33}$$

Suppose that there are a very large number of identical systems of this type in the laboratory, and that the magnetic moment vectors of these systems are oriented at random. What should be expected if the x component of magnetic moment of every system were measured? In classical mechanics, a continuous distribution of components ranging in magnitude from $+\sqrt{3}\,\gamma\hbar/2$ (corresponding to systems that happened to have their magnetic moments pointing "up" at the time of measurement) to $-\sqrt{3}\,\gamma\hbar/2$ (corresponding to systems that happened to have their magnetic moments pointing "down" at the time of measurement) would be expected. In fact, classical mechanics does not provide an appropriate description of these systems. The actual result, explicable only by means of quantum mechanics, is that the measured value of p_x for half of the systems is $+\gamma\hbar/2$, and for the other half, $-\gamma\hbar/2$. Precisely the same results are obtained by measurements of p_y and p_z.

The *length* of a vector p_M with these components is correctly given by the three-dimensional analog of the Pythagorean theorem:

$$\sqrt{p_x^2 + p_y^2 + p_z^2} = p_M. \tag{4.34}$$

In classical mechanics, the *direction* of the magnetic moment vector $\mathbf{p}_M$ is defined to be the direction along which the component of magnetization equals its total length:

$$\mathbf{p}_M = \sqrt{3}\,\frac{\gamma\hbar\hat{u}_1}{2}. \tag{4.35}$$

The unit vector $\hat{u}_1$, together with two other mutually orthogonal unit vectors $\hat{u}_2$ and $\hat{u}_3$, defines a coordinate system that is most convenient for describing the behavior of the particle (particle reference frame). The orientation of the axes of the $\hat{u}_1, \hat{u}_2, \hat{u}_3$ system with respect to the axes of the fixed $\hat{x}, \hat{y}, \hat{z}$ system will vary from particle to particle. In quantum mechanics, Eq. 4.34 is satisfied:

$$\sqrt{(\pm \gamma\hbar/2)^2 + (\pm \gamma\hbar/2)^2 + (\pm \gamma\hbar/2)^2} = \frac{\sqrt{3}\,\gamma\hbar}{2}. \tag{4.36}$$

but Eq. 4.35 is not quantum-mechanically valid in *any* coordinate system. (This fact will be proved in Chapter 6.)

A completely new way must be found to define the direction of the magnetic moment. Suppose that the particle were bathed in a uniform static field of induction, **H** (the symbol **B** is not used in magnetic resonance):

$$\mathbf{H} = H_x\hat{x} + H_y\hat{y} + H_z\hat{z}. \tag{4.37}$$

The energy $\mathcal{E}$ of a magnetic dipole in a uniform field is given by a scalar product like that of Eq. 3.13:

$$\mathcal{E} = -\mathbf{p}_M \cdot \mathbf{H}. \tag{4.38}$$

In other words, the energy of the system (purely magnetic energy in this case) will now depend on the orientation. In particular, suppose that

$$\mathbf{H} = H_0\hat{u}_1. \tag{4.39}$$

Now one can write

$$\mathbf{p}_M = p_{u_1}\hat{u}_1 + p_{u_2}\hat{u}_2 + p_{u_3}\hat{u}_3, \tag{4.40}$$

and the energy becomes (from Eq. 4.38)

$$\mathcal{E} = -p_{u_1}H_0. \tag{4.41}$$

Because of the quantum-mechanical nature of $\mathbf{p}_M$, there can only be two possible eigenvalues of p_{u_1}:

$$p_{u_1} = \frac{\pm \gamma\hbar}{2}. \tag{4.42}$$

Hence, there are only two eigenvalues of the energy:

$$\mathcal{E} = \frac{\pm \gamma\hbar H_0}{2}. \tag{4.43}$$

Suppose that the system is put into the state having the lower eigenvalue. This could be done by placing the particle in thermal contact with a heat bath at a low temperature;

$$k_0 T \ll \gamma \hbar H_0 \tag{4.44}$$

(k_0 is Boltzmann's constant, and T is the absolute temperature) and allowing a sufficiently long time to elapse:

$$t \gg T_1 \tag{4.45}$$

(T_1 is the relaxation time; see Chapter 5). In this state,

$$p_{u_1} = \frac{+\gamma\hbar}{2}. \tag{4.46}$$

In other words, the component of the magnetic moment parallel to the $\hat{u}_1$ axis will be nearly certain; repeated measurements of that component will yield reproducible results.

The same cannot be said of the u_2 and u_3 components. If the particle is put into the magnetic eigenstate represented by the eigenvalue in Eq. 4.46 by cooling it in a magnetic field in the u_1 direction, a measurement of p_{u_2} will yield the result $+\gamma\hbar/2$ half of the time and the result $-\gamma\hbar/2$ the other half. These two values will occur at random, and the result of any single measurement will be completely unpredictable. The same thing will happen if p_{u_3} is measured.

It is understood that the spin-$\frac{1}{2}$ particles must be returned to their initial states between successive measurements of any one component of $\mathbf{p}_M$. This might be accomplished by allowing each of them to "soak" in the field $\mathbf{H}$ for a time $t \gg T_1$ while again in contact with the heat bath. (This precaution may not be necessary after measurements of p_{u_1} because such measurements need not change the state of the particle.)

4.6   A geometrical model of the transition process

Imagine a pair of concentric spheres, the inner one of radius $\gamma\hbar/2$ and the outer of radius $\sqrt{3}\ \gamma\hbar/2$, as shown in Figure 4.3. The magnetic moment of the particle can be represented by a vector $\mathbf{p}_M$, with its tail at the center of the spheres, and its tip somewhere on the larger sphere. The poles of both spheres are their intersection points with the z axis. Any attempt to measure $\mathbf{p}_M$ by measuring its projection along any direction in space will produce a component vector with its tail at the center and its tip on the smaller sphere.

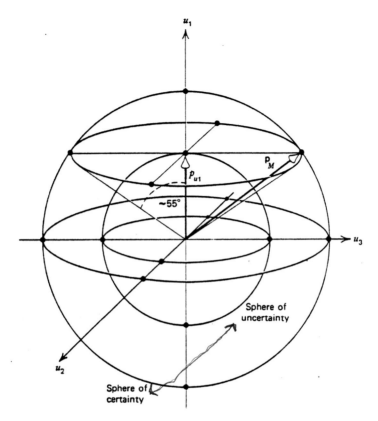

Figure 4.3. Spheres of certainty and uncertainty for a spin-$\frac{1}{2}$ particle. The total magnetic moment vector $\mathbf{p}_M$ (of length $\sqrt{3}\,\gamma\hbar/2$) makes an angle of about 55° with its certain (measurable) component, p_{u_1} (of length $\gamma\hbar/2$).

It is therefore possible to single out a particular direction in space (call it $\hat{u}_1$) and to put the system in a particular eigenstate of the magnetization along that direction. One way of doing this, as was just mentioned, is to put a magnetic field $\mathbf{H}$ along that direction and to let the system sit for a long time in thermal contact with a low-temperature heat bath. (There are other ways of accomplishing the same task, but they need not be described here.) Now, if p_{u_1} is measured, the tip of the component vector will certainly be found at the point where the u_1 axis intersects the small sphere. The possible locations of $\mathbf{p}_M$ consistent with this fact will describe a cone of half angle

$$\cos^{-1}\left(\frac{1}{\sqrt{3}}\right) = 54°44'8.2'', \qquad (4.47)$$

and the axis of this cone will be the u_1 axis. Therefore the locus of the head of $\mathbf{p}_M$ will describe a circle where the cone intersects the large sphere, and that circle in turn will lie in a plane tangent to the small sphere at the head of p_{u_1}. Finally, the locus of possible outcomes of measurements of p_{u_2} and p_{u_3} is a great circle on the small sphere in a plane perpendicular to $\hat{u}_1$.

Since the only information available with certainty by direct experimental observation of this system can be represented by a component vector with its head on the small sphere, that sphere will be called the *sphere of certainty*. Since the exact location of the head of $\mathbf{p}_M$ on the larger sphere is uncertain, that sphere will be called the *sphere of uncertainty*. The difference in the radii of the two spheres is a consequence of the uncertainty principle, and is larger for spin-$\frac{1}{2}$ particles than for any other kind. [The ratio of the radii in the general case of a spin-s particle is $\sqrt{s(s+1)}\,/s$, and goes to 1 as s becomes very large. This fact is a consequence of the correspondence principle.] Also, p_{u_1} will be called the *certain component* of $\mathbf{p}_M$, since only that component can be measured many times in succession with reproducible results, and the u_1 axis will be termed the *axis of certainty*. (This axis is usually called the "axis of quantization," but since that term is sometimes also applied to the magnetic field axis, a new name has been invented for use in this discussion.)

After the static magnetic field has been used to line up p_{u_1}, it will be realigned with the z axis:

$$\mathbf{H} = H_0 \hat{z}. \tag{4.48}$$

The result of this choice is that, whenever the system is in an eigenstate of the energy, the axis of certainty will be the $\hat{z}$ axis. Any measurement of p_z will yield a reproducible result. If the system is in the low-energy eigenstate, called 1, $p_z = \gamma\hbar/2$. If the system is in the high-energy eigenstate, called state 2, $p_z = -\gamma\hbar/2$. The results of the measurement of p_x and p_y (or the components along any other direction) will be indeterminate.

This information can now be used to visualize the difference between Heisenberg and Schrödinger jumps. Suppose that a spin-$\frac{1}{2}$ particle is put into state 1, and at time $t=0$ the particle is suddenly embedded in a circularly polarized electromagnetic wave of frequency ω. In particular, suppose that the wave propagates along the $\hat{z}$ axis and has a spatially uniform magnetic amplitude H_1. (Since the dipole moment of the particle is purely magnetic, there is no need to be concerned with the electric amplitude.) The total magnetic field will therefore become

$$\mathbf{H} = H_0\hat{z} + H_1(\hat{x}\cos\omega t + \hat{y}\sin\omega t). \tag{4.49}$$

It will be shown in Chapter 6 that H_0 is associated with the H_0 term in the Hamiltonian operator, and H_1, with the perturbation represented by V —see Eqs. 4.18, 4.19, and 4.24. It will also be shown that the magnitude of the perturbation in this case will be

$$V = \gamma \hbar H_1. \tag{4.50}$$

In Eq. 4.50, it may be seen that V is the difference in the energies of the eigenstates of the same particle placed in a uniform static magnetic field of amplitude H_0. It will also be seen eventually that the general form of V for any spectroscopic transition is

$$V = 2|\mathbf{p} \cdot \mathbf{F}|. \tag{4.51}$$

The symbol $\mathbf{F}$ represents either the magnetic or the electric amplitude in the electromagnetic wave, depending on whether $\mathbf{p}$, the transition dipole moment, is electric or magnetic. By substituting Eq. 4.50 into Eq. 4.24, the time dependence of the parameter θ can be found:

$$\theta = \gamma H_1 t. \tag{4.52}$$

If one remembers that the perturbation will be applied in the form of a pulse of duration Υ such that $c_{A1}(\Upsilon) = 0$ and $c_{A2}(\Upsilon) = 1$, it can be seen from Eqs. 4.22 and 4.23 that the necessary and sufficient condition is

$$\theta(\Upsilon) = n\pi, \tag{4.53}$$

where n is an odd number. With $n = 1$ (the simplest choice), Eqs. 4.52 and 4.53 can be combined to yield

$$\Upsilon = \frac{\pi}{\gamma H_1}. \tag{4.54}$$

A "typical" spectroscopic experiment on a spin-$\frac{1}{2}$ particle in a static magnetic field $H_0 \hat{z}$ can now be described as follows.

1. The system is put into the low-energy eigenstate, so that the certain component of magnetic moment is parallel with the z axis (spin up). All other components of the magnetic moment (e.g., y and x) will be indeterminate.

2. An electromagnetic wave of the type described previously is turned on at time $t = 0$. The frequency of the wave is given by $\omega = \omega_0$ (see Eq. 2.68); from Eq. 4.43,

$$\omega_0 = \frac{(\gamma \hbar H_0/2) - (-\gamma \hbar H_0/2)}{\hbar} = \gamma H_0. \tag{4.55}$$

(These frequencies are ordinarily in the radio-wave region of the spectrum.)

3. The electromagnetic wave is turned off at time $t = \pi/\gamma H_1$. The system now will be in the high-energy eigenstate with the certain component of magnetic moment antiparallel to the z axis (spin down). All other components of the magnetic moment (e.g., y and x) will be indeterminate.

If the experiment described above is interrupted at some time in the interval $0 < t < \pi/\gamma H_1$, the H_1 wave turned off, and the z component of magnetic moment measured, that component will sometimes be found up and sometimes found down. The probability that "up" will result is $\cos^2(\gamma H_1 t)$, and the probability that "down" will be found is $\sin^2(\gamma H_1 t)$; this can be seen from Eqs. 4.22 and 4.23.

To distinguish between the two different kinds of quantum jumps, it is necessary next to find an infinite collection of operators, $\{R\}_t$, associated with the infinite number of superposition states through which the particle passes from spin up to spin down. At a given time t, the superposition coefficients in Eqs. 4.22 and 4.23 uniquely define a state according to Eq. 4.20. This state should be an eigenstate of the property represented by the particular operator R associated with the time t.

The correct choice of that operator is the component of magnetic moment along the direction specified by θ' and Ω, where

$$\Omega = \S - \omega_0 t; \qquad (4.56)$$

$\S$ is defined in Eq. 2.84, and ω_0 in Eq. 4.55. This component is the projection of the dipole moment on the axis of certainty. As will be shown in Chapter 6, the effect of the perturbation V is to tilt that axis away from the z axis through the angle θ'. It will also be shown that the "laboratory-space" angle θ' is always numerically equal to the "spin-space" angle θ. The projection of the axis of certainty upon the yx plane will make an angle Ω with the x axis. If the unit vector in the direction of the axis of certainty is called $\hat{u}_1$, the transition process causes the $\hat{u}_1, \hat{u}_2, \hat{u}_3$ coordinate system to rotate in the $\hat{x}, \hat{y}, \hat{z}$ frame until, at the time the pulse is terminated,

$$\hat{u}_1 = -\hat{z}. \qquad (4.57)$$

The z axis, being the direction of the large static magnetic field, H_0, is fixed in the laboratory reference frame. The energy of the magnetic system is composed almost entirely of the energy associated with the component of magnetic dipole moment in the z direction because of the requirement

$$H_0 \gg H_1. \qquad (4.58)$$

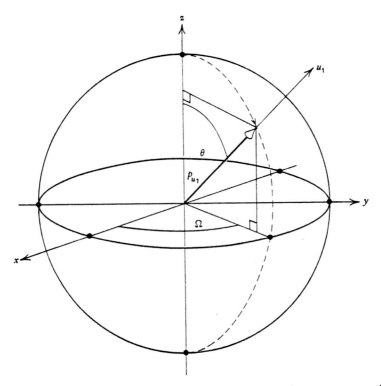

Figure 4.4. Motion of the certain component of the dipole moment, p_{u_1}, during the course of an uninterrupted spectroscopic transition. The u_1 axis is the axis of certainty, and the dotted line is a possible trajectory for the tip of p_{u_1} on the sphere of certainty.

Equation 4.58 follows from Eqs. 4.25, 4.50, and 4.55. Therefore the z axis remains the *energy* axis throughout the transition process. The relationships between the angles and vectors discussed in this section are shown in Figure 4.4.

4.7   Quantum jumps on the sphere of certainty

With this geometrical picture in mind, the consequences of believing in one kind of quantum jump or another can be explored. A belief in Schrödinger quantum jumps is equivalent to a belief that *no* experiment can have a certain outcome unless the u_1 axis is parallel or antiparallel to the z axis. If, on the other hand, one believes in Heisenberg jumps, one must introduce a third axis for complete visualization of the experiment. This is the axis along which the projection of the magnetic moment operator is to be measured. The unit vector in the measurement direction will henceforth be designated as $\hat{v}_1$. In the absence of any disturbing measurement, the axis of certainty, $\hat{u}_1$, lines up parallel to $\hat{z}$, the magnetic field direction in the laboratory, at times $t < 0$; this fact was stated previously in Section 4.5. At $t = 0$, the axis of certainty rotates away from $\hat{z}$; its intersection point with the sphere of certainty is a point with a trajectory determined by Eqs. 4.52 and 4.56, starting at the "north pole" and ending at the "south pole." It follows from Heisenberg's view that each imaginable experiment to measure any Cartesian component of the magnetic dipole moment (in any coordinate system) can be specified by the orientation of the axis of measurement, v_1. The nature of this specification is such that the intersection of the v_1 axis with the sphere of certainty at two different points represents the possible outcomes of the proposed experiment. The act of measurement interrupts the transition process and causes an abrupt change (the Heisenberg quantum jump) in the orientation of the u_1 axis. The point representing the state of the particle (the point of intersection of the axis of certainty with the sphere of certainty) is forced to hop to one of the two "poles" of the measurement axis.

The symbols $|+\rangle$ and $|-\rangle$ will be assigned to the kets representing states with eigenvalues at opposite intersections of the measurement axis with the sphere of certainty. Because of the completeness of the set of eigenkets,

$$|A\rangle = c_{A+}|+\rangle + c_{A-}|-\rangle. \tag{4.59}$$

The coefficients $c_{A\pm}$ are related to the great-circle distance between the intersection points. The probability of the hop from $|A\rangle$ to $|+\rangle$ is given by $|c_{A+}|^2$, and from $|A\rangle$ to $|-\rangle$, by $|c_{A-}|^2$, in accordance with the usual rule. If the measurement axis is the z axis, Eq. 4.59 becomes identical with Eq. 4.20, and all of the previously mentioned results are obtained. If, on the other hand, the measurement axis coincides with the axis of certainty, one of the coefficients (either c_{A+} or c_{A-}) in Eq. 4.59 is zero and there will be no quantum jump. The system will be in an eigenstate of the property being measured. By continually moving the measurement axis to keep it aligned with the axis of certainty, one could make an infinite number of measurements on the system as it travels through the infinite continuum of superposition states. Each measurement would yield a predictable outcome, so that the uncertainty principle would not limit the accuracy of the process. The system could be monitored during the entire transition process without disturbing its behavior in any way.

There is a one-to-one correspondence between each choice of V and the

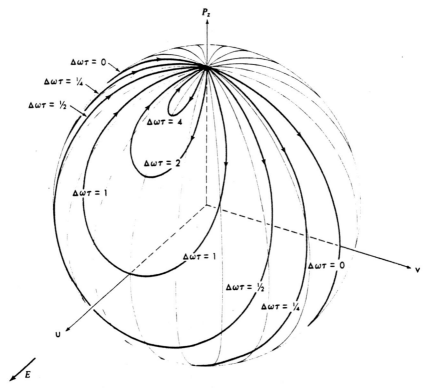

Figure 4.5. Spectroscopic transitions on the sphere of certainty. The trajectories shown are for processes that leave the system in its initial state (see the discussion of self-induced transparency in Chapter 7). Taken from Fig. 5 of *Phys. Rev.* **183**, 457 (1969), by S. L. McCall and E. L. Hahn.

trajectory of the point (representing the superposition state associated with the ket $|A\rangle$) on the surface of the sphere of certainty. If one knew the physical situation well enough, the trajectory could be computed for any kind of quantum transition. One could even discuss processes other than those produced by resonant interaction with electromagnetic radiation (spectroscopy), such as collisions. Although rather complicated spectroscopic trajectories have been described (see Figure 4.5), no work known to this author to date has been done on any of the others.

A geometrical picture of the transition process has been developed in this section, and a description of how the behavior of the system expected for Schrödinger quantum jumps differs from that predicted for jumps of the Heisenberg variety has been given. In the next sections, a thought experiment based on this picture will be described. This experiment will decide the question of which kind of jump actually occurs in nature.

4.8   Magnetic resonance in bulk and in beams

The spectroscopic study of transitions between states representing different orientations of a magnetic dipole moment is called *magnetic resonance*. There are two important kinds of magnetic resonance experiments. The first takes place at low density in a molecular beam apparatus; the second, at high density in a stationary bulk sample.

Bulk experiments are superior in some ways to beam experiments for illustrating facts about transitions. In the crossed-coil bulk magnetic resonance spectrometer, the entire sample is enclosed within a radio-frequency receiver coil, so that the behavior of the quantum systems is monitored directly and continuously throughout the experiment. Usually it is not practical to monitor the behavior of a particle by means of direct observation during its flight through a beam apparatus, however. Instead the apparatus is designed in such a way that it deflects particles exhibiting undesired behavior, and transmits the others to a single detector located at the end of the flight path of the beam. The behavior of quantum systems is then *deduced* from the changes in beam current at the detector produced by changes in the state of the portion of the apparatus that interacts with the beam. The relative advantage of bulk magnetic resonance experiments over beams made it possible for scientists carrying out the former type in the 1950s to make great contributions to the understanding of the topics discussed in this book. This is the work described in Chapter 1.

Beam experiments, however, also have some strong points. First, as will be seen shortly, it is relatively easy to put every particle in the beam into the same eigenstate. The only way to accomplish this task in bulk matter, on the other hand, is by cooling down the sample in accordance with Eq. 4.44. Easily obtainable laboratory magnetic fields are of the order of 1 or 2 T (webers per square meter), and in most cases the sizes of γ found in nature are so small that temperatures below 0.01 K would be required to satisfy the inequality presented in that equation. A more important advantage of beam experiments is that they afford the opportunity to study the particles one at a time. This is much different from the situation in bulk experiments, where one is always measuring the ensemble-averaged behavior of a very large number of particles. It will be shown in Chapter 5 that, if the ensemble is excited by a coherent perturbation, ensemble-averaged behavior mimics the behavior of the expectation value of an individual particle. There is, however, a difference (pointed out in Chapter 2) between the expectation value of a property for an individual system and the value of that property measured in a single experiment on the same system (unless the system is in an eigenstate of the property).

Both kinds of experiments are discussed in this book. Magnetic resonance in bulk will be considered in Chapter 6, and the rest of the present chapter will be devoted to a *Gedanken* magnetic resonance experiment in a beam apparatus. An excellent monograph on beam experiments has been written by Ramsey.[4]

4.9 The Stern-Gerlach experiment

In a typical beam experiment (see Figure 4.6) the atoms, ions, or molecules under study are vaporized in an oven. They are then allowed to escape from the oven through a hole (oriented to produce a stream of particles symmetrically distributed about the x axis of the laboratory coordinate system) into an evacuated chamber. Apertures are used to collimate the beam, eliminating systems with any appreciable component of velocity perpendicular to the beam axis. A one-to-one correspondence between the position of a particle in the apparatus and the time elapsed since it left the oven can be produced by giving all the particles in the beam very nearly the same speed. A pair of notched disks (or a spiral-grooved cylinder rotating about an axis parallel to $\hat{x}$) can be used to remove from the beam any quantum system having an undesired component of velocity along the beam direction. The particles that survive passage through the apertures and velocity selector have nearly identical velocities,

$$\mathbf{v} = v\hat{x}. \tag{4.60}$$

These particles enter the "interaction region" of the apparatus, where the desired experiment is performed upon them. All particles that are not removed from the beam by the experimental apparatus strike the detector.

As the beam particles pass into the interaction region, their angular momentum vectors are presumably oriented at random in the laboratory coordinate system. Each particle then passes between the pole faces of a horseshoe magnet (usually called the *A magnet* by beam scientists). The pole faces of the A magnet are sculpted to produce a linear field gradient in the z direction:

$$\mathbf{H}_A = G_M z\hat{z}. \tag{4.61}$$

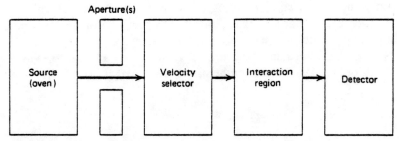

Figure 4.6.   Block diagram of a typical beam apparatus.

This gradient exerts a force upon an atom or molecule of mass m_0 to which the dipole is attached, and produces an acceleration **a** in accordance with the discussion given in Chapter 3:

$$\mathbf{a} = \frac{\hat{z} p_z G_M}{m_0}. \qquad (4.62)$$

If the length of the pole faces (measured in the x direction) is l_A, each particle will spend a time l_A/v in the inhomogeneous field. It will therefore acquire a component of momentum in the z direction, so that the total momentum,

$$\boldsymbol{\mu} = m_0 v \hat{x}, \qquad (4.63)$$

becomes

$$\boldsymbol{\mu} = m_0 v \left[\hat{x} + \left(\frac{p_z G_M l_A}{m_0 v^2} \right) \hat{z} \right]. \qquad (4.64)$$

The momentum increment produced by the A magnet will cause the beam to fan out in the xz plane. The atoms or molecules which had magnetic moments oriented in such a way that p_z was positive will be directed upwards, ($\| \hat{z}$), whereas those with negative z components will be directed downwards ($\| - \hat{z}$). The experiment just described was first performed by Stern and Gerlach,[5] using silver atoms ($s = \frac{1}{2}$) as the beam particles. The detector was a cold glass plate oriented perpendicularly to the beam axis. Silver atoms that struck the plate condensed and eventually produced a mirror. The extent of the mirror in the z direction indicated the amount of deflection, and therefore the magnitude of p_z. Stern and Gerlach found that the distribution of beam trajectories in the "fan" was not continuous. Instead, as described in Section 4.5, there were only two beam components, corresponding to "spin up" and "spin down"—see Eq. 4.42. It would be hard to exaggerate the importance of this experiment in stimulating the development of quantum theory.

Several conditions must be imposed on the parameters of this experiment in order to make the mathematics tractable:

$$\Delta v_z, \Delta v_y \ll \frac{\gamma \hbar G_M l_A}{2 m_0 v} \ll v \ll c. \tag{4.65}$$

The first condition in Eq. 4.65 ensures that the spreading of the beam (due to the residual momentum transverse to the beam direction, brought about by insufficient collimation) will not mask the separation of the incident beam into subbeams by the A magnet. The second condition ensures that the kinetic energy of the beam particle is not changed appreciably by the dipole-inhomogeneous field interaction, while the third obviates the necessity for consideration of relativistic effects. It is also assumed that the beam separation will not be appreciable during the flight of the particle through the A field (impulse approximation). After the beam leaves the A magnet, however, the z momentum acquired by the atoms and molecules will eventually separate the subbeams by an amount that exceeds the beam radius. At this point it is possible to block one of the subbeams, so that only the atoms or molecules with some desired z component of spin will be transmitted.

Constraints are also imposed in order to allow study of the beam particles in isolation, before they have a chance to interact with each other or their surroundings. If such interactions were permitted, they would have the effect of permitting particles in state 2 to relax down into state 1 exponentially, with a characteristic time constant T_1, mentioned in Section 4.5. The total length, L, for the beam chamber is therefore chosen sufficiently short so that particles of speed v do not stay in the apparatus long enough to relax appreciably:

$$v T_1 \gg L. \tag{4.66}$$

4.10   State selection in beam experiments

The experiments described in subsequent sections also take place in the apparatus diagramed in block form in Figure 4.6, with one difference. The interaction region contains an A magnet similar to that described in the preceding sections, but is enlarged over that used by Stern and Gerlach to permit investigation of the properties of spin-oriented particles.

It is convenient to return the transmitted subbeams to the x axis for ease in subsequent experimentation or detection. This may be accomplished by causing the beam to pass through another inhomogeneous magnetic field, having its gradient oriented *anti*parallel to $\hat{z}$. The conventional designation for such a device is "B magnet":

$$\mathbf{H}_B = -G_M z\hat{z}. \tag{4.67}$$

(A combination of A and B magnets that will accomplish the desired refocusing of the beam is shown in Figure 4.7.) In the region between the first and second B magnets, the subbeams are well separated, so that it is possible to insert an obstruction into the path of either one without affecting the intensity of the other.

The direction of the field gradient in the A magnet at the entrance to this device is the axis of measurement, usually oriented parallel to the z axis:

$$\hat{v}_1 = \hat{z}_1. \tag{4.68}$$

If the subbeam deflected in the $+\hat{v}_1$ direction is blocked, all of the particles that survive passage through this device will have their certain components of spins oriented in the $-\hat{v}_1$ direction, and vice versa. This

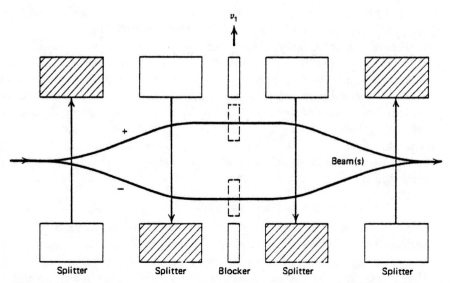

Figure 4.7. Block diagram of a state selector; directions of field gradients are shown by vertical arrows.

arrangement of magnetic field gradients and blockers will therefore be designated henceforth as a "Stern-Gerlach spin selector" ("SG" for short). From the point of view of a believer in Heisenberg jumps, a particle propagating in the $\hat{x}$ direction that enters an SG with its certain component of spin pointing along an arbitrary direction $\hat{u}_1 \neq \hat{v}_1$ may have any one of six different experiences. Depending on how the two beam stops are placed, (1) it may pass through without change in spin direction (both beam stops withdrawn). The particle may encounter one beam stop placed to block the plus beam, precipitating a quantum jump into either the plus or minus state: in the former case, (2) it would be blocked, and in the latter, (3) transmitted. It may encounter the blocker in the path of the minus beam, which would also precipitate a quantum jump into eigenstates of the v_1 component of angular momentum. This time, a jump into the state represented by $|-\rangle$ would cause the particle to be removed from the beam (4), and a jump into the state represented by $|+\rangle$ would cause it to survive (5). Finally, if both blockers are inserted (6), it is certain that no particles will ever be transmitted.

The SG is therefore a device of the type that is required to put all of the quantum systems into the same initial state, namely, that represented by the wavefunction ψ_1. Each beam particle that leaves an SG will be, at that instant of time ($t = 0$), certainly in the eigenstate of spin associated with the unblocked path. One cannot exactly determine the relationship between the time t "seen" by any one quantum system and the time measured on a clock in the laboratory. This information, if it were available, could be used to determine the position of the beam particle in question. It is because of the uncertainty relations between the position of a particle and its momentum, that such a measurement would produce a Heisenberg quantum jump into an unpredictable state of momentum, undoing the work of the velocity selector. In the experiments to be described in subsequent sections of this chapter, it will be necessary to know closely the amount of time spent by each particle in each portion of the apparatus (and therefore the velocity must be known). Also a shutter to closely determine position will be required. Fortunately, in practice the accuracy permitted by the uncertainty principle is sufficient.

4.11 The Rabi magnetic resonance experiment

The desired beam experiment must conform to the pattern described in Section 4.4: spin-$\frac{1}{2}$ particles must travel from the velocity selector into a transition region that has three different sections, as shown in Figure 4.8. The initial and final state selectors can be SGs oriented with initial gradients ($\hat{v}_1$ axes) in the $+\hat{z}$ direction. Beam stops are inserted into the path of the minus beam in the initial SG and into the path of the minus

·beam in the final SG. Particles that exit from the initial detector are certainly in the plus or "spin-up" state, represented by $|1\rangle$. Any particle that changes its state in the transition region will surely be blocked by the final SG and will therefore not strike the detector.

The transition will not properly be called *spectroscopic* unless (1) the two states have different energies, and (2) the perturbation is an electromagnetic wave. To satisfy the first requirement, the entire interaction region will be inserted between the pole faces of a magnet that produces a uniform magnetic field in the z direction. This device is usually called a C magnet, and its magnitude is H_0, as described in Eq. 4.39. The C magnet therefore will give the two quantum states the energies expressed in Eq. 4.43. All of the particles that survive passage through the initial SG will be in the state having the lower of the two energies: recall Eqs. 4.41 and 4.46. (The magnetic energy added by the A and B magnets is zero because the beam propagates along the x axis, where $z=0$. Therefore, from Eqs. 4.61 and 4.67,

$$H_A = H_B = 0.)$$ (4.69)

To satisfy the second requirement for a spectroscopic transition, an oscillating magnetic field is produced in the transition region at the frequency ω_0 (see Eq. 4.55). An rf oscillator operating at that frequency is connected to a transmitter coil elongated in the x direction, with its magnetic axis oriented along the y direction. The amplitude of the mag-

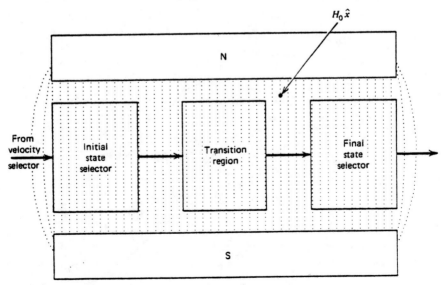

Figure 4.8.   Block diagram of interaction region.

netic field produced by the coils is adjusted to $2H_1$ by controlling the power output of the oscillator. This oscillating field will be equivalent to two rotating fields of constant amplitude H_1, one of which rotates in the same sense (clockwise or counterclockwise) as the axis of certainty and the other in the opposite sense (see Figure 4.9). The influence of the latter

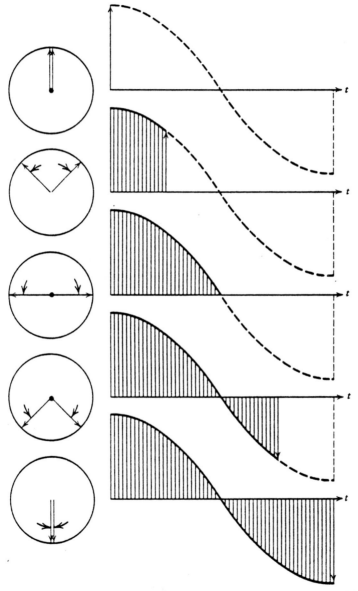

Figure 4.9. A plane-polarized wave (amplitude shown on right) resolved into two circularly polarized waves (amplitude shown on left).

rotating field will be negligible;[6] the former will produce all of the desired effects, as one can see from Eq. 4.49.

The time of flight of the particles through the transition region of length l will determine the irradiation period Υ:

$$\Upsilon = \frac{l}{v}. \qquad (4.70)$$

Either the velocity v or the magnitude of H_1 should be adjusted until the irradiation period is sufficient to supply a π pulse to each particle, as indicated in Eq. 4.54.

When everything has been properly adjusted, each particle that leaves the initial SG will have rotated its axis of certainty by exactly 180° during its passage through the transition region and will be blocked with 100% probability by the final state selector. Equivalently, one may say that each quantum system has swallowed exactly one photon and has changed its state from that represented by $|+\rangle$ with energy $\mathcal{E}_1$, to that represented by $|-\rangle$ with energy $\mathcal{E}_2$. A believer in Schrödinger jumps may claim that the photon-swallowing act occurred at any arbitrarily chosen point along the x axis within the transition region ($0 \leqslant x \leqslant l$), and hence at any time in the interval $l/v(0 \leqslant t \leqslant \Upsilon)$. This apparatus therefore cannot distinguish between the two kinds of jumps.

Beam experiments with C magnets and rf waves were developed by I. I. Rabi[7] and his co-workers to provide very accurate measurements of the magnetic moments of nuclei and molecules. The apparatus actually used was far simpler than that described above, however. Instead of eight inhomogeneous-field magnets and four beam stops to prepare and detect the initial and final quantum states, implied by the use of two SGs, Rabi employed only a single A magnet as the initial spin selector, and single B magnet as the final spin selector. By careful adjustment of the beam trajectories and detector position, such a device can even be made to work without using velocity selection. If SGs of the type described above are employed, however, velocity selection is required.

4.12   The Ramsey separated oscillating fields experiment

N. F. Ramsey[8] modified the Rabi magnetic apparatus in the following way. Instead of one transmitter coil for the $\mathbf{H}_1$ field (of length $l_1 = l_C$), he used two coils of length $l_1/2 < l/2$—one located after the exit end of the initial SG and one just before the entrance end of the final SG.

Note that in both the Rabi experiment and in Ramsey's modification thereof, the certain component of the magnetic dipole moment makes an angle $\theta' = 0$ with the z axis at the beginning of the $\mathbf{H}_1$ irradiation region and an angle $\theta' = \pi$ with the z axis at the end of that period. Recall from

Section 4.6 that the angle θ' in laboratory coordinates happens to equal the
"angle" θ that appears in the algebraic expressions for the superposition
coefficients. This means that in both the Rabi and the Ramsey experiments, $\theta = \theta' = \pi/2$ at the half-irradiation point. The difference is that in
the Rabi apparatus the beam particles are described by the wavefunction

$$\Psi = \frac{1}{\sqrt{2}}(\psi_1 + \psi_2) \tag{4.71}$$

at only one instant of time, $t = \Upsilon/2$, and at that instant the particles
themselves are experimentally inaccessible. By way of contrast, in the
Ramsey apparatus the axis of certainty for the spin of each particle is
located in the xy plane over nonzero portions of the beam path, $l - l_1$, and
over a correspondingly long interval of time, $(l - l_1)/v$. This space can be
made long enough to accommodate additional experimental apparatus.
The apparatus could be chosen to verify that the quantum systems are
indeed in an eigenstate of "spin sideways" when they are in a superposition of eigenstates of "spin up" and "spin down."

Ramsey's purpose in designing the separated oscillating fields method
was not to verify the existence of superposition states, however. He simply
wanted to determine ω_0 to greater precision than was possible in the
Rabi-type apparatus, and was able to show that merely separating the ω_1
fields would accomplish this purpose. The modification of the Ramsey
apparatus required to disprove the Schrödinger jump picture of quantum
transitions will be described in the next section.

4.13   A thought experiment

The desired experiment could, in principle, measure a property of a
quantum system in a superposition state and not produce any quantum
jumps. Such an experiment can be performed, using the Ramsey separated
oscillating fields equipment, if some device that can measure the y component of magnetization is inserted into the space between the two
oscillating fields.

The obvious choice for such an apparatus is an SG oriented along the y
axis. If the atoms and molecules are still in either the spin-up or spin-down
state (having undergone—or not undergone—their Schrödinger jumps),
they would have a 50% probability of being deflected into the left-hand
subbeam and a 50% chance of being deflected into the right-hand one. On
the other hand, if they have not undergone any jumps, they ought to be
in an eigenstate of the y component of angular momentum. *Which* of these
two eigenstates they would be in (i.e., whether they would be "spin left" or

"spin right") depends on the algebraic sign of γ.

Unfortunately, the experiment just described would not work in the apparatus devised by Ramsey. The presence of the H_0 field in the space between the two irradiation regions causes components of the magnetic moment in the xy plane to precess about the z axis at the Larmor frequency. This means that the actual orientation of the axis of certainty in laboratory coordinates is given by

$$\hat{u}_1 = \cos\Omega \sin\theta' \hat{x} + \sin\Omega \sin\theta' \hat{y} + \cos\theta' \hat{z}, \tag{4.72}$$

where Ω was defined in Eq. 4.56. Since Ω changes very rapidly with time (ω_0 for protons exceeds 1 MHz even if H_0 is only 25 mT), the direction of the certain component of spin will reverse many, many times during the flight of the quantum system through the field of the A magnet. A large number of impulses $[\omega_0(l_C - l_1)/\pi v]$ will be delivered to each particle, half pushing it to the left and half to the right. The net y components of linear momentum acquired will therefore be zero, and the beam will not split into two subbeams.

To make the beam split into two subbeams, one with a trajectory to the left and one to the right in stationary laboratory coordinates, it is necessary to stop the Larmor precession. This can be done by replacing the C magnet of length l_C by two C magnets, each of length $l_C/2$. The first of these, in conjunction with the H_1 field of length $l_1/2$, will produce the first $\pi/2$ pulse (i.e., $\theta' = \pi/2$ for particles leaving this portion of the apparatus). The angle θ' will remain at $\pi/2$ for the entire region of length $l_C - l_1$ in between the two C magnets. Furthermore, in this intermediate region, the angle Ω will remain constant because $\omega_0 = 0$. The amplitude of the field produced by the C magnet should be adjusted until the spins precess through $n + \frac{1}{2}$ Larmor half cycles:

$$\frac{2\omega_0}{l_C} = (n + \tfrac{1}{2})\pi. \tag{4.73}$$

Since the H_1 field and the time of arrival of each particle may be synchronized by means of a shutter in the path of the beam, one can make $\S = \pi$. Therefore, in the intermediate region,

$$|\Omega| = (n - \tfrac{1}{2})\pi. \tag{4.74}$$

The result of these adjustments is to align the axis of certainty either parallel or antiparallel to the laboratory y axis:

$$\hat{u}_1 = \pm\hat{y}. \tag{4.75}$$

Blocking one of the two (left or right) subbeams should reduce the beam intensity to zero; blocking the other should produce no change in beam intensity. In the latter case, the effect of the sideways Stern-Gerlach apparatus in the intermediate region is to perform a measurement upon each beam particle without producing a Heisenberg quantum jump.

The spin-$\frac{1}{2}$ particles will then enter the field of the second C magnet and resume their precessional motion. The second H_1 field will then produce the second $\pi/2$ pulse (i.e., $\theta = \pi$ for particles leaving this portion of the apparatus). It will probably be necessary to adjust the phase of the radio frequency used in the second oscillator to ensure that absorption of energy by the particles (rather than stimulated emission) will occur.

Now imagine that the C magnet and the H_1 field are divided into N_s segments of equal length. This would create $N_s - 1$ gaps between these sections, and a Stern-Gerlach apparatus could be inserted into each gap (see Figure 4.10). The direction of the magnetic field gradient in successive SGs will make successively larger angles with the laboratory z axis, so that at each point it is aligned with the direction of the axis of certainty for the beam particles. If the direction of the field gradient in the jth SG is $\hat{u}_{1,j}$, then

$$\hat{u}_{1,j} \cdot \hat{u}_{1,j+1} = \cos\left(\frac{\pi}{N_s}\right) \tag{4.76}$$

and

$$\hat{u}_{1,j} \cdot \hat{z} = \cos\left(\frac{j\pi}{N_s}\right). \tag{4.77}$$

In each SG, the subbeam which intersects the negative branch of the $\hat{u}_1$ axis could be blocked without reducing the transmitted intensity. In this way, $N_s - 1$ measurements could be made upon each quantum system during its transition between the energy eigenstates represented by ψ_1 and ψ_2. Each measurement would have an eigenvalue as its result, so that no Heisenberg jumps would ever occur. A schematic drawing of a typical segment of the proposed apparatus appears in Figure 4.11.

4.14 Difficulties with the proposed experiment

There are two major practical problems with the *Gedanken* experiment proposed in the preceding section. The first of these can be solved by ensuring that the magnetic field intensity due to the C magnet increases (decreases) gradually from 0 to H_0 (H_0 to 0). An abruptly changing electric

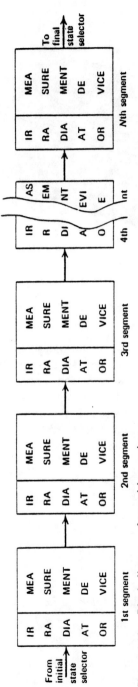

Figure 4.10. Block diagram of transition region.

131

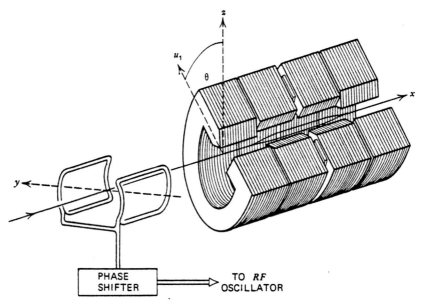

Figure 4.11.   Sketch of one segment of the transition region.

or magnetic field can be expressed as a sum of sinusoidally oscillating electromagnetic waves; the amplitude of these waves can be calculated by means of Fourier analysis. This analysis shows that the amplitudes are appreciable at frequencies as high as the reciprocal of the transit time of a quantum system through the "fringing field" region. If this region for the last C magnet (for example) begins at x_0 and ends at $x_0 + \Delta l$,

$$H_C = \begin{cases} \dfrac{H_0 x}{\Delta l}, & x_0 < x < x_0 + l, \\ H_0, & x > x_0 + l. \end{cases} \tag{4.78}$$

The oscillating fields then have frequencies

$$\omega' < \frac{v}{\Delta l} \tag{4.79}$$

and are capable of producing transitions (called *Majorana flops*[9]) whenever

$$\omega' \sim \omega_0. \tag{4.80}$$

Therefore the condition (called the *adiabatic condition*) that must be satisfied to keep the beam particles in whatever state they happen to be while entering the C magnet is

$$\Delta l > \frac{v}{\omega_0}. \tag{4.81}$$

An alternative statement of the adiabatic condition, therefore, is that each spin must precess through many Larmor cycles during its stay in the fringing field. The adiabatic condition can be met by careful design of the C magnets.

A more serious problem is ensuring that the spins in the intermediate regions point exactly along the y axis, instead of along some other direction in the xy plane. The requirement is that the number of cycles of precession during passage through each C magnet be controllable, so that Eq. 4.73 will be satisfied. Unfortunately there is a limitation in principle on the accuracy of ω_0. Due to the fact that the beam particles only "see" the field that causes their axes of certainty to precess for a time T/N_s, the energy difference $\mathcal{E}_2 - \mathcal{E}_1$ is uncertain by an amount $\Delta \mathcal{E}$, which satisfies the uncertainty relationship

$$\frac{T \Delta \mathcal{E}}{N_s} > \frac{\hbar}{2}. \tag{4.82}$$

This leads to an uncertainty in the Larmor frequency;

$$\Delta \mathcal{E} = \hbar \Delta \omega_0. \tag{4.83}$$

These two equations can be combined to yield

$$\Delta \omega_0 T = 1. \tag{4.84}$$

Equation 4.84 can be obtained without the use of quantum mechanics; it is simply the Fourier relationship between the spread of frequencies $\Delta \omega_0$ in a wave packet which persists for a duration T. (Remember the previous discussion of the adiabatic theorem.) Since the quantum systems precess for a time T/N_s, the uncertainty in precession frequency leads to an uncertainty $\Delta \Omega$ in the accumulated phase:

$$\Delta \Omega = \frac{\Delta \omega_0 T}{2}. \tag{4.85}$$

The angle Ω in the regions between the C magnets therefore cannot be determined within limits narrower than about $\pm \frac{1}{2}$ radian. This means that the maximum intensity ratio of the left- and right-hand beams cannot be the desired $1.00:0.00$. Instead, the best that can be expected will be of the order of

$$\cos^2 \tfrac{1}{4} : \sin^2 \tfrac{1}{4} :: 0.94 : 0.06. \tag{4.86}$$

The estimate given in Eq. 4.86 is decidedly optimistic.

These errors would occur at each SG in the transition region and accumulate in such a way that the transmitted intensity would be very low if N_s were large. A "perfect" experiment with a larger number of SG magnets is not necessary, however. If the results of a single measurement between C magnets (e.g., at the half-way point with a field gradient $H_A = G_M y \hat{y}$) produced anything but a $50:50$ beam, the hypothesis of Schrödinger jumps would be disproved.

4.15 The Bloom transverse Stern-Gerlach effect

The *Gedanken* experiment just described is supposed to prove that superposition states have properties that can be measured without producing quantum jumps. It is essential to the argument that the superposed states be eigenstates of the energy with different eigenvalues. Although the states in the proposed experiment did have different energies while they were in the fields produced by the C magnets, they had the same magnetic energy (namely, zero) while the crucial measurement was being performed. For this reason, it would be desirable to perform an experiment on spin-$\tfrac{1}{2}$ particles during their passage through the field of a C magnet and attempt to separate spin-left particles from spin-right particles in the rotating coordinate system. Myer Bloom and his co-workers[10] have accomplished this separation in a remarkable experiment demonstrating what they called the *transverse Stern-Gerlach effect*.

In the Bloom experiment, a beam of neutral potassium atoms was directed along the z axis of a solenoidal C magnet. The detector then recorded a beam profile having an intensity maximum on the axis (i.e., at the origin of the xy plane). Four wires were placed inside the solenoid parallel to the z axis in symmetrical positions (in the north, east, south, and west electric quadrupole arrangement described in Chapter 3) about the beam. An rf voltage applied alternately to these wires created an inhomogeneous magnetic field directed along the $\hat{x}'$ axis in a coordinate system rotating at the frequency ω. The magnetic field of the solenoid was increased until the Larmor frequency, ω_0, equaled ω. At that point, the beam split into a number of subbeams corresponding to the number of eigenstates of the angular momentum of potassium atoms.

4.16   Quantum jumps and superposition states: conclusion

If the experiment described in Section 4.13 is performed, the apparatus will have produced a transition of the system from state 1 to state 2, and will have performed N_s measurements upon the system during the process. If there were such things as Schrödinger quantum jumps in nature, the performance of these N_s experiments would have the effect of reducing the beam intensity nearly to zero.

The fact is that Schrödinger jumps do not occur in nature. The only quantum jumps that exist are those of the Heisenberg variety. Since the experiment was designed to avoid Heisenberg jumps, only those jumps necessitated by the considerations outlined in Section 4.14 will occur. As a consequence, the beam intensity will be minimally affected by the N_s measurements. If the experiment were actually performed, the failure of the beam intensity to diminish to zero could be taken as proof of the reality of superposition states.

In terms of the geometrical picture developed previously to describe the transition process, the rf irradiation of a quantum system in the first segment causes the point representing the state of the system to move away from the "north" pole on the sphere of certainty at the angular frequency $\omega_1 = \gamma H_1$. At the same time, the point circulates rapidly about the pole at the much larger rate ω_0 because of the field H_0. The resultant trajectory of the point is a tightly wound spiral on the sphere of certainty, originating at the "north" pole (see Figure 4.12a). At the end of the irradiation period of the first segment, the particle passes out of the field H_0 and the precessional motion ceases. The representative point will come to rest on the sphere at the point $\theta = \pi / N_s$ and $\Omega = -\pi/2$ (see Eq. 4.72). The ray drawn from the sphere's center through to the representative point defines the axis of certainty, $\hat{u}_1$. The SG portion of the first segment is represented in this picture by a measurement axis, $\hat{v}_1$. Since $\hat{u}_1$ and $\hat{v}_1$ coincide, the measurement process does not alter the position of the representative point (see Figure 4.12b). As the particle exits from the SG, the $\hat{v}_1$ axis disappears. The representative point resumes its spiral downward course as it becomes subject to the static and oscillatory magnetic fields associated with the second segment (see Figure 4.12c).

Finally, the differences between the two kinds of jumps can be illustrated by analogy. Suppose that an extraterrestrial being who wishes to learn the history of this planet asks the question, "Who was Richard Evelyn Byrd?" A well-informed earthling can reply, "He was an explorer." "And what did he explore?" asks the being. "The polar regions of the planet," replies the earthling. The being has the power to look backward in time and therefore is able to see Byrd first at the North Pole and then at

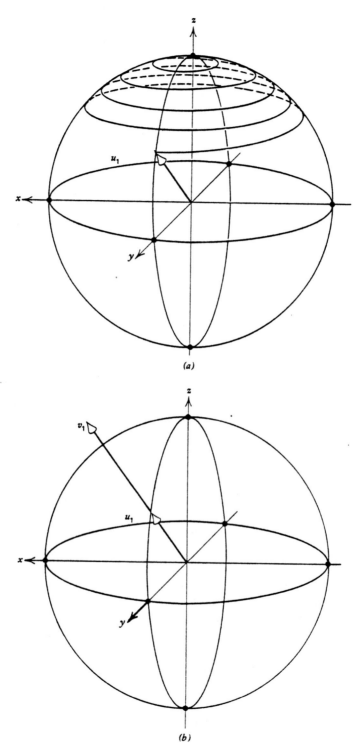

Figure 4.12. (*a*) Spectroscopic trajectory of a precessing particle. (*b*) Measurement of the dipole moment of a nonprecessing particle.

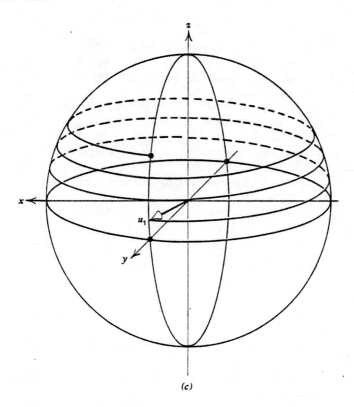

(c)

(c) Resumption of precessional motion by the particle.

the South Pole. The being notes the change in Byrd's position and asks itself the question, "How did Byrd get from one pole to the other?" Since it knows that the poles are the intersection points of the earth's axis with the sphere representing the surface of the earth's crust (and since it has x-ray eyes), it carefully examines the interior of the earth along the axis over a period of time to see whether it can find Byrd in transit. All measurements performed along this axis have the result that Byrd is always either at the South Pole or the North Pole, but never in between. The being concludes on this basis that the mode of travel used by Byrd to progress from one pole to the other is a discontinuous process called a "quantum jump." Another extraterrestrial being might think to look at other portions of the earth's surface during the transition process. If it did so, it might detect Admiral Byrd moving in a continuous trajectory upon that sphere from one pole to another, and therefore reach a different conclusion about the dynamics of polar exploration.

4.17 References

1. E. T. Jaynes and F. W. Cummings, "Comparison of quantum and semiclassical radiation theories with application to the beam maser," *Proc. IEEE*. **51**, 89

(1963).

2. E. Schrödinger, "Are there quantum jumps?", *What Is Life?* (Doubleday Anchor Books, Garden City, N. Y., 1956), pp. 132–160.

3. W. Heisenberg, *Physics and Philosophy* (Harper and Bros., New York, 1958), pp. 142 ff.

4. N. F. Ramsey, *Molecular Beams* (Clarendon Press, Oxford, 1956).

5. a. O. Stern, "Ein Weg zur experimentellen Pruefung der Richtungsquantelung in Magnetfeld," *Zs. Phys.* **7**, 249 (1921).

   b. W. Gerlach and O. Stern, "Ueber die Richtungsquantelung im Magnetfeld," *Ann. Phys.* **74**, 673 (1924).

   c. W. Gerlach, "Ueber die Richtungsquantelung im Magnetfeld, II," *Ann. Phys* **76**, 163 (1925).

6. a. F. Bloch and A. Siegert, "Magnetic resonance for nonrotating fields," *Phys. Rev.* **57**, 522 (1940).

   b. A. F. Stevenson, "On the theory of the magnetic resonance method of determining nuclear moments," *Phys. Rev.* **58**, 1061 (1940).

7. a. I. I. Rabi, J. R. Zacharias, S. Millman, and P. Kusch, "A new method of measuring nuclear magnetic moment," *Phys. Rev.* **53**, 318 (1938).

   b. I. I. Rabi, S. Millman, P. Kusch, and J. R. Zacharias, "The molecular beam resonance method for measuring nuclear magnetic moments," *Phys. Rev.* **55**, 526 (1939).

8. N. F. Ramsey, "A molecular beam resonance method with separated oscillating fields," *Phys. Rev.* **78**, 695 (1950).

9. E. Majorana, "Atomi orientati in campo magnetico variabile," *Nuovo Cimento* **9**, 43 (1932).

10. a. M. Bloom and K. Erdman, "The transverse Stern-Gerlach experiment," *Can. J. Phys.* **40**, 179 (1962).

    b. M. Bloom, E. Enga, and H. Lew, "Observation of the transverse Stern-Gerlach effect in neutral potassium," *Can. J. Phys.* **45**, 1481 (1965).

4.18 Problems

4.1. At what temperature (kelvins) is $kT = \gamma \hbar H_0$ for protons ($\gamma/2\pi = 42$ MHz T^{-1}) in a magnetic field of 1.4 T?

4.2. Calculate $\langle x \rangle_{12}$, $\langle y \rangle_{12}$, and $\langle z \rangle_{12}$ for hydrogen in a "halfway" superposition of the $1s$ and $2s$ states ($c_1 \equiv c_{1s} = c_2 \equiv c_{2s} = 1/\sqrt{2}$).

$$\psi_{2s}(\mathbf{r}, t) = (32\pi a_0^3)^{-1/2} \exp\left(\frac{-i \mathcal{E}_2 t}{\hbar} \right) \left[2 - \left(\frac{r}{a_0} \right) \right] \cdot \exp\left(\frac{-r}{2a_0} \right).$$

4.3. Calculate the perturbation energy V (in joules) required to produce a π pulse of duration $\Upsilon = 1.0 \times 10^{-9}$ s.

4.4. What is the minimum angle between the total angular momentum and its certain component for $s = 1$? $s = 10$? $s = 100$?

4.5. Calculate the value of H_1 (in teslas) required to produce a π pulse for protons (γ in Problem 4.1) of duration $\Upsilon = 1.0 \times 10^{-6}$ s.

5 Ensembles of radiating systems

5.1 Reasons for the use of statistical methods

The quantum systems that interact with light waves in spectroscopic experiments have been treated in preceding chapters as if these systems were to be studied one at a time. In practice, however, one ordinarily deals with macroscopic samples of matter, each of which consists of very large numbers ($\approx 10^{23}$) of microscopic chromophores. Statistical methods must be used in such cases to predict the behavior of the sample, and it is the purpose of this chapter to develop appropriate techniques.

It might be imagined that the statistical problem in quantum mechanics had already been solved when it was discovered how to calculate expectation values. If some physically observable property of the system is represented by the operator R, the expectation value of that property, $\langle R \rangle$, may be calculated by means of Eq. 2.78. The interpretation of $\langle R \rangle$ is that each of N repeated measurements of that property made upon a single system produces a result r_n, drawn from the set of M eigenvalues $\{r_n\}_M$. The average of these measurements approaches $\langle R \rangle$ as N becomes very large:

$$\lim_{N \to \infty} \frac{1}{N} \sum_{n=1}^{N} r_n = \langle R \rangle. \tag{5.1}$$

If a single measurement is made simultaneously upon each of N identical particles (the ensemble), the same average is to be expected. (The theoretical justification for the equality of these two averages is called the *ergodic hypothesis* in statistical mechanics.) If this were all there was to the problem, the ensemble average would in every case be the expectation value, and there would be no need for additional discussion of quantum statistical mechanics.

The N-particle ensemble average will not necessarily equal the N-measurement single-particle average, however, unless certain conditions are met. First, whenever repeated measurements are being made upon a single system, it is necessary to return that system exactly to its initial state between each pair of measurements. (Whenever this precaution is *not* taken, the measurements will be called *successive* rather than *repeated*.) The corresponding requirement in regard to the equivalent experiment in which simultaneous measurements are made upon a large number of identical systems is that each of these systems be in the same state.

These conditions (which make the collection of systems a *microcanonical ensemble*) are not always met in practice. Measurements are more commonly performed upon quantum systems, the states of which are determined by an equilibrium Boltzmann distribution among the several stationary energy levels associated with an absolute temperature $T > 0$. Collections of systems so distributed are called *canonical ensembles*. Whenever averages of physical properties are computed for such ensembles, one must perform both "quantum" averaging (i.e., calculations of expectation values), and "classical" or ensemble averaging over the various states that are present. The decision was made in Chapter 2 to indicate the former type of averaging by means of triangular brackets—for example, $\langle R \rangle$. The latter type of averaging will be represented by the symbol used in Chapter 2 for a strictly classical average, a superior bar (e.g., by $\bar{R}$), and the combination of the two types by both symbols (e.g., by $\langle \bar{R} \rangle$).

The main concern here is with systems that are in the process of changing their states. It may well be that the processes which are producing the changes of state do not affect every system in the same way. This means that, even if all of the systems start out in the same state, so that $\langle \bar{R} \rangle = \langle R \rangle$ at the start, they will very shortly be in different states. Therefore $\langle \bar{R} \rangle \neq \langle R \rangle$, and ensemble averaging will have to be used (in addition to the calculation of expectation values) in order to predict accurately the physical properties of the sample.

5.2   Coherent and incoherent perturbations

Perturbations that affect every system of the ensemble in the same way are called *coherent*. The most important examples for the purposes of this chapter are the following ones.

1. The oscillating electric and magnetic fields produced by inductors, capacitors, or antennas connected to tuned LC circuits. These produce coherent perturbations at radio frequencies and cause transitions between states representing different orientations of nuclear spins in beams (as described in Chapter 4) and bulk samples (nuclear magnetic and electric quadrupole resonance). They also produce transitions in beams between states representing different orientations of molecular rotation axes whenever a rotational magnetic moment is present (molecular magnetic

resonance) or when a change in the orientation of an electric dipole or quadrupole moment is possible (molecular electric resonance).

2. The oscillating electric and magnetic fields produced in waveguides or cavities connected to klystrons or similar devices. These produce coherent perturbations at microwave frequencies and cause transitions between states representing different orientations of electron spins (electron para-magnetic, ferromagnetic, antiferromagnetic, and similar types of resonance experiments), and between states representing different molecular rota-tional frequencies (microwave rotational spectroscopy). They also produce transitions between states representing different orbital patterns for char-ged particles about the lines of force in a magnetic field (cyclotron resonance).

3. The oscillating electric and magnetic fields produced in waveguides or microwave cavities by masers. These produce coherent perturbations at microwave frequencies and can therefore, in principle, be used to do any of the things that klystrons can do. In addition, they can produce useful power at some shorter wavelengths, so that the two sources together can also explore transitions between states representing different low-frequency vibrational states of molecules. These include inversion, ring puckering, wagging, and torsional oscillations.

4. The oscillating electric and magnetic fields produced in and radiated by the cavities of optical masers (lasers). These produce coherent perturba-tions in the near- and far-infrared, the visible, and the near-ultraviolet regions of the spectrum. They cause transitions between states representing different frequencies of stretching vibrations in molecules, and states representing different electronic states of all kinds in atoms, molecules, and ions.

It is likely that the list of sources and source wavelengths will be extended, and in the future many more areas of spectroscopy will have routine access to coherent sources. By way of contrast, Globars (used to produce infrared radiation) and heated filaments and electric discharges (used to produce incandescent and fluorescent light) give rise to incoherent radiation. The theoretical description of ensembles of systems irradiated by means of these sources must include ensemble averaging from the outset. Even the rf, microwave, maser, and laser sources are not *perfectly* coherent, and there are cases in which this fact has to be considered in computing the ensemble-averaged behavior of a system irradiated in such a way.

The most pervasive incoherent perturbations in spectroscopic experi-ments are relaxation processes. Their importance lies in the fact that whereas absorption or stimulated emission can always be brought about by means of a coherent perturbation (at least in principle), spontaneous emission and radiationless de-excitation nearly always occur as random processes. In other words, no two systems in a canonical ensemble necessarily "feel" each other or the heat bath in the same way at the same time, and therefore ensemble averaging is required to predict the effect of relaxation on the sample. Such processes may ordinarily be characterized by relaxation times T_1 and T_2, to be described later. A rigorous quantum-mechanical description of coherent states of the radiation field has been given by Glauber.[1]

5.3   Strongly coupled and weakly coupled systems

It has been suggested that, in order to obtain good agreement between theory and experiment, calculations of expectation values must be supplemented by calculations of ensemble averages. The results of some ensemble-averaging processes can be anticipated. Consider a charged spinning particle, such as an electron or a proton. In Chapter 4 it was shown that such particles have a magnetic dipole moment, and there are only two eigenstates of the operator representing the projection of that dipole moment along any direction (e.g., the z axis of the laboratory coordinate system). The eigenvalues are $\pm \gamma \hbar / 2$ (see Eq. 4.42). The magnetogyric ratio can be subscripted to indicate whether the spin of the electron (γ_e) or that of nucleus (γ_n) is being discussed.

Imagine a mole of metal atoms (e.g., thallium), each of which has a nucleus containing one unpaired proton. The total z component of nuclear magnetic moment of the *ensemble* should be the vector sum of all the individual nuclear moments, and therefore could range between $+ N_0 \gamma_n \hbar / 2$ and $- N_0 \gamma_n \hbar / 2$ $(N_0 = 6 \times 10^{23})$, depending on the distribution of systems between the two eigenstates. With a small magnetic field along the z direction to line up the spins, the value of $+ N_0 \gamma_n \hbar / 2$ would correspond to the state of lowest energy, and therefore would be the limiting value of the z component of magnetic moment at low temperatures. Hence the ensemble-averaged nuclear magnetic moment would be $\gamma_n \hbar / 2$. The ensemble-averaged electron magnetic moment under the same conditions would, however, *not* be $\gamma_e \hbar / 2$. Instead, it would be very much smaller than that amount and perhaps would even have the opposite sign.

The nuclei, being separated from one another by about 10^4 nuclear radii, have very little spatial overlap among their wavefunctions. Wavefunctions of the unpaired electrons on each of the thallium atoms, however, are spread out over the entire metal crystal, so that there is a very large amount of spatial overlap among them. Whenever appreciable spatial overlap exists, the fundamental indistinguishability of the particles becomes very important, cooperative phenomena appear, and the ensemble-averaged properties cannot be computed by the simple statistical methods employed in classical mechanics. The two special types of quantum statistics developed to treat such cases are called *Fermi-Dirac* and *Bose-Einstein* *statistics.*

Most of the attention of this book will be focused on systems that do not have much spatial overlap of their wavefunctions. Indeed, it will be assumed that these systems are coupled together only in two ways. They all are being irradiated by the same radiation field, and they all are relaxing by transfer of energy to the same heat bath. Therefore it will not be necessary to use Bose-Einstein or Fermi-Dirac statistics, and ensemble averages can be computed by the straightforward techniques of classical statistics. In particular, the ensemble-quantum average of the property represented by the operator R can be calculated as follows:

$$\langle \overline{R} \rangle = \frac{1}{N} \sum_{n=1}^{N} \langle R \rangle_n. \tag{5.2a}$$

The conditions under which Eq. 5.2a yields the correct ensemble-quantum average are as follows.

1. The wavefunctions for the constituent systems must have little spatial overlap.

2. The systems must interact with one another only weakly (this condition is not independent of the first).

Equation 5.2a reduces to

$$\langle \overline{R} \rangle = \langle R \rangle \tag{5.2b}$$

if the following conditions are met.

3. Any perturbation that is applied to the system in order to produce absorption or stimulated emission must be coherent.

4. At the time that the perturbation is "switched on," all the systems of the ensemble must be in identical states (i.e., the internal degrees of freedom for each quantum system must be represented by the same wavefunction).

5. The experiment must not last longer than $\Upsilon \ll T_1, T_2$ (to be discussed later), so that relaxation effects will not be important.

A convenient technique for calculating average values when these five requirements are satisfied is presented in the next two sections.

5.4 Computing expectation values from superposition coefficients

Just as was the case in Chapter 4 (Eqs. 4.12 and 4.20), it is necessary to consider a quantum system that is in a superposition of eigenstates. Only two eigenstates will be considered, as before. Equations 2.24 and 2.50 may be combined to provide an expression for the wavefunction:

$$\Psi(q,t) = c_1(t)T_1(t)\phi_1(q) + c_2(t)T_2(t)\phi_2(q). \tag{5.3}$$

It is convenient to combine all of the time-dependent factors on the right hand side of Eq. 5.3:

$$a_j(t) = c_j(t)T_j(t), \quad j = 1, 2. \tag{5.4}$$

In Chapters 2 and 4, superposition wavefunctions were used to calculate the expectation value of some physically observable property of the system, R (see Eqs. 2.83 and 4.13). The same thing must be done here. Equation 5.3 may be substituted into Eq. 2.82, using the notation introduced in Eq. 5.4, to produce

$$\langle R(t) \rangle_{\Psi\Psi} = |a_1(t)|^2 R_{11} + |a_2(t)|^2 R_{22} + 2\mathrm{Re}[a_1^*(t)a_2(t)R_{12}]. \tag{5.5}$$

Equation 5.5 expresses, in slightly modified form, exactly the same information as is contained in Eq. 2.83. The R_{jk}'s are defined in Eq. 2.85, where it may be seen that they all are independent of the time.

The products $a_j a_k^*$ can be arranged to form a 2×2 matrix, just as can the quantities R_{jk}. In the latter case, the matrix represents some operator (e.g., the dipole moment). It may be imagined that the matrix $a_j^* a_k$ also represents an operator, which may be called D:

$$D_{jk} \equiv a_j a_k^*. \tag{5.6}$$

Equation 5.5 can then be rewritten, replacing quantities that appear on the right-hand side by the elements of the corresponding matrices:

$$\langle R(t) \rangle_{\Psi\Psi} = D_{11}R_{11} + D_{22}R_{22} + D_{21}R_{12} + D_{12}R_{21}. \tag{5.7}$$

What are the states represented by $\psi_1 = T_1\Phi_1$ and $\psi_2 = T_2\Phi_2$ in Eq. 5.3? Suppose that they are eigenfunctions of an operator representing another physically observable property of the system (e.g., the energy). In that case, ψ_1 and ψ_2 are members of a complete set, $\{\psi\}_E$. (In the interest of simplicity, it will be assumed that they are the *only* members of the set $\{\psi\}_E$.) Each member of the set depends on the independent variables q and t and is factorable into two terms, $\Phi(q)$ and $T(t)$, as in Eq. 2.24. These facts imply that Φ_1 and Φ_2 together also constitute a complete set of functions that can be used in linear combination to represent any state of the system at any given point in time. The only limitation is that the values of the coefficients of Φ_1 and Φ_2 which are appropriate at one instant of time are, in general, not satisfactory at any other instant in time. This causes no problem, however, because the coefficients themselves can be considered to be continuous scalar functions of t.

What happens, then, if an operator operates upon Φ_1? The result will be another state function. This state function can be written as a linear combination of Φ_1 and Φ_2 because, as has just been stated, they constitute a complete set. In particular,

$$\mathsf{D}\Phi_1(q) = b_{11}(t)\Phi_1(q) + b_{12}(t)\Phi_2(q). \tag{5.8}$$

From the preceding discussion, it can be seen why b_{11} and b_{22} are, in general, time dependent. If both sides of Eq. 5.8 are multiplied by Φ_1^* and integrated over the entire range of q, Eq. 5.8 becomes

$$\int \Phi_1^*(q)\mathsf{D}\Phi_1(q)\,dq = \int b_{11}|\Phi_1(q)|^2\,dq + \int b_{12}\Phi_1^*(q)\Phi_2(q)dq. \tag{5.9}$$

The coefficients b_{11} and b_{12} are independent of q and may be taken out of the integrals on the right-hand side. It has previously been assumed (Eq. 2.46) that the Φ's are orthogonal, and the integral on the left-hand side is, by definition, D_{11}. Therefore

$$D_{11} = b_{11}. \tag{5.10}$$

This entire process can be repeated using Φ_1^*, Φ_2, and Φ_2^* in place of Φ_1 on the left-hand side of Eq. 5.8, and Φ_1, Φ_2^*, and Φ_2 in place of Φ_1^* on the left-hand side of Eq. 5.9. The results can be expressed by a generalization of Eq. 5.10:

$$D_{jk} = b_{jk}, \qquad j = 1, 2. \tag{5.11}$$

These results can be substituted back into Eq. 5.8:

$$\mathsf{D}\Phi_j = D_{j1}\Phi_1 + D_{j2}\Phi_2. \tag{5.12}$$

Now, the entire process described by Eqs. 5.8 to 5.12 is repeated, using the operator R in place of D. The result, analogous to Eq. 5.12, is

$$R\Phi_k = R_{k1}\Phi_1 + R_{k2}\Phi_2. \tag{5.13}$$

Next, D operates upon both sides of Eq. 5.13:

$$\mathsf{DR}\Phi_k = \mathsf{D}(R_{k1}\Phi_1 + R_{k2}\Phi_2). \tag{5.14}$$

On the right-hand side of Eq. 5.14, the operator D commutes with the scalars R_{kj}, so that each of the two terms is of the form $R_{kj}\mathsf{D}\Phi_j$. Therefore the expression in Eq. 5.12 may be substituted into each term on the right-hand side of Eq. 5.14, to obtain

$$\mathsf{DR}\Phi_k = R_{k1}(D_{11}\Phi_1 + D_{12}\Phi_2) + R_{k2}(D_{21}\Phi_1 + D_{22}\Phi_2). \tag{5.15}$$

It was pointed out in Chapter 2 that the product of operators DR is itself an operator. Therefore an expression for $\mathsf{DR}\Phi_k$ might have been obtained using the procedure outlined in Eqs. 5.8 to 5.12. The result would have been as follows:

$$\mathsf{DR}\Phi_k = (\mathsf{DR})_{k1}\Phi_1 + (\mathsf{DR})_{k2}\Phi_2. \tag{5.16}$$

A comparison of the right-hand sides of Eq. 5.15 and 5.16, term by term, shows that

$$(\mathsf{DR})_{kj} = R_{k1}D_{1j} + R_{k2}D_{2j}. \tag{5.17}$$

Equation 5.17 is merely the general formula for computing an element of the product of two 2×2 matrices. If a system with more eigenstates were chosen $(M>2)$, Eq. 5.17 would have contained the general formula for computing an element of the product of two $M \times M$ matrices. All operators in quantum mechanics can be represented by matrices that obey these multiplication rules.

The reason for introducing matrices at this point, however, is rather special. The first and last terms on the right-hand side of Eq. 5.7 can be grouped together and compared with the right-hand side of Eq. 5.17. The second and third terms on the right-hand side of Eq. 5.7 can be similarly grouped and compared. It is seen that

$$\langle R(t)\rangle_{\Psi\Psi} = (\mathsf{DR})_{11} + (\mathsf{DR})_{22}. \tag{5.18}$$

Equation 5.18 is usually written as

$$\langle R(t)\rangle_{\Psi\Psi} = \mathrm{Tr}\,[\mathsf{DR}]. \tag{5.19}$$

The symbol Tr [x] (read "trace of x") means the sum of the diagonal elements of the square matrix x_{jk} with elements.

The formula in Eq. 5.19 is remarkable for several reasons. In the first place, although it was suggested in Eq. 5.5 that the operator R represented the dipole moment of the system, no use was made of any particular properties of the dipole moment in order to derive the formula. Therefore Eq. 5.19 is valid for *any* operator R representing a physically observable property of the system (e.g., energy, angular momentum, or linear momentum). Next, in the particular picture of quantum mechanics that has been used, the operator R will not ordinarily explicitly contain the time. Since the basis set of functions used to form the matrix, namely, Φ_1 and Φ_2, have only time-independent members, the elements of the matix of R found in this basis will also be time independent. All of the time dependence of the problem, both from the time-dependent parts of the complete wavefunctions ψ_1 and ψ_2 and from the c's, has been lumped together in the matrix of D. Finally, although it was suggested (in the discussion following Eq. 5.7) that Φ_1 and Φ_2 might be eigenfunctions of the energy operator, no use was made of any particular properties of those eigenfunctions to derive the formula. Therefore the validity of Eq. 5.19 is independent of the basis set used to form the matrices of D and R, save only that the *same* basis must be used for both.

A universal procedure for finding the time-dependent expectation value of any property has therefore been discovered. First, choose any complete orthonormal set of time-independent wavefunctions $\{\psi_j\}$. In that basis, form the time-independent matrix of the operator R representing the physically observable property of interest. Also form the matrix of the time-dependent operator D in the same basis. Multiply the two $M \times M$ matrices together, and sum the M diagonal elements of the resultant $M \times M$ product matrix. The result will be the expectation value of the property of interest, with the correct time dependence. It was stated at the outset that this derivation would utilize a particular choice of M, namely, 2. A more general treatment, appropriate for any value of M, may be found in the book by Slichter.[2]

5.5   Equations of motion for the operator D

It has been established that the operator D is a remarkably important one in time-dependent quantum mechanics. It is therefore of great interest to discover how to compute its matrix elements. This can be done by substituting from Eq. 5.3 into the time-dependent Schrödinger equation (Eq. 2.23), using the definition of the a_j's from Eq. 5.4 and the distributive law:

$$a_1 H\Phi_1 + a_2 H\Phi_2 = i\hbar \left[\Phi_1 \left(\frac{\partial a_1}{\partial t} \right) + \Phi_2 \left(\frac{\partial a_2}{\partial t} \right) \right]. \qquad (5.20)$$

The fact that the coefficients a_j do not depend on spatial or spin coordinates (and are therefore not affected by the Hamiltonian operator, H) has been used on the left-hand side of Eq. 5.20.

Both sides of Eq. 5.20 may be multiplied by Φ_1^* and then integrated over q. The result is

$$i\hbar\left(\frac{\partial a_1}{\partial t}\right) = a_1 H_{11} + a_2 H_{12}. \tag{5.21}$$

If both sides had instead been multiplied by Φ_2^* and then integrated, the result would have been

$$i\hbar\left(\frac{\partial a_2}{\partial t}\right) = a_1 H_{21} + a_2 H_{22}. \tag{5.22}$$

To find a differential equation for a particular matrix element of D, the definition in Eq. 5.6 may be used:

$$\frac{\partial D_{11}}{\partial t} \equiv \frac{\partial(a_1^* a_1)}{\partial t}. \tag{5.23}$$

Therefore, from the chain rule,

$$\frac{\partial D_{11}}{\partial t} = \left[\frac{\partial a_1^*}{\partial t}\right]a_1 + a_1^*\left[\frac{\partial a_1}{\partial t}\right]. \tag{5.24}$$

The second term on the right-hand side of Eq. 5.24 may be obtained by multiplying Eq. 5.21 by $a_1^*/i\hbar$, and the first term, by multiplying the complex conjugate of Eq. 5.21 by $-a_1/i\hbar$. The results, when substituted into Eq. 5.24, yield

$$\frac{\partial D_{11}}{\partial t} = \frac{-a_1}{i\hbar}(a_1^* H_{11}^* + a_2^* H_{12}^*) + \frac{a_1^*}{i\hbar}(a_1 H_{11} + a_2 H_{12}). \tag{5.25}$$

On the right-hand side of Eq. 5.25, the definition of D_{jk} from Eq. 5.6 may be used again:

$$\frac{\partial D_{11}}{\partial t} = -\frac{1}{i\hbar}\left[(D_{11}H_{11}^* + D_{12}H_{12}^*) - (D_{11}H_{11} + D_{21}H_{12})\right]. \tag{5.26}$$

The Hamiltonian, H, like all operators in quantum mechanics, satisfies the Hermitian condition, Eq. 2.104. By using that fact and a slight rearrangement of terms, Eq. 5.26 may be rewritten as follows:

$$\frac{\partial D_{11}}{\partial t} = -\frac{1}{i\hbar}\left[(D_{11}H_{11}+D_{12}H_{21})-(H_{11}D_{11}+H_{12}D_{21})\right]. \quad (5.27)$$

Each sum in parentheses on the right-hand side of Eq. 5.27 may be recognized (with the aid of Eq. 5.17) as the matrix element of the product of two matrices:

$$\frac{\partial D_{11}}{\partial t} = -\frac{1}{i\hbar}\left[(DH)_{11}-(HR)_{11}\right]. \quad (5.28)$$

Now, the term in square brackets on the right-hand side of Eq. 5.28 may be recognized (with the aid of Eq. 2.7) as a matrix element of the commutator of the operators D and H:

$$\frac{\partial D_{11}}{\partial t} = -\frac{1}{i\hbar}[D,H]_{11}. \quad (5.29)$$

More generally,

$$i\hbar\frac{\partial D_{jk}}{\partial t} = [H,D]_{jk}, \qquad 1<j<M, \quad 1<k<M. \quad (5.30)$$

It is customary to rewrite Eq. 5.30 as a relationship between the operators D and H themselves,

$$i\hbar\left[\frac{\partial D}{\partial t}\right] = [H,D]. \quad (5.31)$$

It is to be understood that the matrix elements of Eq. 5.31 must be used in performing the indicated computations.

Equation 5.31, then, represents M^2 equations in the M^2 unknown matrix elements of D. All these equations are first-order differential equations, and therefore M^2 arbitrary constants will appear in their solutions. These M^2 constants must be fixed by boundary conditions, and this is ordinarily done by specifying the entire D matrix at time $t=0$. Once the initial state is specified, one may obtain (in principle) exact expressions for the time dependence of the matrix elements of D. These formulas, in turn, may be used in calculating the product of the D matrix and that of any other operator. Once this product is obtained, the time-dependent behavior of the expectation value of any physically observable property may be calculated by means of Eq. 5.19.

It can be seen from this discussion that the material presented in this section is an outline of the general solution to any problem one might wish to undertake in time-dependent quantum mechanics (but only if Eqs. 5.2a and 5.2b are satisfied). The circumstances under which this condition is met are limited to single particles, or ensembles of particles satisfying all five of the requirements listed in Section 5.3. It is now necessary to generalize this treatment so that there will be adequate theoretical means for the description of ensembles which satisfy only Eq. 5.2a. Such ensembles fail to meet one or more of the requirements numbered 3, 4, and 5 in Section 5.3.

5.6 The density matrix

In a canonical ensemble consisting of N identical quantum systems, the nth system has internal coordinates q_n and a wavefunction

$$\Psi_n(q_n, t) = c_{n1}\psi_1(q_n, t) + c_{n2}\psi_2(q_n, t). \tag{5.32}$$

Note that Eq. 5.32 is identical with Eq. 5.3 except for the additional subscript.

By following the procedure outlined in Section 5.5, an operator D_n with elements defined as in Eq. 5.6 may be obtained:

$$D_{jk}^{(n)} = a_j^{(n)} a_k^{(n)*}. \tag{5.33}$$

This operator can be used to compute expectation values of any physical quantity, for example, the quantity represented by R (see Eq. 5.19):

$$\langle R(t) \rangle_n = \mathrm{Tr}[D_n R]. \tag{5.34}$$

Note that the operator R is the same for every system in the ensemble and therefore need not bear the subscript n.

Because all ensembles with appreciable spatial overlap of wavefunctions representing different systems have been excluded from consideration, the computation of the ensemble average, $\langle \overline{R} \rangle$, is very simple:

$$\langle \overline{R} \rangle = \frac{1}{N} \sum_{n=1}^{N} \langle R \rangle_n. \tag{5.35}$$

Now Eq. 5.34 may be used on the right-hand side of Eq. 5.35:

$$\langle \overline{R} \rangle = \frac{1}{N} \sum_{n=1}^{N} \mathrm{Tr}[D_n R]. \tag{5.36}$$

Calculating the trace of a matrix is an operation that follows the distributive law (because the multiplication of matrices obeys that law):

$$\mathrm{Tr}\,(AB) + \mathrm{Tr}\,(AC) = \mathrm{Tr}\,[A(B+C)]. \tag{5.37}$$

Equation 5.37 may be used on the right-hand side of Eq. 5.36 to obtain

$$\langle \bar{R} \rangle = \mathrm{Tr}\left[\left(\frac{1}{N}\sum_{n=1}^{N} D_n\right)R\right]. \tag{5.38}$$

The result expressed algebraically in Eq. 5.38 can be stated in ordinary language as follows. The ensemble-quantum averaged value of R is the trace of the product of the matrices of R and ρ, where the matrix of ρ is the linear average of the D_n matrices representing individual systems of the ensemble:

$$\underline{\rho} \equiv \frac{1}{N}\sum_{n=1}^{N} D_n. \tag{5.39}$$

The operator $\underline{\rho}$ is called the *density operator*, and its matrix, the *density matrix*. It is easy to show that the equation of motion for $\underline{\rho}$ is the same as that for each D separately (see Eq. 5.31):

$$1\hbar\left(\frac{\partial \underline{\rho}}{\partial t}\right) = [H, \underline{\rho}]. \tag{5.40}$$

An equation like Eq. 5.40 occurs in classical statistical mechanics, where it is called the *Liouville equation*.

The average values of physical observables (e.g., the one represented by R) are calculated by means of a formula analogous to Eq. 5.34:

$$\langle \overline{R(t)} \rangle_N = \mathrm{Tr}\left[\underline{\rho}(t)R\right]. \tag{5.41}$$

In summary, the procedure for calculating the result of any experiment by means of quantum mechanics is as follows. Choose an initial state for the ensemble by choosing the complex elements of the density matrix, $\underline{\rho}$, at time $t=0$. Using these M^2 constants [only $M(M-1)$ of them are independent because the diagonal elements must be real], solve Eq. 5.40 for the values of the matrix elements of $\underline{\rho}$ at the time of measurement, t. Calculate the time-independent matrix of the operator representing the desired physical property (e.g., R), using the same basis. Multiply the two matrices and sum the diagonal elements as indicated in Eq. 5.41; the result will be the experimental value of the desired property at time t, correctly averaged over all systems of the ensemble.

5.7 Properties of the density matrix

Before the calculations for various cases of interest are performed, some general remarks can be made. If the macrosystem (ensemble) is a closed one, the identification of the terms on the right-hand side of Eq. 5.39 with particular microsystems may not change with time. Since the trace of each of the $[D_n]$ matrices is 1, the trace of $[\rho]$ will also be 1, for all time. The invariance of the unit trace of $[\rho]$ therefore reflects the law of conservation of matter in a closed macrosystem (ensemble).

The Hamiltonian matrix, which drives the density matrix in accordance with Eq. 5.40, ordinarily contains terms of three different kinds. One group of terms, called collectively H_0, is time independent and has relatively large matrix elements. It establishes the stationary states of the system (see Eqs. 4.18 and 4.19) and is therefore the object of greatest attention in conventional quantum mechanics. Another group of terms, called H_1 (or sometimes V— see Eqs. 4.24 and 4.25), is time independent and provides the mechanism for transitions to occur between the eigenstates of H_0. The third group of terms, called H_R, describes the processes by means of which the quantum systems can exchange energy with each other or with the heat bath. The H_R terms provide the mechanism by means of which the ensemble of systems will relax back to an equilibrium distribution among the states of H_0, whenever it is displaced from equilibrium by H_1.

The question of the choice of basis (complete set of eigenstates defined in Chapter 2) for the matrices $[D_n]$, $[H]$, and $[R]$ has been left open. The only thing decided is that, for each system in the ensemble, the same basis must be used for all three matrices. The most convenient choice of basis is the set of eigenfunctions of the operator H_0. Since all of the $[D_n]$'s are Hermitian, $[\rho]$ will also be Hermitian. (This is the reason for the previously mentioned fact that each diagonal element is a real number.) The complex off-diagonal elements of $[D_n]$ can be written (see Eq. 5.33) as

$$D_{jk}^{(n)} = |D_{jk}^{(n)}| \exp\left[i\Omega_{jk}^{(n)} \right].\tag{5.42}$$

The corresponding off-diagonal element of $[\rho]$ can therefore be written (see Eq. 5.39):

$$\rho_{jk} = \frac{1}{N} \sum_{n=1}^{N} |D_{jk}^{(n)}| \left\{ \cos\left[\Omega_{jk}^{(n)} \right] + i \sin\left[\Omega_{jk}^{(n)} \right] \right\}.\tag{5.43}$$

For a sufficiently large ensemble ($N \to \infty$), the sums in Eq. 5.43 can be replaced by integrals. For example, the first term can be written as

$$\frac{1}{N} \sum_{n=1}^{N} |D_{jk}^{(n)}| \cos[\Omega_{jk}^{(n)}] = \lim_{\Delta \to \infty} \frac{1}{2} \int_{-\Omega}^{\Omega} |D(x)| \cos x \, dx. \qquad (5.44)$$

One of the basic assumptions of statistical mechanics is the *principle of equal apriori probabilities.* This hypothesis states that all configurations of any system (or ensemble of systems) which have the same energy are equally likely at equlibrium. Since the energy of a state is not affected by the phase of the corresponding wavefunction, the principle of equal apriori probabilities will ensure that the phases Ω_{jk} of D_{jk} are distributed at random throughout the ensemble. The integral on the right-hand side of Eq. 5.44 represents the net effect of an infinite number of oscillations at an infinite number of frequencies, all with amplitudes bounded by $0 < |D(\Omega)| < 1$. (Remember the definition of D in Eq. 5.33, and the fact that $|a_j|$ must lie between $+1$ and -1.) In this jumble of oscillations, positive values of $\cos \Omega$ must be as numerous as negative ones, and the integral in Eq. 5.44 must therefore be zero. In other words, in an ensemble at equilibrium, all the off-diagonal elements of the density matrix must be zero, because of the destructive interferences among the corresponding elements of the constituent matrices. This result is called the *hypothesis of random phases.*

The elements of the density matrix that do not vanish when the ensemble represented by ρ is at thermodynamic equilibrium are the diagonal ones:

$$\rho_{jk} = \frac{1}{N} \sum_{n=1}^{N} D_{jj}^{(n)} = \frac{1}{N} \sum_{n=1}^{N} |a_j^{(n)}|^2. \qquad (5.45)$$

It is obvious from inspection of Eq. 5.45 that the jth diagonal element at equilibrium merely represents the fraction of the systems of the ensemble which will give the answer E_j if their energy is measured. In other words, the diagonal elements are the energy-eigenstate-occupation probabilities, which, in an ensemble of semi-isolated systems, are given by the Boltzmann factors:

$$\overline{|a_j^{(n)}|^2} = \frac{\exp(-\mathcal{E}_j/k_0 T)}{Q}, \qquad (5.46)$$

where Q is the partition function:

$$Q \equiv \sum_{j=1}^{M} \exp\left(\frac{-\mathcal{E}_j}{k_0 T}\right). \qquad (5.47)$$

5.8 Effect of relaxation on the density matrix

In this book, several different quantum-mechanical problems will be considered, and the corresponding H_0 and H_1 terms will be characterized explicitly. The same will not be done for H_R, however, because it is ordinarily much more complicated than the others. Instead, a phenomenological approach will be adopted as follows. First, the density matrix at equilibrium, $[\underline{\rho}^e]$, is given:

$$[\underline{\rho}^e] = \frac{1}{Q}
\begin{bmatrix}
\exp\left(-\mathcal{E}_1/k_0 T\right) & 0 & \cdots & 0 \\
0 & \exp\left(-\mathcal{E}_2/k_0 T\right) & \cdots & 0 \\
0 & 0 & & 0 \\
\vdots & \vdots & & \vdots \\
0 & \cdots & \cdots & \exp\left(-\mathcal{E}_M/k_0 T\right)
\end{bmatrix}.$$

$$(5.48)$$

Next, it will be assumed that the perturbation represented by H_1 commences, drives the ensemble away from equilibrium, and then ceases to act. At this point, each element of the density matrix will begin to decay back to its equilibrium value:

$$\frac{d\rho_{jk}}{dt} = -\frac{(\rho_{jk} - \rho_{jk}^e)}{T_{jk}}. \qquad (5.49)$$

There may be terms in addition to the one shown on the right-hand side of Eq. 5.49, but the simplest assumption is to neglect them and imagine that all the decays are first order, with a rate constant T_{jk}^{-1}. Not all the T_{jk}'s are independent of one another; T_{jk} must equal T_{kj}, for example, because ρ_{jk} is merely the complex conjugate of ρ_{kj} and must therefore decay to equilibrium at the same rate (remember that ρ is Hermitian). There are also strictures upon the relaxation times for diagonal elements because, regardless of the choice of the set $\{T_{jk}\}_M$, one must always have

$$\sum_{j=1}^{M} \rho_{jj} = 1. \qquad (5.50)$$

In the simplest nontrivial case, there are only two stationary states ($M = 2$) and therefore only two rate constants. The relaxation times for the diagonal elements must be exactly equal. Conventionally, this time is called the *longitudinal relaxation time* and has the symbol T_1. Since there are only two off-diagonal elements, $\rho_{12} = \rho_{21}^*$, there is only one possible additional relaxation time, conventionally called the *tranverse relaxation time*, T_2. It should also be remembered that, because of the hypothesis of random phases, $\rho_{jk}^e = 0$ for $j \neq k$.

In summary, the effect of H_R on the density matrix is equivalent to the addition of decay terms of the form shown in Eq. 5.49 to the rate equations. For a quantum system with only two eigenstates, the four differential equations for the elements of $[\rho]$ are as follows:

$$\frac{d\rho_{11}}{dt} = \frac{\left[(H_0 + H_1), \underline{\rho}\right]_{11}}{i\hbar} - \frac{\rho_{11} - \rho_{11}^e}{T_1}, \tag{5.51}$$

$$\frac{d\rho_{22}}{dt} = \frac{\left[(H_0 + H_1), \underline{\rho}\right]_{22}}{i\hbar} - \frac{\rho_{22} - \rho_{22}^e}{T_1}, \tag{5.52}$$

$$\frac{d\rho_{12}}{dt} = \frac{\left[(H_0 + H_1), \underline{\rho}\right]_{12}}{i\hbar} - \frac{\rho_{12}}{T_2}, \tag{5.53}$$

and

$$\frac{d\rho_{21}}{dt} = \frac{\left[(H_0 + H_1), \underline{\rho}\right]_{21}}{i\hbar} - \frac{\rho_{21}}{T_2}. \tag{5.54}$$

In obtaining Eqs. 5.51 to 5.54, use has been made of Eqs. 5.40, 5.49, and 5.50, the hypothesis of random phases, and the fact that the total Hamilitonian, H, is given by

$$H = H_0 + H_1 + H_R. \tag{5.55}$$

5.9 Equations of motion for the density matrix

Equations 5.53 and 5.54 may be simplified further, using the facts that the basis of the density matrix is the set of eigenfunctions of H_0 and that the distributive law holds for commutators:

$$\left[(H_0 + H_1), \underline{\rho}\right] = \left[H_0, \underline{\rho}\right] + \left[H_1, \underline{\rho}\right], \tag{5.56}$$

$$\left[H_0, \underline{\rho}\right] = H_0 \underline{\rho} - \underline{\rho} H_0, \tag{5.57}$$

$$\left(H_0 \underline{\rho}\right)_{pq} = \sum_{r=1}^{M} (H_0)_{pr} \rho_{rq}, \tag{5.58}$$

and

$$(H_0)_{pr} = (H_0)_{pp} \delta_{pr}, \tag{5.59}$$

where δ_{pr} is the Kronecker delta defined in Eq. 2.47. Therefore

$$(H_0 \underline{\rho})_{pq} = (H_0)_{pp} \rho_{pq} \tag{5.60}$$

and

$$[H_0, \underline{\rho}]_{pq} = [(H_0)_{pp} - (H_0)_{qq}] \rho_{pq}. \tag{5.61}$$

It can now be seen that the choice of the set of eigenfunctions of H_0 as the bases for all of the matrices has had two useful consequences. First, it has made it possible to interpret the diagonal elements of $[\rho]$ as the fractional occupancies of the various stationary states of H_0 by the quantum systems in the ensemble (Eqs. 5.45 to 5.47). Second, the matrix of H_0 in this basis has elements of magnitude zero everywhere except on the principal diagonal (Eq. 5.59). The fact that the matrix of H_0 is diagonal permits a simplification of the $[H_0, \rho]$ term in the Liouville equation, as has been seen.

It is also possible to simplify the $[H_1, \rho]$ term slightly by insisting that this matrix of H_1 have nonzero elements only *off* the principal diagonal. If the operator H_1 as initially chosen has nonzero elements both on and off the diagonal, both H_0 and H_1 can be redefined in such a way that the new H_0 is the sum of the old H_0 plus the diagonal elements of the old H_1; the remaining off-diagonal elements constitute the new H_1:

$$[H_1, \underline{\rho}] = H_1 \underline{\rho} - \underline{\rho} H_1. \tag{5.62}$$

$$(H_1 \underline{\rho})_{pq} = \sum_{r=1}^{M} (H_1)_{pr} \rho_{rq}. \tag{5.63}$$

For $M = 2$,

$$(H_1 \underline{\rho})_{pq} = (H_1)_{p1} \rho_{1q} + (H_1)_{p2} \rho_{2q} \tag{5.64}$$

and

$$(H_1)_{rs} = 0 \quad \text{unless } r \neq s. \tag{5.65}$$

Therefore

$$[H_1, \underline{\rho}]_{11} = 2i \operatorname{Im} [(H_1)_{12} \rho_{21}] = -[H_1, \underline{\rho}]_{22}. \tag{5.66}$$

and

$$[H_1, \underline{\rho}]_{12} = (H_1)_{12}(\rho_{22} - \rho_{11}) = -[H_1, \underline{\rho}]^*_{21}. \tag{5.67}$$

Equations 5.56, 5.64, 5.66, and 5.67 may be used in Eqs. 5.51 to 5.54, together with

$$[(H_0)_{pp} - (H_0)_{qq}] \equiv \mathcal{E}_p - \mathcal{E}_q \tag{5.68}$$

and the definition of ω_0 in Eq. 2.68, to obtain

$$\frac{d\rho_{11}}{dt} = \frac{2\,\text{Im}\left[(H_1)_{12}\rho_{21}\right]}{\hbar} - \frac{\rho_{11} - \rho_{11}^e}{T_1}, \tag{5.69}$$

$$\frac{d\rho_{22}}{dt} = -\frac{2\,\text{Im}\left[(H_1)_{12}\rho_{21}\right]}{\hbar} - \frac{\rho_{22} - \rho_{22}^e}{T_1}, \tag{5.70}$$

$$\frac{d\rho_{12}}{dt} = i\omega_0\rho_{12} + \frac{(H_1)_{12}(\rho_{22} - \rho_{11})}{i\hbar} - \frac{\rho_{12}}{T_2}, \tag{5.71}$$

and

$$\frac{d\rho_{21}}{dt} = -i\omega_0\rho_{21} - \frac{(H_1)^*_{12}(\rho_{22} - \rho_{11})}{i\hbar} - \frac{\rho_{21}}{T_2}. \tag{5.72}$$

5.10   Coherence in ensembles of quantum radiators

No further progress in the solution of Eqs. 5.69 to 5.72, the equations of motion for the elements of the density matrix, will be made in this chapter.

Instead, the dependence of the elements of both (ρ) and $[D_n]$ on the phases $\Omega_{jk}^{(n)}$, given in Eqs. 5.42 to 5.44, will be discussed. The definition of the elements of $[D_n]$ (Eqs. 5.33 and 5.42) and the definition of the a's (Eq. 5.4) may be combined to obtain

$$D_{jk}^{(n)} = |c_j^{(n)}||c_k^{(n)}|\exp\left[i\Omega_{jk}^{(n)}\right]. \tag{5.73}$$

By analogy to Eq. 4.56,

$$\Omega_{jk}^{(n)} = \S_{jk}^{(n)} + \frac{(\mathcal{E}_j - \mathcal{E}_k)t}{\hbar}. \tag{5.74}$$

The behavior of the ensemble-averaged properties is very sensitively dependent on the values of the M phase constants, $\Omega_{jk}^{(n)}(0) = \S_{jk}^{(n)}$. It has already been stated that if they are distributed at random all of the off-diagonal elements of the density matrix will vanish. But suppose that they are all the same. This means that all of the matter waves are oscillating in step with one another, in a way which is analogous to the synchrony among coherent light waves. The importance of phase coherence among the wavefunctions of quantum systems can be seen by examining Eqs. 5.42 to 5.44.

It is a cliché of statistical mechanics that one cannot deduce all the properties of microsystems from the ensemble-averaged behavior of the macrosystem. The reason for this can be seen from Eq. 5.44. When the Ω's start to differ from one another, even very slightly, the ensemble-averaged properties of the sample begin to blur as the off-diagonal elements start to cancel out. The difference between ensemble-averaged properties and the properties of individual microsystems is always of the same nature: the microsystems have a greater repertoire and display a wider variety of behavior. The system can do everything that the ensemble can do, and more; but the ensemble cannot do anything that an individual system in the ensemble cannot do. This is due to the fact that the systems are only weakly interacting, so that the matrix $[\rho]$ is simply a sum of the matrices $[D_n]$ (see Eq. 5.39).

Now it can be seen (from Eq. 5.43) that as the phases $\Omega_{jk}^{(n)}$ of the systems within the ensemble become more and more nearly the same, the density matrix approaches more and more closely the typical $[D_n]$ matrix in all of its elements. With perfect coherence among the matter waves of the systems, perfect mimicry of the expectation value of behavior of each system by the entire ensemble will be achieved. In this way, microscopic (quantum) behavior of individual atoms, ions, and molecules will be "seen" in the macroscopic world. This is contrary to the claims of universal validity for the cliché which says that one cannot visualize quantum-mechanical behavior from macroscopic laboratory experiments. The cliché is wrong in principle, but usually correct in practice because it is ordinarily difficult in the laboratory to bring about the phase coherence necessary to produce counter-examples. At first sight, in fact, the reader might imagine that bringing about coherence between the phases of Avogadro's number of quantum systems would be completely impossible. Apparently, a quantum-mechanical version of Maxwell's demon would be required! However, Dicke[3] has described how the phases in an ensemble of excited quantum systems could spontaneously achieve coherence in a radiative process. His work gives a great deal of insight into the process by which laser action is initiated. Dicke introduced a new quantum number (the cooperation number) to describe the circumstances that give rise to these phenomena, and pointed out several unique properties of the radiation that would be emitted by phase-correlated systems.

One of Dicke's results can be made plausible by an argument based on classical electromagnetic theory. The radiating atom has been viewed as a tiny dipole, oscillating at the beat frequency between two stationary-state wavefunctions. In order for emission to occur, it is necessary that the dipole first receive energy from some external source. Suppose that the driving field is represented in this case by a tiny transmitter connected to the dipole, as would be the case if the atom and its driver were really a tiny radio or television station. The resultant electromagnetic waves are broadcast in all directions (except along the dipole axis), just as one calculates in classical electromagnetic theory. Now, imagine a second antenna placed next to the first. This antenna is identical in every way to the first one and is driven by a transmitter at exactly the same frequency (there being no govermental regulatory agency in Hilbert space to prevent this). The waves radiated by these two dipoles will overlap one another spatially, and the corresponding electric and magnetic fields will constructively and destructively interfere. The resultant pattern of broadcast energy flux will no longer be as symmetric as it was when there was only one dipole; zones of "darkness" and "brightness" will appear. Precisely where these zones appear depends on the relative values of the phase constants of the two antennas.

More antennas can be added to the first two. If a pair of these is selected at random, and a point of observation is chosen, the electric fields E_1 and E_2 will add to form a resultant. The square of this resultant will be proportional to the irradiance, J_{12}, at the point of observation (see Eq. 1.6):

$$J_{12} \propto |\mathbf{E}_1 + \mathbf{E}_2| \cdot |\mathbf{E}_1 + \mathbf{E}_2| = |E_1|^2 + |E_2|^2$$
$$+ 2|E_1||E_2| \cos \theta_{12}. \qquad (5.75)$$

The angle θ_{12} in Eq. 5.75 depends on many different factors—the orientation of the two dipoles, the distance between them, and the location of the point of observation are examples. But it also depends on the difference between the phases of oscillation of the two dipoles, and this is the most important for the present discussion. While the antennas are being driven, this phase difference will be determined primarily by the difference in the phases of oscillation of the two transmitters. As will be seen in subsequent chapters, the phase of a transmitter affects the phase constant $\Omega_{jk}^{(n)}$ (see Eq. 5.74) of a particular off-diagonal element of the D_n matrix for the quantum system being driven thereby, and this in turn determines the phase of $\langle R \rangle_n$. In any event, when all relevant factors are taken into account, θ_{12}

can be calculated. Suppose that $|E_1| = |E_2| = |E|$. Then, from Eq. 5.75,

$$J_{12} \propto 2|E|^2(1 + \cos\theta_{12}). \tag{5.76}$$

If $\theta_{12} = 180°$ (destructive interference), the resultant intensity will be 0. If $\theta_{12} = 90°$, the resultant intensity will be exactly twice that expected for a single dipole,

$$J_1 = J_2 \propto |E|^2. \tag{5.77}$$

On the other hand, if $\theta_{12} = 0$ (constructive interference), J_{12} will be four times that expected from a single dipole.

These results can be generalized to N dipoles as follows:

$$J_N \propto \left| \sum_{p=1}^{N} \mathbf{E}_p \cdot \sum_{q=1}^{N} \mathbf{E}_q \right| = \sum_{n=1}^{N} |E_n|^2 + \sum_{p=1}^{N} \sum_{q=1}^{N} |E_p||E_q|\cos\theta_{pq}. \tag{5.78}$$

If it is assumed, as before, that all $|E_n|$ are equal, then

$$J_N \propto |E|^2 \left(N + \sum_{p=1}^{N} \sum_{q=1}^{N} \cos\theta_{pq} \right). \tag{5.79}$$

Complete destructive interference can be achieved in a number of ways. For example, $\theta_{pq} = 0°$ for $p + q$ even and $\theta_{pq} = 180°$ for $p + q$ odd will produce complete destructive interference if N is even, and nearly complete if N is odd. If, instead of complete destructive interference between the waves radiated by N dipoles, complete constructive interference is desired, it can be achieved by $\theta_{pq} = 0°$ for all p and q:

$$J_N \propto |E|^2[N + N(N-1)] = N^2|E|^2. \tag{5.80}$$

It should be remembered that the values of θ_{pq} ordinarily depend on the point of observation, so that the radiation emitted from a particular array can vary from 0 to an amount proportional to $N^2|E|^2$, depending on the direction from which the array is viewed (see Figure 5.1). Finally, if the values of θ_{pq} are distributed at random over the ensemble of N dipoles, the double sum in Eq. 5.78 is proportional to the average value of $\cos\theta$ over the interval $(0, 2\pi)$ and is therefore zero (see Eq. 5.44 et seq). Therefore, in this case,

$$J_N \propto N|E|^2. \tag{5.81}$$

Figure 5.1. Radiation pattern produced by a phased classical array of dipoles. Four dipoles, located at $(x/\lambda, y/\lambda) = (1, 1)$, $(1, -1)$, $(-1, -1)$, and $(-1, 1)$, are radiating with identical phase constants. The area shown is that portion of the principal quadrant of the xy plane bound by the lines $x = 5\lambda$ and $y = 5\lambda$ (the full pattern has four-fold symmetry). The number of dots per square inch at any location is proportional to

$$\left| \sum_{n=1}^{4} E_n \right|^2.$$

Note constructive interference along the axes and destructive interference elsewhere. The figure was prepared with the assistance of Henry Streiffer using the facilities of the LSU computer center.

Also, in this case, the directionality of the radiation is completely lost; the pattern shown in Figure 5.1 would be replaced by a uniformly gray field.

The discussion concluded above must be summarized. The radiation emitted by N dipoles differs in character from the radiation emitted by one dipole. If N dipoles are driven by a common transmitter (or individual transmitters with synchronized phases), the off-diagonal elements of the corresponding D_n matrices will also be synchronized and the off-diagonal elements of ρ will be nonzero. As a result, the dipole moments of the quantum systems in the ensemble will radiate electromagnetic waves having synchronized phases (coherent radiation). This radiation will be highly directional, because of the geometric factors that, in addition to the phase constants $\Omega_{jk}^{(n)}$, determine the angles θ_{pq}. It also will be very intense in the direction in which it is emitted; it will be N^2 times as intense as the radiation expected in that direction from a single dipole. An example is given in Figure 5.2.

On the other hand, if the N dipoles radiate under the influence of transmitters having phases distributed at random, the phase constants $\Omega_{jk}^{(n)}$ of the off-diagonal elements of the associated D_n matrices will also be random. Therefore the corresponding elements of the density matrix ρ will vanish because of phase cancellation, and no net macroscopic (experimentally observable) oscillating polarization will be associated with the radiation process. The emitted electromagnetic waves will be incoherent, isotropic, and of modest intensity (N times that to be expected from a single quantum radiator).

The utilization of a phased array of dipoles to produce an intense unidirectional coherent beam of electromagnetic radiation is well known to electronics engineers in the macroscopic world; it is employed in radio astronomy and radio direction finding.

Most light sources in conventional emission spectroscopy produce an incoherent jumble of electromagnetic waves. After this light passes through a monochromater, it is analogous to a collection of N transmitters, each operating at the same frequency but with a different phase. The antennas in this case are microscopic quantum systems (atoms, ions, or molecules). The D_n matrix for each of these microsystems has nonzero off-diagonal elements, oscillating at frequencies corresponding to all of the absorption lines in the spectrum. Associated with the off-diagonal elements of $[D_n]$ are oscillating microscopic dipole moments (e.g., $\langle p_E \rangle_n$) which interact with the incoming radiation fields. Since the driving electromagnetic waves are unsynchronized, the constants $\Omega_{jk}^{(n)}$ for the off-diagonal elements of $[D_n]$ are randomly distributed throughout the ensemble. Therefore the density matrix associated with the ensemble $[\rho]$ remains totally diagonal throughout the absorption process; the off-diagonal elements vanish be-

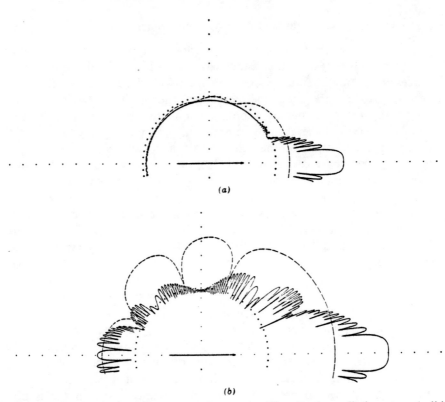

Figure 5.2. (a) Radiation patterns from two right circular cylinders, one (solid line) of length $500\lambda/\pi$ and radius $5\lambda/\pi$, and the other (broken line) of length $5\lambda/\pi$ and radius $\lambda/2\pi$. Both have 61.2 excited chromophores per unit volume (λ^3). The dotted line is the incoherent radiation pattern from either cylinder when all of the atoms are excited. The radiation pattern is initiated by a weak coherent pulse propagating along the cylinder axis, shown by the arrow. (b) Same as (a), but with 61.2×10^4 chromophores per unit volume (λ^3). Taken from *Phys. Rev.* **A3**, 1735 (1971) by N. E. Rehler and J. H. Eberly.

cause of phase cancellation. Consequently, there is no (measurable) macroscopic polarization of the spectroscopic sample; the ensemble is a poor mimic of the behavior of the quantum systems of which it is composed. Radiation re-emitted by the sample is isotropic and has an intensity that is proportional to the number of radiators. The latter feature is the basis for one of the important assumptions of emission spectroscopy (fundamental to Beer's law): The oscillator strength is derived from the observed spectrum by assuming that the line intensities are proportional to the concentration of chromophores.

5.11 Creating, observing, and destroying coherence

The features of conventional spectroscopy described in the preceding paragraphs make it clear that a detailed knowledge of the dynamics of the process by which quantum systems interact with the radiation field is not necessary to the practicing spectroscopist. The results of his experiments are equally well explained by adopting a "quantum-jump" picture, because all of the details of the absorption and emission processes are "wiped out" by phase cancellation of the relevant off-diagonal elements of the $[D_n]$ matrices. This phase cancellation is due, in turn, to the fact that the light sources conventionally employed are all incoherent—"As ye sow, so shall ye reap."

Suppose that it is desired to see the details of spectroscopic transitions that cannot be observed in conventional spectroscopic experiments. The first trick, as was suggested above, is to induce phase correlations among the matter waves of the quantum systems in the ensemble. It was mentioned that such correlations can sometimes be produced spontaneously, but the usual method is to produce them by means of coherent radiation. Both of these methods will be discussed in more detail in subsequent chapters. For the purposes of the remaining portion of this chapter, it will be sufficient to suppose that an off-diagonal element of the density matrix (more properly, a pair of such elements, since ρ is Hermitian) has been made nonzero. Suppose that a coherent driving field (H_1) has been used to produce the nonzero element, and that it is now desired to study the behavior of the ensemble after this field has been turned off. There are several ways in which the action of the heat bath, represented by H_R, can return the ensemble to equilibrium (i.e., a Boltzmann distribution of quantum systems among the eigenstates of H_0). For simplicity, the quantum systems will be presumed to have only two energy levels. Equations 5.69 to 5.71 were developed for the purpose of describing the time development of the elements of the density matrix associated with an ensemble of such systems. Since H_1 is supposed to be absent, the only terms that remain in these equations are the relaxation terms, plus terms that are proportional to ω_0 and can be transformed away by mathematical methods to be described in subsequent chapters. The relaxation terms are characterized by the phenomenological constants T_1 and T_2, introduced in Eqs. 5.51 to 5.54, which will now be discussed in more detail.

The first discussion concerns T_1, the longitudinal relaxation time. It is possible to define a quantity T_s, with the dimensions of temperature, to characterize the diagonal elements of the density matrix:

$$T_s \equiv \frac{\mathcal{E}_2 - \mathcal{E}_1}{k_0 \ln (\rho_{22}/\rho_{11})} .$$

$$(5.82)$$

The quantity T_s defined in Eq. 5.82 has been dubbed the "spin temperature" of the ensemble and is to be contrasted with the temperature of the surrounding heat bath, as given by the Boltzmann formula in Eqs. 5.46 and 5.47:

$$T = \frac{\mathscr{E}_2 - \mathscr{E}_1}{k_0 \ln(\rho_{22}^e/\rho_{11}^e)} . \tag{5.83}$$

In Eqs. 5.82 and 5.83, as in Eqs. 5.46 and 5.47, k_0 is Boltzmann's constant. The difference between the spin temperature, T_s, and the actual temperature, T, is a measure of the energy received by the sample (because of excitation by means of H_1) in excess of the amount that one would expect if the ensemble were in thermal equilibrium with the heat bath. It can be seen, therefore, that T_1 characterizes the rate of flow of energy from the ensemble to the heat bath, and vice versa; it is, in effect, the "$1/e$ cooling (heating) time" required to bring T_s and T into coincidence. If the sample is excited by means of incoherent radiation (or any other random process), off-diagonal elements of the density matrix will never appear and T_1 will be the only measurable relaxation time in the system. One mechanism that the ensemble possesses for getting rid of excess energy is radiation (luminescence). It has already been noted that the intensity of the incoherent luminescence is proportional to N, the number of quantum systems in the ensemble. Now it can be seen that the excess of population in state 2 over that in state 1 will decay exponentially with a rate constant $1/T_1$. Therefore the net flux of electromagnetic radiation out of the system will also decay. For this reason, T_1 is called the "fluorescence lifetime" by conventional spectroscopists.

   Now T_2, the transverse relaxation time, can be considered. At the end of the T_1 process, the sample will have returned to Boltzmann equilibrium; the net excess energy in the ensemble will be zero. At a sufficiently low temperature, $T \ll E_2/k_0$, it is accurate to say that every system in the ensemble eventually will be in one of the stationary states of the system— the ground state. Therefore each system in the ensemble, characterized in general by

$$\Psi_n = c_{1n}\psi_{1n} + c_{2n}\psi_{2n}, \tag{5.84}$$

will have $c_{2n} = 0$. Consequently, the off-diagonal elements of every $[D_n]$ matrix, being proportional to the product $c_{1n}c_{2n}^*$, will also be zero. Since each element of the density matrix for the ensemble is proportional to the sum of the corresponding elements of the $[D_n]$ matrices, $\rho_{jk}(j \neq k)$ will also be zero. Finally, it therefore follows that all T_1 processes are also T_2 processes, because T_1 relaxation is sufficient to produce all $\rho_{jk}(j \neq k)$ equal to zero.

It sometimes happens that the T_1 processes are the dominant ones, so that all T_2 relaxation occurs in this way. In such circumstances, $T_1 = T_2$. More generally, however, the universal relationship between the two times is

$$T_2' \leqslant T_1. \tag{5.85}$$

Equation 5.85 states that, although T_1 processes are *sufficient* to bring about T_2 relaxation, they are not necessary. It may be that other processes occurring within the ensemble will cause the decay of off-diagonal elements of the density matrix *faster* than the diagonal elements re-establish Boltzmann equilibrium.

One must return now to the picture of the phased array of dipoles. The cessation of H_1 is equivalent to disconnecting all the transmitters from the antennas abruptly. Each antenna will be "caught" with excess kinetic energy in the motions of its electrons, which it can discharge by continuing to radiate for a time T_2. Suppose that before the antennas complete this process, some other factor causes them to become out of phase with each other ($T_2 < T_1$). The dynamics of the radiation process subsequent to the disconnection of the transmitters will be as follows. Immediately after cessation of the driving forces, the antennas will continue to radiate an intense directional beam. As the synchronization forced on the antennas by the transmitters disappears, the radiators will gradually "forget" their timing because of T_2 processes. The phases of the systems will become "unglued" from one another, and the intensity and directionality of the radiation emitted by them will be lost. Eventually, the radiation from the array will be completely incoherent and isotropic, and will be produced at a greatly reduced rate until T_1 relaxation ends the entire process. It is as if all the radiators are soldiers, called out on a field at night and formed in line by a drill sergeant (the coherent driving field, or transmitter). The drill sergeant marches all of his soldiers (synchronizing their motions) by counting cadence. Disconnecting the transmitter (shooting the drill sergeant) will not produce an immediate breakup of the marching formation, because each soldier will have formed in his own mind a memory of the sergeant's cadence, All of these memories, however, are slightly imperfect and differ from one another. After a time T_2, the cumulative effects of the cadence errors will be quite noticeable; the marching file will have straggled out over the field in a most unmilitary fashion. All of this will ordinarily occur long before the soldiers cease marching, because it takes a long time (T_1) for any of them to drop from exhaustion or to desert the ranks. See Figure 5.3.

The difference in intensity between the initial coherent radiation and the

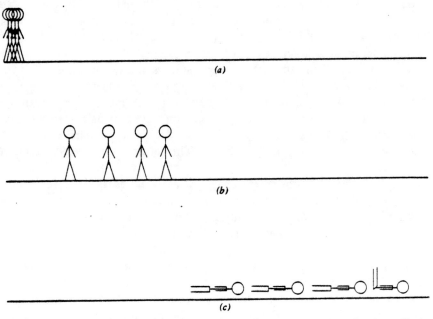

Figure 5.3.   (*a*) Coherently driven soldiers. (*b*) Soldiers marching freely, suffering T_2 relaxation. (*c*) Soldiers after T_1 relaxation.

ultimate incoherent emission can be truly enormous for macroscopic samples of quantum systems—the expected factor-of-N enhancement of the former is of the order of 6×10^{23} (Avogadro's number). This fact is essential to the successful operation of crossed-coil nmr spectrometers, as the ordinary incoherent fluorescence from magnetized nuclei is far too weak to be detected experimentally. Ensembles with a high degree of phase correlation among the constituent systems are called "superradiant"; they are characterized by a high value of the "cooperation" quantum number. The decay of superradiant emission (transitions of the ensemble to states of lower cooperation number) in a time T_2 is called "free-induction decay" by nmr spectroscopists.

In the classical phased array described above, it has been assumed tacitly that the dominant T_1 mechanism was the ohmic electrical resistance of the antennas—friction between the electrons and the internal parts of their conductors. In spectroscopy, such relaxation processes, which convert excess ensemble energy directly into heat, are called "radiationless". In nuclear magnetic resonance it is indeed true that T_1 relaxation is completely dominated by radiationless processes; spontaneous emission (incoherent fluoresence) is so slow that it would take literally forever ($\approx 10^{15}$

years) for Boltzmann equilibrium to be established by this means. In systems undergoing electronic transitions, emitting and absorbing light in the visible and ultraviolet regions of the spectrum, one commonly finds that incoherent spontaneous emission is an important or even dominant T_1 process. If incoherent spontaneous emission is rapid enough so that an appreciable fraction of the excitation energy of an ensemble can escape into the heat bath thereby, imagine how much more energy can be eliminated by coherent superradiant emission! Even in nmr spectroscopy, it sometimes happens that free-induction decay can compete with radiationless relaxation as a T_1 process. This effect is termed "radiation damping."

As will be seen in subsequent chapters, each increase in the relaxation rate $1/T_2$ causes the corresponding spectral line to increase in width. Line broadening due to radiation damping presents a problem in the design of commercial nmr spectrometers. It is solved by decreasing the Q of the receiver circuit; this, in effect, prevents a rapid escape of electromagnetic radiation from the sample. The magnitude of the broadening due to damping depends on the *square* of the concentration of nuclei in the samples, as is expected for a coherent process.

In this chapter, a powerful method for predicting the macroscopic behavior of microscopic quantum systems has been developed. The principle tool used in this method is the density matrix, which contains all of the information about the time-development of an ensemble in statistical quantum mechanics. The notion of phase-coherence among matter waves was introduced, as was the influence of perturbations and of relaxation processes. In the next chapter, the formalism of the density matrix will be used in a discussion of magnetic resonance in bulk samples. Finally, in Chapter 7, these concepts will be applied to all other kinds of spectroscopy.

5.12 References

1. R. J. Glauber, "Coherent and incoherent states of the radiation field," *Phys. Rev.* **131**, 2766 (1963).
2. C. P. Slichter, *Principles of Magnetic Resonance* (Harper and Row, New York, 1963), pp. 127–134, 156–159.
3. a. R. H. Dicke, "Coherence in spontaneous radiation processes," *Phys. Rev.* **93**, 99 (1954).
    b. R. H. Dicke, "Coherence and the quantum," *J. Opt. Soc. Am.* **47**, 527 (1957).
    c. R. H. Dicke, "The coherence-brightened laser," in *Quantum Electronics*, Vol. 1, P. Grivet and N. Bloembergen, Eds. (Columbia University Press, New York, 1964), pp. 35–53.

5.13   Problems

5.1

a.   Find the elements of the matrix D for a spin

$s = \frac{1}{2}$ system in the state represented by

$$\Psi = \exp\left(\frac{i\omega_0 t}{2}\right)\cos\left(\frac{\theta}{2}\right)\alpha + \exp\left(\frac{-i\omega_0 t}{2}\right)\sin\left(\frac{\theta}{2}\right)\beta.$$

b.   Show that, for $\theta = 62°28'34.3''$, the matrix becomes

$$[D] = \frac{1}{1+e}\begin{bmatrix} e & \exp\left(\frac{1}{2} + i\omega_0 t\right) \\ \exp\left(\frac{1}{2} - i\omega_0 t\right) & 1 \end{bmatrix}.$$

c.   What is the expectation value of the energy for this system?

5.2   Consider a particle that has only two eigenstates of the energy, $\mathcal{E} = kT$ and 0.

a.   What is the density matrix for an ensemble of N such particles at equilibrium?

b.   Calculate the total energy of the ensemble.

5.3

a.   What is the density matrix for an ensemble of two level particles, all of which are in the ground state?

b.   What is the density matrix for an ensemble of two level particles, all of which are in the excited state?

5.4   Solve Eqs. 5.69 to 5.72 for $H_1 = 0$ and $\mathcal{E} = kT$. Use the boundary condition that, at time $t = 0$,

$$\rho(0) = \frac{1}{2}\begin{bmatrix} 1 & \exp(i\omega_0 t) \\ \exp(-i\omega_0 t) & 1 \end{bmatrix}.$$

6 Applications to magnetic resonance

6.1 Operators representing orbital angular momentum

The spinning charged particle having an angular momentum quantum number of 1/2 was introduced in Chapter 4 to illustrate the quantum-mechanical nature of spectroscopic transitions. This system is particularly suitable for such a purpose because the component of the transition dipole moment in any direction in space can be made an eigenvalue property by choosing an appropriate state. In Chapter 1 it was noted that the ideas presented in this book were historically first discovered and applied in the study of such systems. For these reasons, and because of the remarkable simplicity of the quantum-mechanical calculations in this case, the first detailed application of material developed in the first five chapters will be made to quantum transitions of spin-1/2 particles in a magnetic field (magnetic resonance spectroscopy). Chapter 4 was devoted to magnetic resonance in molecular beams, so that the quantum systems could be studied one at a time. By way of contrast, in this chapter the emphasis will be placed on spin-1/2 particles in bulk samples, and the statistical methods introduced in Chapter 5 must be employed.

The discussion will be prefaced by a review of various facts about angular momentum. In classical mechanics, the angular momentum L of a particle about a point is given by the cross product of the vector joining the point to the particle, $\mathbf{r}$, and the linear momentum vector of the particle, μ (do not confuse μ with the magnetic permeability, μ_0):

$$\mathbf{L} = \mathbf{r} \times \mu. \tag{6.1}$$

(see Figure 6.1). Each of these three vectors may be written in terms of its Cartesian components:

$$\mathbf{L} = L_x \hat{x} + L_y \hat{y} + L_z \hat{z}, \tag{6.2}$$

$$\mathbf{r} = x\hat{x} + y\hat{y} + z\hat{z}, \tag{6.3}$$

and

$$\mu = \mu_x \hat{x} + \mu_y \hat{y} + \mu_z \hat{z}. \tag{6.4}$$

170

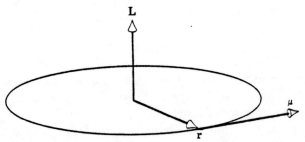

Figure 6.1. Vector relationship between orbital angular momentum, **L**, linear momentum **μ**, and position **r**.

According to the determinantal rule,

$$\mathbf{r} \times \mathbf{\mu} \equiv \begin{vmatrix} x & y & z \\ \mu_x & \mu_y & \mu_z \\ \hat{x} & \hat{y} & \hat{z} \end{vmatrix}. \tag{6.5}$$

By comparing the results of expanding the right-hand side of Eq. 6.5 term by term with the right-hand side of Eq. 6.2, the relationships

$$L_x = y\mu_z - z\mu_y, \tag{6.6}$$

$$L_y = z\mu_x - x\mu_z, \tag{6.7}$$

and

$$L_z = x\mu_y - y\mu_x. \tag{6.8}$$

may be found. Equations 6.6 to 6.8 can be used to find the operators corresponding to the three components of angular momentum (associated, e.g., with the motion of an electron around a nucleus) by the following simple substitutions:

$$\underline{\mu}_x \equiv -i\hbar \left(\frac{\partial}{\partial x} \right)_{y,z,t,} \tag{6.9}$$

$$\underline{\mu}_y \equiv -i\hbar \left(\frac{\partial}{\partial y} \right)_{x,z,t,} \tag{6.10}$$

$$\underline{\mu}_z \equiv -i\hbar \left(\frac{\partial}{\partial z} \right)_{x,y,t,} \tag{6.11}$$

$$\mathsf{X} = x, \tag{6.12}$$

$$\mathsf{Y} = y, \tag{6.13}$$

$$\mathsf{Z} = z, \tag{6.14}$$

$$\mathsf{L}_x = L_x, \tag{6.15}$$

$$\mathsf{L}_y = L_y, \tag{6.16}$$

and

$$\mathsf{L}_z = L_z. \tag{6.17}$$

After these substitutions have been made, Eq. 6.2 may be interpreted as the definition of a vector operator, with its three components being ordinary scalar operators defined by Eqs. 6.6 to 6.17.

It is interesting to find the commutators of the three orbital angular momentum operators. For example, since the commutator rule obeys the distributive law,

$$
\begin{aligned}
[\mathsf{L}_x, \mathsf{L}_y] &= \left[(\mathsf{Y}\,\underline{\mu}_z - \mathsf{Z}\,\underline{\mu}_y), (\mathsf{Z}\,\underline{\mu}_x - \mathsf{X}\,\underline{\mu}_z) \right] \\
&= \left[\mathsf{Y}\,\underline{\mu}_z, \mathsf{Z}\,\underline{\mu}_x \right] - \left[\mathsf{Y}\,\underline{\mu}_z, \mathsf{X}\,\underline{\mu}_z \right] \\
&\quad - \left[\mathsf{Z}\,\underline{\mu}_y, \mathsf{Z}\,\underline{\mu}_x \right] + \left[\mathsf{Z}\,\underline{\mu}_y, \mathsf{X}\,\underline{\mu}_z \right].
\end{aligned} \tag{6.18}
$$

It is easy to see that

$$\left[\mathsf{Y}\,\underline{\mu}_z, \mathsf{Z}\,\underline{\mu}_x \right] = \mathsf{Y}\,\underline{\mu}_x \left[\underline{\mu}_z, \mathsf{Z} \right], \tag{6.19}$$

$$\left[\mathsf{Y}\,\underline{\mu}_z, \mathsf{X}\,\underline{\mu}_z \right] = 0, \tag{6.20}$$

$$\left[\mathsf{Z}\,\underline{\mu}_y, \mathsf{Z}\,\underline{\mu}_x \right] = 0, \tag{6.21}$$

and

$$\left[\mathsf{Z}\,\underline{\mu}_y, \mathsf{X}\,\underline{\mu}_z \right] = \mathsf{X}\,\underline{\mu}_y \left[\mathsf{Z}, \underline{\mu}_z \right]. \tag{6.22}$$

The results in Eqs. 6.19 to 6.22 may be substituted into Eq. 6.18 to produce

$$[\mathsf{L}_x, \mathsf{L}_y] = (\mathsf{X}\,\underline{\mu}_y - \mathsf{Y}\,\underline{\mu}_x)[\mathsf{Z}, \underline{\mu}_z]. \tag{6.23}$$

The first factor in parentheses on the right-hand side of Eq. 6.23 is simply L_z; see Eq. 6.8. The commutator in square brackets may be evaluated by letting it operate upon some state function $f(z)$:

$$
\begin{aligned}
[\mathsf{Z}, \underline{\mu}_z] f &= -i\hbar \left[z \frac{\partial f}{\partial z} - \frac{\partial}{\partial z}(zf) \right] \\
&= -i\hbar \left[z \frac{\partial f}{\partial z} - \left(f + z \frac{\partial f}{\partial z} \right) \right] \\
&= i\hbar f.
\end{aligned} \tag{6.24}
$$

Now that $f(z)$ has done its job, it may be removed from Eq. 6.24 and the resultant equality substituted into Eq. 6.23:

$$\left[L_x, L_y\right] = i\hbar L_z.$$

(6.25)

Similarly, one can show that

$$\left[L_y, L_z\right] = i\hbar L_x$$

(6.26)

and

$$\left[L_z, L_x\right] = i\hbar L_y.$$

(6.27)

Equation 6.25 can be remembered easily because the subscripts of the operators in it are in alphabetical order; Eqs. 6.26 and 6.27 can be obtained from Eq. 6.25 by a cyclic permutation of these subscripts.

6.2   Operators representing spin angular momentum

In the quantum theory of the electron developed by Pauli,[1] a triplet of operators, S_1, S_2, and S_3, were discovered which obeyed the same commutative relations that L_x, L_y, and L_z obeyed. In other words,

$$[S_1, S_2] = i\hbar S_3.$$

(6.28)

Also, the two other equations obtained from Eq. 6.28 by cyclic permutation of the subscripts are obeyed. Therefore it seemed reasonable to define a new vector operator:

$$S = S_x \hat{x} + S_y \hat{y} + S_z \hat{z},$$

(6.29)

where x, y, and z have replaced 1, 2, and 3 as subscripts. The physical property represented by the operator S is called the *spin angular momentum* of the electron.

It was recognized that there must be something rather unusual about the operator S. In particular, the connection between the orbital angular momentum operator L and the vector operators r and $\underline{\mu}$ is clearly defined. It is, in fact, the same relationship found in classical mechanics, as shown in Eqs. 6.1 to 6.8. If an electron were a particle that had a nonzero volume (e.g., a small sphere), one could divide up this volume into N infinitesimal volume elements, the jth having a linear momentum μ_j and located a distance r_j from the center of mass (see Figure 6.2). Then

$$S = \sum_{j=1}^{N} r_j \times \mu_j.$$

(6.30)

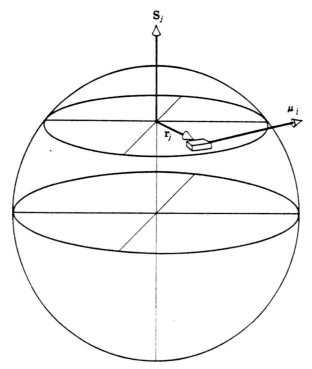

Figure 6.2. Vector relationship between spin angular momentum S, and the positions r_j and linear momenta μ_j of differential mass elements for a classical sphere.

The spin angular momentum would then be exactly like the momentum associated with the rotation of the earth on its axis, for which an equation like Eq. 6.30 holds. This would complete the analogy between the motion of the earth around the sun and the motion of the electron around a nucleus. Just as L determines the length of the "year" of both earth and electron, S would determine the "day" of both. Although this may still be a useful analogy, one cannot write an equation of the form of Eq. 6.30 for an electron. The reason is that the electron acts as if it were a mathematical point, and hence the properties r_j and μ_j of the infinitesimal volume are undefined.

Nevertheless, it will be shown that all of the most important measurable physical consequences of L lie in the commutative relations expressed in Eqs. 6.25 to 6.27. It has therefore been decided to adopt the commutative relations as the fundamental *definition* of angular momentum, rather than Eqs. 6.1 and 6.30 (which were utilized for that purpose in classical mechanics). This is in accord with a time-honored tradition in physics—

old definitions are generalized so that new discoveries can be fitted into theoretical frameworks which have proved their utility in the past.

If $\mathbf{S}$ is a vector in the laboratory coordinate system, it ought to be possible to define its length. Actually, it is found to be more convenient to deal with the square of the length of $\mathbf{S}$,

$$S^2 \equiv \mathbf{S} \cdot \mathbf{S} = S_x^2 + S_y^2 + S_z^2. \tag{6.31}$$

Since S^2 is a sum of products of operators, it is itself an operator.

To find the commutator of S^2 with S_x, the distributive law must be used:

$$[S^2, S_x] = [S_x^2, S_x] + [S_y^2, S_x] + [S_z^2, S_x]. \tag{6.32}$$

The first commutator on the right-hand side of Eq. 6.32 is zero because every operator commutes with any power of itself. The second commutator can be written, using the associative law, as

$$[S_y^2, S_x] = S_y(S_y S_x) - (S_x S_y) S_y$$

$$= S_y(S_x S_y - [S_x, S_y]) - (S_y S_x + [S_x, S_y]) S_y$$

$$= -(S_y[S_x, S_y] + [S_x, S_y] S_y). \tag{6.33}$$

Using the commutative relation in Eq. 6.28 yields

$$[S_y^2, S_x] = -i\hbar(S_y S_z + S_z S_y). \tag{6.34}$$

Next,

$$[S_z^2, S_x] = -(S_z[S_x, S_z] + [S_x, S_z] S_z)$$

$$= i\hbar(S_z S_y + S_y S_z). \tag{6.35}$$

Equations 6.34 and 6.35 may be substituted into Eq. 6.32 to give

$$[S^2, S_x] = 0. \tag{6.36}$$

Similarly, it can be shown that

$$[S^2, S_y] = 0 \tag{6.37}$$

and

$$[S^2, S_z] = 0. \tag{6.38}$$

6.3 Eigenkets of spin; raising and lowering operators

In Chapter 2 it was shown that a single set of eigenkets will suffice for two operators that commute with one another. The operator S^2 will commute with any of the three components, S_x, S_y, or S_z. The latter, however, do not commute with each other. Physically, this means that the system may move in such a way that the length of the total angular momentum, plus the length of any one Cartesian component, will be conserved in a stationary state. Whichever component is picked to be a constant of the motion, the other two components will not be constant. Therefore there are three choices of a complete set of linearly independent eigenkets of spin: one is the set of eigenkets of S_x; the second, of S_y; and the third, of S_z. Whichever is picked, it will automatically be an eigenket of S^2. In what follows, the set of eigenkets of S_z is selected arbitrarily as the representation.

Let us choose a particular member of this set (call it $|j\rangle$) and operate upon it with S_z. Since S_z represents angular momentum, its eigenvalues will have to have the *units* of angular momentum. This will be taken care of automatically if each eigenvalue is written as a product of a dimensionless constant with $\hbar$;

$$S_z|j\rangle = \hbar m_j|j\rangle. \tag{6.39}$$

Similarly, the eigenvalues of S^2 will have to have units of angular momentum squared:

$$S^2|j\rangle = \hbar^2 \Lambda_j|k\rangle. \tag{6.40}$$

The allowed values of m and Λ for all members of the set $\{|S_z\rangle\}$ plus the number of states M must be determined.

What happens when S_y and S_x operate upon $|j\rangle$ must also be discovered. As things turn out, it is more convenient to attack this question first. Rather than investigate the problem directly, it is simpler to define two new operators,

$$S_+ \equiv S_x + iS_y \tag{6.41}$$

and

$$S_- \equiv S_x - iS_y, \tag{6.42}$$

and see what *they* do to $|j\rangle$. It is easy to see that if what S_+ and S_- do to $|j\rangle$ is known, what S_y and S_x do can be discovered by inverting Eqs. 6.41 and 6.42. All that is known at this stage is that the result of operating upon a ket with any operator is to turn that ket into another ket:

$$S_+|j\rangle = |+\rangle \tag{6.43}$$

and

$$S_-|j\rangle = |-\rangle. \tag{6.44}$$

The results in Eqs. 6.43 and 6.44 are disconcertingly vague because there are literally an infinite number of possibilities for $|+\rangle$ and $|-\rangle$. The only thing $|\pm\rangle$ *cannot* be is simply a constant multiplied by $|j\rangle$ itself. This is known because S_+ and S_- are linear combinations of S_y and S_x, and neither of the latter commute with S_z. Since $|j\rangle$ is an eigenket of S_z, it will not be simultaneously an eigenket of S_+ or S_-. In general, then,

$$|\pm\rangle = c_{\pm 1}|1\rangle + c_{\pm 2}|2\rangle + \cdots + c_{\pm N}|N\rangle, \tag{6.45}$$

where at least one $c_{\pm k}$ $(k \neq j)$ is nonzero.

The *simplest* possiblity for $|\pm\rangle$ would be for all but one of the $c_{\pm k}$'s in Eq. 6.45 to be zero. In that case, Eqs. 6.43 and 6.44 could be written as follows:

$$S_+|j\rangle = c_{+k}|k\rangle, \qquad k \neq j, \tag{6.46}$$

and

$$S_-|j\rangle = c_{-l}|l\rangle, \qquad l \neq j. \tag{6.47}$$

Perhaps the nicest thing about the hypotheses in Eqs. 6.46 and 6.47 is that they can be tested. If $|+\rangle$ and $|-\rangle$ were just other members of the same set of eigenkets from which $|j\rangle$ was drawn, they would have to satisfy the same equations that gave $|j\rangle$ its identity in the first place. In particular, then, the tests are

$$S_z|\pm\rangle \stackrel{?}{=} \text{const.} \times |\pm\rangle \tag{6.48}$$

and

$$S^2|\pm\rangle \stackrel{?}{=} \text{const.} \times |\pm\rangle. \tag{6.49}$$

It is also necessary that

$$|\pm\rangle \neq 0, \tag{6.50}$$

because even though $|\pm\rangle = 0$ satisfies Eqs. 6.48 and 6.49, it corresponds to no particle at all being present and is therefore of no interest.

Applying the test in Eq. 6.49 first yields

$$S^2|\pm\rangle = S^2S_\pm|j\rangle$$

$$= S^2(S_x \pm iS_y)|j\rangle$$

$$= (S^2S_x \pm iS^2S_y)|j\rangle$$

$$= (S_xS^2 \pm iS_yS^2)|j\rangle$$

$$= (S_x \pm iS_y)S^2|j\rangle. \tag{6.51}$$

In the above, the distributive law has been used, plus the fact that S^2 commutes with S_y and S_x (see Eqs. 6.36 and 6.37).

The fact that multiplication by a scalar commutes with all other operators may be applied to combine Eqs. 6.40 and 6.51:

$$S^2|\pm\rangle = S_\pm\hbar^2\Lambda_j|j\rangle$$

$$= \hbar^2\Lambda_jS_\pm|j\rangle$$

$$= \hbar^2\Lambda_j|\pm\rangle. \tag{6.52}$$

Also used were the definitions of $S_\pm$ and $|\pm\rangle$, as expressed in Eqs. 6.41 to 6.44. It can be seen from Eq. 6.52 that the wavefunctions $|+\rangle$ and $|-\rangle$ indeed pass the test expressed in Eq. 6.49.

The test in Eq. 6.48 may now be applied:

$$S_z|\pm\rangle = S_zS_\pm|j\rangle$$

$$= S_z(S_x \pm iS_y)|j\rangle$$

$$= (S_zS_x \pm iS_zS_y)|j\rangle. \tag{6.53}$$

The operator products in parentheses to the right of the equality sign in Eq. 6.53 may be rewritten with the aid of the commutative relations; Eq. 6.53 then becomes

$$S_z|\pm\rangle = (\{S_xS_z + [S_z,S_x]\} \pm i\{S_yS_z - [S_y,S_z]\})|j\rangle$$

$$= \{(S_x \pm iS_y)S_z + ([S_z,S_x] \mp i[S_y,S_z])\}|j\rangle$$

$$= [S_\pm S_z + (i\hbar S_y \mp i^2\hbar S_x)]|j\rangle$$

$$= [S_\pm S_z \pm \hbar(S_x \pm iS_y)]|j\rangle$$

$$= S_\pm(S_z \pm \hbar)|j\rangle$$

$$= S_\pm(S_z|j\rangle \pm \hbar|j\rangle). \tag{6.54}$$

Equation 6.39 may now be used to rewrite Eq. 6.54 as follows:

$$S_z|\pm\rangle = S_\pm(\hbar m_j|j\rangle \pm \hbar|j\rangle)$$
$$= S_\pm[\hbar(m_j \pm 1)]|j\rangle$$
$$= \hbar(m_j \pm 1)S_\pm|j\rangle$$
$$= \hbar(m_j \pm 1)|\pm\rangle. \tag{6.55}$$

It can be seen from Eq. 6.55 that the kets $|+\rangle$ and $|-\rangle$ indeed pass the test expressed in Eq. 6.48.

In summary, not only has it been discovered that the result of operating upon $|j\rangle$ with $S_+(S_-)$ is another member of the set of eigenkets of S_z, but also it has been learned *which* member of the set—the member with the same value of Λ as $|j\rangle$, but with a value of m higher (lower) by one unit. For this reason, S_+ and S_- are called *raising* and *lowering operators*. A notation frequently used for this ket is

$$|j\rangle \equiv |\Lambda, m\rangle. \tag{6.56}$$

Equations 6.46 and 6.47 therefore may now be rewritten as follows:

$$S_\pm|\Lambda, m\rangle = c_{\pm, m \pm 1}|\Lambda, m \pm 1\rangle. \tag{6.57}$$

6.4 Number of states, normalization, and eigenvalues

The facts expressed in Eq. 6.57 make it possible to start with any one of the eigenkets $|\Lambda, m\rangle$ representing a particular stationary state of the system, and to generate from it the eigenkets representing all other stationary states having angular momentum vectors of the same length (Λ), but different projections of these vectors on the z axis (m). For example, by repeated operation using S_+,

$$\underbrace{S_+ S_+ \cdots S_+}_{u \text{ times}} |\Lambda, m\rangle \equiv S_+^u|\Lambda, m\rangle$$

$$= c_{+, m+1} c_{+, m+2} \cdots c_{+, m+u}|\Lambda, m+u\rangle \tag{6.58}$$

Common sense indicates that there must be some limit to the process expressed in Eq. 6.58; surely the component of the angular momentum along the z axis cannot exceed the length of the total vector. In other words, there must be some limit upon $m + u$. Similarly,

$$S_-^v|\Lambda, m\rangle = c_{-, m-1} c_{-, m-2} \cdots c_{-, m-v}|\Lambda, m-v\rangle; \tag{6.59}$$

there must be a limit on $m - v$ also.

The easiest way to obtain automatic upper and lower bounds on m would be to have $c_{+,m}$ be zero if m becomes too high and $c_{-,m}$ be zero if m becomes too low. It will be necessary to compute these quantities anyway, in order to normalize the wavefunctions generated by means of Eq. 6.57. First, S_-S_+ is computed using the definitions in Eqs. 6.41 and 6.42, the commutator in Eq. 6.28, the definition of S in Eq. 6.31, and the distributive law:

$$S_-S_+ = (S_x - iS_y)(S_x + iS_y)$$

$$= (S_x^2 + S_y^2) + i(S_x S_y - S_y S_x)$$

$$= (S^2 - S_z^2) - S_z\hbar. \tag{6.60}$$

Then $|+\rangle$ is normalized, using Eqs. 6.43 and 6.57:

$$(S_+|\Lambda, m\rangle)^\uparrow S_+|\Lambda, m\rangle = |c_{+,m+1}|^2\langle\Lambda, m+1|\Lambda, m+1\rangle. \tag{6.61}$$

The superscript $\uparrow$ means that the ket vector in parentheses should be replaced by the corresponding bra. To discover the identity of this bra, one must make use of what is called the *Hermitian property of Hilbert space* (defined previously in Eq. 2.104). It can be shown that, because of this property, corresponding bras and kets are Hermitian adjoints of one another. When operators, bras, and kets are represented by matrices (as was done, e.g., in Chapter 5), their Hermitian adjoints can be defined very simply. The transpose $[A]_T$ of any row, column, or square matrix $[A]$ is formed by interchanging rows and columns. In other words, the elements of the nth row of $[A]$ become the elements of the nth column of $[A]_T$. The Hermitian adjoint, $[A]^\dagger$, of any matrix $[A]$ is formed by replacing each element of $[A]_T$ by its complex conjugate. Using this definition and Eqs. 6.41 and 6.42, one can show that the Hermitian adjoint of S_+ is S_-. Assume that $|j\rangle$, the starting eigenket, is already normalized. Then, from Eq. 6.61,

$$|c_{+,m+1}|^2 = (S_+|\Lambda, m\rangle)^\uparrow S_+|\Lambda, m\rangle$$

$$= (\langle\Lambda, m|S_-)S_+|\Lambda, m\rangle. \tag{6.62}$$

Next, the associative and distributive laws are used, and Eq. 6.60 is substituted into Eq. 6.62:

$$|c_{+,m+1}|^2 = \langle \Lambda, m | S_- S_+ | \Lambda, m \rangle$$

$$= \langle \Lambda, m | S^2 | \Lambda, m \rangle - \langle \Lambda, m | S_z^2 | \Lambda, m \rangle - \hbar \langle \Lambda, m | S_z | \Lambda, m \rangle. \tag{6.63}$$

Equations 6.39 and 6.40 are then used to find

$$|c_{+,m+1}|^2 = \hbar^2 \Lambda - \hbar^2 m^2 - \hbar^2 m$$

$$= \hbar^2 [\Lambda - m(m+1)]. \tag{6.64}$$

Similarly, starting with the operator $S_+ S_-$, one has

$$|c_{-,m-1}|^2 = \hbar^2 [\Lambda - m(m-1)]. \tag{6.65}$$

Whenever the expressions in square brackets on the right-hand sides of Eq. 6.64 and 6.65 are *not* zero, Eq. 6.50 is satisfied. This means that $|+\rangle$ and $|-\rangle$ have completely satisfied the tests laid down for them, and they indeed qualify as members of the set $\{|S_z\rangle\}$, as hoped. Whenever they *are* zero, they provide boundaries for the allowed values of m in Eq. 6.57. From Eq. 6.64,

$$\Lambda - m_{MAX}(m_{MAX} + 1) = 0. \tag{6.66}$$

From Eq. 6.65,

$$\Lambda - m_{MIN}(m_{MIN} - 1) = 0. \tag{6.67}$$

From Eqs. 6.66 and 6.67, a relationship is obtained between m_{MAX} and m_{MIN}:

$$m_{MAX}(m_{MAX} + 1) = m_{MIN}(m_{MIN} - 1). \tag{6.68}$$

The numerical values of m_{MAX} and m_{MIN} are still not known. It is known from Eq. 6.58, however, that it must be possible to start at some arbitrarily chosen m and, by repeated applications of the S_+ operator, reach m_{MAX} in an integral number of steps:

$$m_{MAX} = m + u. \tag{6.69}$$

Similarly, according to Eq. 6.59, it must be possible to start at the same point, step down an integral number of times by applying S_-^v, and arrive at m_{MIN}:

$$m_{MIN} = m - v. \tag{6.70}$$

Equation 6.70 may be subtracted from Eq. 6.69 to find

$$m_{MAX} - m_{MIN} = u + v \equiv q. \tag{6.71}$$

Since u and v are integers, q must also be an integer. Next, Eq. 6.71 can be substituted into Eq. 6.68 to obtain

$$(m_{MAX})^2 + m_{MAX} = (m_{MAX} - q)^2 - (m_{MAX} - q). \tag{6.72}$$

Equation 6.72 may be easily solved by

$$m_{MAX} = \frac{q}{2}. \tag{6.73}$$

Therefore m_{MAX} and all other values of m are either integers or half integers, depending on whether q is even or odd.

The fact that m_{MAX} must be either integral or half integral, as indicated by Eq. 6.73, severely restricts the possible solutions to Eq. 6.68. In fact, there are only two corresponding possibilities for m_{MIN}:

$$m_{MIN} = m_{MAX} + 1 \tag{6.74}$$

and

$$m_{MIN} = -m_{MAX}. \tag{6.75}$$

The "solution" in Eq. 6.74 may be disregarded because it contradicts the very concepts of minimum and maximum. If m_{MAX} is denoted by the symbol s, in accordance with the usual custom, it is found from Eq. 6.66 that

$$\Lambda = s(s+1). \tag{6.76}$$

The same result may be obtained from Eqs. 6.67 and 6.75. A schematic presentation of the relationship between m and s is given in Figure 6.3.

6.5 Spinning particles in nature

In summary, the following has been learned. Whenever one finds in quantum mechanics a system described within a Hilbert space containing

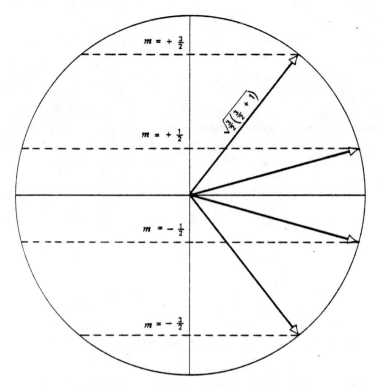

Figure 6.3. Quantum states of a spinning particle; relationships between m and s for $s = \frac{3}{2}$.

three operators, S_x, S_y, and S_z, obeying the rule

$$[S_x, S_y] = S_z \tag{6.77}$$

and cyclic permutations thereof, one has found a system that can exist in states represented by

$$|j\rangle \equiv |s(s+1), m_s\rangle. \tag{6.78}$$

When the system is in any one of these states, the length of the angular momentum vector is a constant of the motion. The square of that length is the eigenvalue of the operator S^2,

$$S^2|s(s+1), m_s\rangle = \hbar^2 s(s+1)|s(s+1), m_s\rangle, \tag{6.79}$$

where s is a positive integer or half integer. The component of angular momentum along one of the Cartesian axes (e.g., z) will also be a constant of the motion. The length of that component is the eigenvalue of the operator S_z,

$$S_z|s(s+1),m_s\rangle = \hbar m_s|s(s+1),m_s\rangle, \tag{6.80}$$

where the values of m_s are integrally spaced and bounded from above and below by s and $-s$, respectively. If a particular ket corresponding to one of these states of stationary angular momentum is known, the other may be found by repeated applications of the raising and lowering operators:

$$(S_x \pm iS_y)|s(s+1),m_s\rangle = \hbar[s(s+1)-m_s(m_s \pm 1)]^{1/2}$$
$$\times \exp(i\zeta_{s,m_s \pm 1})|s(s+1),m_s \pm 1\rangle, \tag{6.81}$$

where all kets are normalized to unity, and $\zeta_{s,ms \pm 1}$ is an arbitrary phase constant that can ordinarily be neglected (see Eq. 2.49).

These results, although derived with the spin angular momentum of the electron specifically in mind, apply to any angular momentum whatsoever. In Table 6.1 the symbols used in different systems for the quantum numbers are employed to display the otherwise identical formulas.

TABLE 6.1 Similarities among quantum systems possessing angular momentum

Type of Angular Momentum	Length of Total Vector	Length of z Component	Restrictions on Total Length	Restrictions on Length of z Component
Electron spin	$\hbar[s(s+1)]^{1/2}$	$\hbar m_s$	$s = \frac{1}{2}$	$m_s = \pm\frac{1}{2}$
Proton spin	$\hbar[I(I+1)]^{1/2}$	$\hbar m_I$	$I = \frac{1}{2}$	$m_I = \pm\frac{1}{2}$
Electron orbit	$\hbar[l(l+1)]^{1/2}$	$\hbar m_l$	$l = 0,1,\ldots,\infty$	$m_l = -l, -l+1,\ldots,l$
Total electron	$\hbar[j(j+1)]^{1/2}$	$\hbar m_j$	$j = l+s$	$m_j = -j, -j+1,\ldots,j$
Total H atom	$\hbar[F(F+1)]^{1/2}$	$\hbar m_F$	$F = j+I$	$m_F = -F, -F+1,\ldots,F$
Molecular rotation	$\hbar[J(J+1)]^{1/2}$	$\hbar M$ (laboratory axis)	$J = 0,1,\ldots,\infty$	$M = -J, -J+1,\ldots,J$
		$\hbar K$ (molecular axis)		$K = -J, -J+1,\ldots,J$

It has already been mentioned that a clear classical analog of spin angular momentum is possible only if the electron is imagined to be a ball of nonzero volume. Then the ball could be subdivided into infinitesimal volume elements, and S could be calculated by means of Eq. 6.30. Of course, each of these infinitesimal volume elements would have associated with it not only a tiny chunk of mass, but a tiny bit of negative electrical charge as well. The rotation of the ball would therefore carry these elements of charge around the axis in circular loops, and associated with each loop would be a magnetic field. Therefore a rotating charged sphere should have a magnetic dipole moment. If the infinitesimal charges are rigidly fixed to the infinitesimal masses that constitute the sphere, the dipole moment vector and the angular momentum vector will be parallel (or antiparallel, depending on the algebraic sign of the charge) (see Figure 6.4).

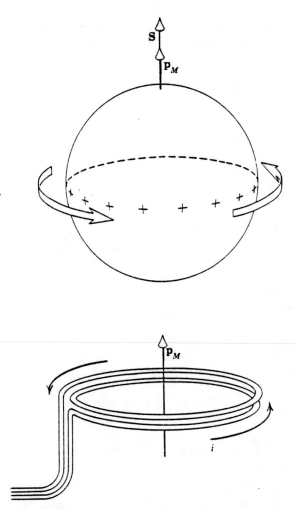

Figure 6.4. (a) Magnetic moment of a classical spinning charged sphere. (b) Magnetic moment of a coil of wire carrying a current.

As was previously stated, electrons are points, not balls. This fact does not prevent them from having spin angular momentum, however, nor does it prevent them from having magnetic dipole moments. Other particles of importance in this chapter (in addition to electrons) are atomic nuclei. All nuclei with nonzero spin angular momenta also have magnetic moments due to their charge. Even the neutrons, of charge zero, have magnetic moments. To explain this, it is imagined that neutrons are composed of both positive and negative charges in equal amounts, with the negative charges located nearer the surface of the sphere than the positive charges. In this way, the negative charges have greater tangential velocities than the positive charges and, therefore, give rise to greater equivalent currents. The area enclosed by the equivalent "loop of wire" is greater for charges on the outside of the neutron. Since the magnetic field associated with the rotation of a charge is proportional to the product of the current and the loop area, the magnetic field associated with the negative charges of the neutron is bigger than that associated with the positive charges. The former cancels the latter and gives rise to a net magnetic moment for the neutron comparable in magnitude to nuclear moments, but opposite in sign to the proton. The relationship between the electromagnetic multipole moments possessed by a nucleus and the magnitude of the associated angular momentum is shown in Table 6-2.

TABLE 6.2   Relationship between spin quantum number and nuclear multipole moment

Moment	Spin quantum number				
	0	$\frac{1}{2}$	1	$\frac{3}{2}$	2
Electric monopole	Yes	Yes	Yes	Yes	Yes
Magnetic dipole	No	Yes	Yes	Yes	Yes
Electric quadrupole	No	No	Yes	Yes	Yes
Magnetic octopole	No	No	No	Yes	Yes
Electric hexadecapole	No	No	No	No	Yes

Each nonzero multipole moment higher than the monopole, or charge, constitutes a "handle" on the nucleus which may be "grasped" by the appropriate term in the Taylor series expansion of the external electromagnetic field, as outlined in Chapter 3. Fluctuations of the distribution of charges and currents in the environment of each nucleus grasp the appropriate handle and attempt to alter the spin orientation. This produces transitions between pairs of m states of the quantum systems. Since the net result is an exchange of energy between the surroundings and the ensemble of nuclear (or electronic) spins, the relaxation times, T_1 and T_2, discussed in Chapter 3 are effectively shortened by these interactions. As a consequence, the easiest way to observe interesting effects in nuclear magnetic resonance experimentally is to investigate them in $I = \frac{1}{2}$ nuclei, where the relaxation times are long enough so that coherence effects persist and can be observed. In electron paramagnetic resonance, of course, there is no choice—$s = \frac{1}{2}$ is a fixed property of the electrons. For this reason, the spin-$\frac{1}{2}$ particles have been the subject of special attention in the study of magnetic resonance, and the special symbols α and β are used for the appropriate eigenkets:

$$|1\rangle = |\tfrac{3}{4}, \tfrac{1}{2}\rangle = \alpha \exp\left[-i\left(\zeta_1 + \frac{\mathcal{E}_1 t}{\hbar}\right)\right] \tag{6.82}$$

and

$$|2\rangle = |\tfrac{3}{4}, -\tfrac{1}{2}\rangle = \beta \exp\left[-i\left(\zeta_2 + \frac{\mathcal{E}_2 t}{\hbar}\right)\right]. \tag{6.83}$$

6.6 The effect of a static magnetic field

To proceed with this analysis, it is necessary to obtain the Hamiltonian operator for the spin-$\frac{1}{2}$ particle. The operator corresponding to the magnetic dipole, $\mathbf{p}_M$, should be proportional to the angular momentum operator:

$$\mathbf{p}_M = \gamma \mathbf{S}. \tag{6.84}$$

The magnetogyric ratio, γ, was introduced in Chapter 4, where it was defined by Eq. 4.35. Classically, the energy of a magnetic dipole in a uniform induction field, $\mathbf{H}$ ($\mathbf{B}$ in all but magnetic resonance), is given by

$$\mathcal{E} = -\mathbf{p}_M \cdot \mathbf{H}. \tag{4.38}$$

By the usual procedure in quantum mechanics, the Hamiltonian is constructed from the classical expression for the energy by replacing all quantities appearing therein by the corresponding operator equivalents:

$$H = -\gamma \mathbf{S} \cdot \mathbf{H}. \tag{6.85}$$

In accordance with Eq. 5.55, the Hamiltonian is broken up into three terms. The first of these, H_0, should be associated with the establishment of the stationary states of the system:

$$H_0 = -\gamma \mathbf{S} \cdot \mathbf{H}_0. \tag{6.86}$$

In conformance with the previously adopted convention, the z component of angular momentum is the one that is invariant in the stationary states of the system. This implies that the coordinate system should be oriented so that $\mathbf{H}_0$ points along the z axis (see Eq. 4.48):

$$\mathbf{H}_0 = H_0 \hat{z}. \tag{6.87}$$

Therefore, using Eqs. 6.29 and 6.87, one may rewrite Eq. 6.86 to obtain

$$\mathbf{H}_0 = -\omega_0 S_z. \tag{6.88}$$

The symbol ω_0 used in Eq. 6.88 was defined previously in Eq. 4.55. The first step in solving the problem is to determine the energy eigenvalues, $\mathcal{E}_1$ and $\mathcal{E}_2$. From Eq. 6.82,

$$\mathbf{H}_0|1\rangle = \mathcal{E}_1|1\rangle$$

$$= -\gamma H_0 S_z |{\tfrac{3}{4}}, {\tfrac{1}{2}}\rangle$$

$$= -\gamma H_0 \hbar (\tfrac{1}{2})|1\rangle. \tag{6.89}$$

Therefore

$$\mathcal{E}_1 = \frac{-\hbar \omega_0}{2}. \tag{6.90}$$

Similarly, from Eq. 6.83,

$$\mathcal{E}_2 = \frac{+\hbar \omega_0}{2}. \tag{6.91}$$

These results were presented without proof in Eq. 4.43.

The orientation of the spin magnetic moment when the particle is in a superposition state will now be calculated. The ket for the particle in this state can be written, as suggested by Eqs. 2.73, 6.82, 6.83, 6.90, and 6.91:

$$|A\rangle = \cos\left(\frac{\theta}{2}\right)\left\{\alpha \exp\left[i\left(\eta_1 + \frac{\omega_0 t}{2}\right)\right]\right\}$$

$$+ \sin\left(\frac{\theta}{2}\right)\left\{\beta \exp\left[i\left(\eta_2 - \frac{\omega_0 t}{2}\right)\right]\right\}. \tag{6.92}$$

To calculate the orientation of the magnetic moment of the system when in the state described by Eq. 6.92, the expectation value of each of the three components, p_x, p_y, and p_z, of the magnetic moment vector, $\mathbf{p}_M$, must be calculated using Eq. 6.84. In Chapter 4 the sense in which the results of such a calculation can indeed be called the orientation of *the* magnetic moment was discussed. It was found that not the orientation of the true (total, instantaneous) dipole moment, but only what was called the *certain component* thereof, would be obtained. This component is of interest because of the fact that, in the course of its interaction with the radiation field, the spin behaves as if this "component" receives the torque and is therefore responsible for the transition.

In performing these calculations, the formula given in Eq. 2.83 may be used. For example,

$$\langle p_x \rangle = \gamma \left[(S_x)_{11} \cos^2\left(\frac{\theta}{2}\right) + (S_x)_{22} \sin^2\left(\frac{\theta}{2}\right) \right.$$

$$\left. + 2\cos\left(\frac{\theta}{2}\right) \sin\left(\frac{\theta}{2}\right) \operatorname{Re}\left\{ (S_x)_{12} \exp\left[i(\S - \omega_0 t) \right] \right\} \right]. \quad (6.93)$$

Equations similar to Eq. 6.93 hold for $\langle p_y \rangle$ and $\langle p_z \rangle$.

Evidently, it will be necessary to compute the elements of the S_x, S_y, and S_z matrices in the basis $\{\alpha, \beta\}$. First, Eqs. 6.41 and 6.42 must be solved for the desired S_y and S_x operators in terms of the raising and lowering operators:

$$S_x = \frac{S_+ + S_-}{2} \quad (6.94)$$

and

$$S_y = \frac{S_+ - S_-}{2i}. \quad (6.95)$$

From Eq. 6.81, ignoring phase constants, it can be computed that, for an $s = \frac{1}{2}$ particle,

$$S_+ \alpha = S_- \beta = 0, \quad (6.96)$$

$$S_- \alpha = \hbar \beta, \quad (6.97)$$

and

$$S_+ \beta = \hbar \alpha. \quad (6.98)$$

Note that α and β are orthonormal kets:

$$(\alpha, \alpha) \equiv \langle \tfrac{3}{4}, \tfrac{1}{2} | \tfrac{3}{4}, \tfrac{1}{2} \rangle = 1, \tag{6.99}$$

$$(\beta, \beta) \equiv \langle \tfrac{3}{4}, -\tfrac{1}{2} | \tfrac{3}{4}, -\tfrac{1}{2} \rangle = 1, \tag{6.100}$$

and

$$(\beta, \alpha) = (\alpha, \beta) \equiv \langle \tfrac{3}{4}, \pm\tfrac{1}{2} | \tfrac{3}{4}, \pm\tfrac{1}{2} \rangle = 0. \tag{6.101}$$

This fact, plus Eqs. 6.94 to 6.98, may be used to calculate

$$(S_x)_{11} = (S_x)_{22} = (S_y)_{11} = (S_y)_{22} = 0, \tag{6.102}$$

and

$$(S_x)_{12} = i(S_y)_{12} = \frac{\hbar}{2}. \tag{6.103}$$

Also, from Eq. 6.80, for an $s = \tfrac{1}{2}$ particle,

$$S_z \alpha = \frac{\hbar \alpha}{2} \tag{6.104}$$

and

$$S_z \beta = \frac{\hbar \beta}{2}. \tag{6.105}$$

Therefore,

$$(S_z)_{11} = -(S_z)_{22} = \frac{\hbar}{2} \tag{6.106}$$

and

$$(S_z)_{21} = (S_z)_{12} = 0. \tag{6.107}$$

Next, Eqs. 6.102, 6.103, 6.106, and 6.107 are substituted into Eq. 6.93 and its analogs. The results are

$$\langle p_y \rangle = \gamma \hbar \cos\left(\frac{\theta}{2}\right) \sin\left(\frac{\theta}{2}\right) \cos(\S - \omega_0 t), \tag{6.108}$$

$$\langle p_x \rangle = \gamma \hbar \cos\left(\frac{\theta}{2}\right) \sin\left(\frac{\theta}{2}\right) \sin(\S - \omega_0 t), \tag{6.109}$$

and

$$\langle p_z \rangle = \frac{\hbar \left[\cos^2(\theta/2) - \sin^2(\theta/2) \right]}{2}. \tag{6.110}$$

Finally, the substitutions

$$p_M = \frac{\gamma\hbar}{2} \tag{6.111}$$

and

$$\Omega = \S - \omega_0 t \tag{6.112}$$

(see Eq. 4.56) are made into Eqs. 6.108 to 6.110 to produce

$$\langle \mathbf{p}_M \rangle = p_M \cos\theta\, \hat{z} + p_M \sin\theta \cos\Omega\, \hat{x} + p_M \sin\theta \sin\Omega\, \hat{y}. \tag{6.113}$$

It can be seen from Eq. 6.113 that $\langle \mathbf{p}_M \rangle$ is a vector of length $p_M = \gamma\hbar/2$, making an angle θ with respect to the z axis, and having its projection on the xy plane at an angle $\Omega = \S - \omega_0 t$, measured counterclockwise from the x axis. In other words, $\langle \mathbf{p}_M \rangle$ precesses around the z axis at a constant frequency, ω_0 (called the *Larmor frequency*), in such a way that its length is constant. The cone angle is determined by the relative amounts of α and β in the superposition. The vector $\langle \mathbf{p}_M \rangle$ is shown in Figure 6.5 (note the similarity to Figure 4.4).

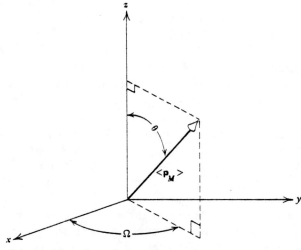

Figure 6.5.   Expectation value of the spin-angular-momentum vector of an $s = \frac{1}{2}$ particle.

In accordance with what was stated previously in Chapter 4, $\langle \mathbf{p}_M \rangle$ carries around with it another vector of length $\sqrt{3}\ \gamma\hbar/2$. This vector is the total angular momentum. Its location cannot be determined precisely, because of the uncertainty principle, but one can be sure that it is somewhere on a cone whose apical angle is $54°44'8''$ and whose axis is $\langle \mathbf{p}_M \rangle$. The location of $\langle \mathbf{p}_M \rangle$, on the other hand, can be determined as precisely as one desires; no limit is imposed on the accuracy of the measurement of Ω or θ by the uncertainty principle.

6.7   The effect of an oscillating magnetic field

The second term in the Hamiltonian operator, Eq. 5.55, will be discussed next. This term, H_1, describes the interaction between the spinning particle and the electromagnetic radiation. It was stated in Chapter 2 that this interaction must proceed by means of the fields associated with the light waves pushing monopoles and/or twisting dipoles. Every particle under consideration in this chapter has a magnetic dipole moment and will therefore feel a torque in the spatially uniform magnetic field $\mathbf{H}$. Every one but the neutron also has an electric monopole moment and will be pushed by the spatially uniform electric field, $\mathbf{E}$.

These fields will have a large effect on quantum systems containing spin-$\frac{1}{2}$ particles only if the motions they excite oscillate at frequencies near those of the corresponding quantum-mechanical transitions (resonance). The torques exerted by $\mathbf{H}$ (in typical large laboratory magnetic fields of $\sim 1\,T$) excite precessional motions in nuclei and electrons that will be at resonance with the oscillations of $\mathbf{H}$ at radio-wave or microwave frequencies. The pushes of $\mathbf{E}$ upon nuclei will tend to excite displacement motions of the nuclear framework (e.g., molecular rotation and vibration). The quantum-mechanical transition frequencies for these motions are much too high for resonance with rf waves to occur. (Microwaves can produce rotational transitions in gas-phase molecules, but only liquid and solid samples are of concern here.) The pushes of $\mathbf{E}$ upon electrons will tend to excite spatial redistributions of their probability densities (e.g., electronic transitions) at frequencies even higher than those of molecular rotation and vibration. Because only rf and microwave-frequency "light" will be considered in this chapter, only $\mathbf{H}$ is important; the influence of the $\mathbf{E}$ field may be neglected.

It can be seen from Eqs. 6.108 and 6.109 that the oscillations of the magnetic dipole moment vector occur in the xy plane, perpendicular to the direction of the field $H_0\hat{z}$. Therefore, in order to drive these dipoles, the oscillations of the magnetic vector associated with the light wave must occur in this same plane. Since electromagnetic waves are transverse (like water waves) rather than longitudinal (like sound waves in air), the oscillating field vectors are perpendicular to the direction of propagation. Therefore the light waves must propagate along the z axis of the coordinate system (i.e., parallel or antiparallel to H_0).

In practice, of course, the wavelength of the radiation employed in nuclear magnetic resonance is too long for anything remotely resembling propagation to occur. The rf oscillations are delivered to the sample by means of a transmitter coil, wound in such a way as to produce a magnetic field that is spatially uniform in the neighborhood of the sample. The axis of this coil is usually parallel to the x axis of the laboratory coordinate system. The resulting field oscillations are equivalent to those that would be produced by a linear superposition of traveling waves (phased to produce standing wave patterns) propagating in all directions in the yz plane. In electron spin resonance, the wave length of the radiation employed is small in comparison to the dimensions of the apparatus, but frequently still large in comparison to the sample. The radiation is piped about in waveguides rather than by means of wires because the electrical resistance of the latter is inconveniently high at microwave frequencies. In nuclear magnetic resonance the sample is usually supplied with radiation by a pair of Helmholz coils; in electron paramagnetic resonance the sample is placed in a microwave cavity at the end of a waveguide.

Regardless of the considerations outlined in the preceding paragraphs, it is accurate to describe the total magnetic field felt by the sample by means of the equation

$$\mathbf{H}(t) = H_0 \hat{z} + H_1(t)\hat{x} \tag{6.114}$$

in any magnetic resonance experiment. The expression in Eq. 6.114 may be substituted into Eq. 4.38 to obtain a classical expression for the energy:

$$\mathcal{E} = -[p_z H_0 + p_x H_1(t)]. \tag{6.115}$$

By analogy to Eq. 6.85, the corresponding Hamiltonian operator is obtained from Eq. 6.115:

$$\mathsf{H} = -\gamma[H_0 \mathsf{S}_z + H_1(t)\mathsf{S}_x]. \tag{6.116}$$

A comparison of Eq. 6.116 with Eqs. 5.55 and 6.86 permits identification of the term in the former that corresponds to the perturbation H_1:

$$\mathsf{H}_1 = -\gamma H_1(t)\mathsf{S}_x. \tag{6.117}$$

Can Eq. 6.117 be questioned by offering an alternative explanation for Eq. 6.116? The field vector **H** presented in Eq. 6.114 is the vector sum of components in the $\hat{x}$ and $\hat{z}$ directions. It therefore describes a vector in the xz plane (see Figure 6.6). If H_1 oscillates sinusoidally with time, then **H** oscillates back and forth about the z axis. What is to prevent the magnetic moments from simply following these oscillations, waving back and forth as reeds in a breeze, without any transitions occurring? Imagine, for example, that the big magnet used to produce $\mathbf{H_0}$ is mounted on a disk-shaped platform in the laboratory xz plane, and that the disk undergoes rapid, small-amplitude oscillations. This arrangement would produce a magnetic field of the same form as that expressed in Eq. 6.114 if $\hat{x}, \hat{y}$, and $\hat{z}$ are understood to be fixed laboratory coordinates. Would these oscillations be capable of producing transitions just as an electromagnetic field is supposed to do?

These objections are legitimate—there are circumstances in which the field $H_1(t)$ does *not* produce transitions, and there are also circumstances in which a mere change in the relative coordinates of the sample and the magnet that produces $\mathbf{H_0}$ *does* produce transitions. Any oscillations (in magnitude or direction) of the total magnetic field **H**, regardless of how they are produced, may or may not cause transitions to take place; what

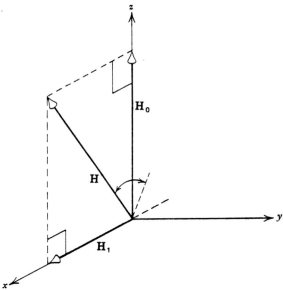

Figure 6.6. Static and oscillating magnetic fields in a spin-resonance experiment.

actually happens in any particular case is determined by the *adiabatic theorem*. This theorem can be stated precisely and proved rigorously, but for the moment it will be sufficient to state it loosely. If H_1 is small in comparison to H_0, *and* if H_1 oscillates slowly in comparison with the Larmor precession frequency, transitions will not occur: the dipoles will "follow" the vector sum of the fields, **H**. If H_1 is large *or* oscillates at a frequency near $\omega_0 = \gamma H_0$, *or* both, transitions will occur. The discussion that follows will be restricted to the latter case.

   If the electromagnetic oscillations H_1 are sinusoidal (i.e., if the "light" is monochromatic),

$$H_1(t) = H_1^0 \cos \omega t. \tag{6.118}$$

As has just been stated, the assumptions

$$H_1^0 \ll H_0 \tag{6.119}$$

and

$$\omega \cong \gamma H_0 \tag{6.120}$$

will be made. The condition stated in Eq. 6.119 makes it possible to assume that the stationary states of the system that were appropriate when only H_0 was present (namely, α and β) are very nearly the same as the stationary states appropriate for the system when both H_0 and H_1 are applied. Therefore α and β will be used as the representation for both the Hamiltonian and density matrices.

6.8   The density matrix for magnetic resonance

The equations of motion for the elements of the density matrix for a general two-level system were presented in Chapter 5 (Eqs. 5.69–5.72). The analysis was interrupted because an explicit expression for the elements of the matrix representing H_1 was lacking at that time. Now that the correct form for the H_1 operator (Eq. 6.117) and the matrix elements of S that appear therein (Eq. 6.102 and 6.103) have been presented, it can be shown that

$$(H_1)_{12} = (H_1)_{21} = -\frac{\gamma \hbar H_1(t)}{2} \tag{6.121}$$

and

$$(H_1)_{11} = (H_1)_{22} = 0. \tag{6.122}$$

Therefore, from Eqs. 5.69 to 5.72 and the above,

$$\frac{d\rho_{11}}{dt} = -\gamma H_1(t)\,\mathrm{Im}\,(\rho_{21}) - \left(\frac{\rho_{11}-\rho_{11}^e}{T_1}\right), \tag{6.123}$$

$$\frac{d\rho_{22}}{dt} = \gamma H_1(t)\,\mathrm{Im}\,(\rho_{21}) - \left(\frac{\rho_{22}-\rho_{22}^e}{T_1}\right), \tag{6.124}$$

$$\frac{d\rho_{12}}{dt} = i\omega_0\rho_{12} + \frac{i\gamma H_1(t)(\rho_{22}-\rho_{11})}{2} - \frac{\rho_{12}}{T_2}, \tag{6.125}$$

$$\frac{d\rho_{21}}{dt} = -i\omega_0\rho_{21} - \frac{i\gamma H_1(t)(\rho_{22}-\rho_{11})}{2} - \frac{\rho_{21}}{T_2}. \tag{6.126}$$

Equations 6.123 to 6.126 can be simplified by doing a little thinking. It is already known that all magnetic moments in the sample are precessing in cones about the z axis at the Larmor frequency, ω_0. This fast motion in the laboratory coordinate system interferes with visualization of the problem and may be eliminated by transforming everything into a rotating coordinate system:

$$\rho_{12}^\dagger = \rho_{12}\exp(-i\omega_0 t) \tag{6.127}$$

and

$$\rho_{21}^\dagger = \rho_{21}\exp(+i\omega_0 t). \tag{6.128}$$

From this it can be calculated that

$$\frac{d\rho_{12}^\dagger}{dt} = \frac{d\rho_{12}}{dt}\exp(-i\omega_0 t) - i\omega_0\rho_{12}\exp(-i\omega_0 t) \tag{6.129}$$

and

$$\frac{d\rho_{21}^\dagger}{dt} = \frac{d\rho_{21}}{dt}\exp(i\omega_0 t) + i\omega_0\rho_{12}\exp(i\omega_0 t). \tag{6.130}$$

Also, it is useful to define

$$\omega_1 = \gamma H_1^0 \tag{6.131}$$

and use the expression for $H_1(t)$ given by Eq. 6.118 to write

$$\frac{d\rho_{11}}{dt} = -\omega_1 \cos \omega t \, \text{Im}\left[\rho_{21}^\dagger \exp(-i\omega_0 t)\right] - \left(\frac{\rho_{11}-\rho_{11}^e}{T_1}\right), \quad (6.132)$$

$$\frac{d\rho_{22}}{dt} = \omega_1 \cos \omega t \, \text{Im}\left[\rho_{21}^\dagger \exp(-i\omega_0 t)\right] - \left(\frac{\rho_{22}-\rho_{22}^e}{T_1}\right), \quad (6.133)$$

$$\frac{d\rho_{12}^\dagger}{dt} = \frac{i\omega_1 \cos \omega t\,(\rho_{22}-\rho_{11})}{2} \exp(-i\omega_0 t) - \frac{\rho_{12}^\dagger}{T_2}, \quad (6.134)$$

and

$$\frac{d\rho_{21}^\dagger}{dt} = -\frac{i\omega_1 \cos \omega t\,(\rho_{22}-\rho_{11})}{2} \exp(i\omega_0 t) - \frac{\rho_{21}^\dagger}{T_2} \quad (6.135)$$

Next, Eqs. 6.132 and 6.133 may be added and subtracted from one another:

$$\frac{d(\rho_{22}+\rho_{11})}{dt} = -\frac{\left[(\rho_{22}+\rho_{11})-(\rho_{22}^e+\rho_{11}^e)\right]}{T_1} \quad (6.136)$$

and

$$\frac{d(\rho_{22}-\rho_{11})}{dt} = +2\omega_1 \cos \omega t \, \text{Im}\left[\rho_{21}^\dagger \exp(-i\omega_0 t)\right]$$
$$-\frac{\left[(\rho_{22}-\rho_{11})-(\rho_{22}^e-\rho_{11}^e)\right]}{T_1}. \quad (6.137)$$

Also, Eqs. 6.134 and 6.135 may be added and subtracted:

$$\frac{d(\rho_{12}^\dagger+\rho_{21}^\dagger)}{dt} = \left[\frac{i\omega_1 \cos \omega t\,(\rho_{22}-\rho_{11})}{2}\right]\left[\exp(-i\omega_0 t)-\exp(i\omega_0 t)\right]$$
$$-\frac{(\rho_{12}^\dagger+\rho_{21}^\dagger)}{T_2} \quad (6.138)$$

and

$$\frac{d(\rho_{12}^\dagger-\rho_{21}^\dagger)}{dt} = \left[\frac{i\omega_1 \cos \omega t\,(\rho_{22}-\rho_{11})}{2}\right]\left[\exp(-i\omega_0 t)+\exp(i\omega_0 t)\right]$$
$$-\frac{(\rho_{12}^\dagger-\rho_{21}^\dagger)}{T_2}. \quad (6.139)$$

Next, four real quantities are defined, using notation suggested by Dicke:[2]

$$R_1 \equiv \frac{\rho_{12}^\dagger - \rho_{21}^\dagger}{i} = 2\,\mathrm{Im}(\rho_{12}^\dagger), \qquad (6.140)$$

$$R_2 \equiv \rho_{12}^\dagger + \rho_{21}^\dagger = 2\,\mathrm{Re}(\rho_{12}^\dagger), \qquad (6.141)$$

$$R_3 \equiv \rho_{11} - \rho_{22}, \qquad (6.142)$$

and

$$\Sigma \equiv \rho_{11} + \rho_{22}. \qquad (6.143)$$

Equations 6.140 to 6.143 may be substituted into Eqs. 6.136 to 6.139. The results are as follows:

$$\frac{d\Sigma}{dt} = -\frac{(\Sigma - \Sigma^e)}{T_1}, \qquad (6.144)$$

$$\frac{dR_3}{dt} = +\omega_1 \cos \omega t\,(R_2 \sin \omega_0 t + R_1 \cos \omega_0 t)$$

$$\qquad\qquad -\left(\frac{R_3 - R_3^e}{T_1}\right), \qquad (6.145)$$

$$\frac{dR_2}{dt} = -\omega_1 \cos \omega t\, R_3 \sin \omega_0 t - \frac{R_2}{T_2}, \qquad (6.146)$$

and

$$\frac{dR_1}{dt} = -\omega_1 \cos \omega t\, R_3 \cos \omega_0 t - \frac{R_1}{T_2}. \qquad (6.147)$$

Note that Σ is proportional to the total number of systems in the ensemble (the trace of the density matrix). Since the trace is invariant (matter being conserved), the right-hand side of Eq. 6.144 is zero. Therefore the solution to the equation is

$$\Sigma = \text{const.} = 1. \qquad (6.148)$$

Note that R_3 is proportional to the difference in population between the ground and excited states. At ordinary (positive) spin temperatures, R_3 is positive. For inverted systems (pumped to negative spin temperatures), R_3 will be negative. A physical interpretation of R_1 and R_2 will be obtained shortly.

Next, the simplification of Eqs. 6.145 to 6.147 will be continued. Trigonometric identities may be used to rewrite the time-dependent terms:

$$\frac{dR_3}{dt} = \frac{\omega_1}{2} R_2 \{ \sin[(\omega+\omega_0)t] - \sin[(\omega-\omega_0)t] \}$$

$$+ \frac{\omega_1}{2} R_1 \{ \cos[(\omega+\omega_0)t] + \cos[(\omega-\omega_0)t] \}$$

$$- \left(\frac{R_3 - R_3^e}{T_1} \right), \tag{6.149}$$

$$\frac{dR_2}{dt} = - \frac{\omega_1 R_3 \{ \sin[(\omega+\omega_0)t] - \sin[(\omega-\omega_0)t] \}}{2} - \frac{R_2}{T_2}, \tag{6.150}$$

and

$$\frac{dR_1}{dt} = - \frac{\omega_1 R_3 \{ \cos[(\omega+\omega_0)t] + \cos[(\omega-\omega_0)t] \}}{2} - \frac{R_1}{T_2}. \tag{6.151}$$

Remember that it already has been assumed that ω is very close to ω_0. This means that terms which oscillate at the difference frequency ($\cong 0$) are very much slower than those which oscillate at the sum frequency ($\cong 2\omega_0$). What will be the effect of the $2\omega_0$ terms? They push the elements of the density matrix first in one direction and then in the other, reversing sign tens (even hundreds) of millions of times a second under usual experimental conditions. The effect of these terms must be very small (rotating wave approximation). On the other hand, the slowly varying terms can have some long-run effect on the magnitude of R_1, R_2, and R_3. Therefore

$$\frac{dR_1}{dt} \cong \frac{-\omega_1 R_3 \cos[(\omega-\omega_0)t]}{2} - \frac{R_1}{T_2}, \tag{6.152}$$

$$\frac{dR_2}{dt} \cong \frac{+\omega_1 R_3 \sin[(\omega-\omega_0)t]}{2} - \frac{R_2}{T_2}, \tag{6.153}$$

and

$$\frac{dR_3}{dt} \cong \frac{\omega_1 \{ R_1 \cos[(\omega-\omega_0)t] - R_2 \sin[(\omega-\omega_0)t] \}}{2}$$

$$- \frac{R_3 - R_3^e}{T_1}. \tag{6.154}$$

One final rotation of the coordinate system may be made:

$$R_1 = S \cos \delta t + C \sin \delta t \tag{6.155}$$

and

$$R_2 = - S \sin \delta t + C \cos \delta t, \tag{6.156}$$

where

$$\delta \equiv \omega - \omega_0. \tag{6.157}$$

From Eq. 6.155,

$$\frac{dR_1}{dt} = \left(\frac{dS}{dt} + \delta C \right) \cos \delta t - \left(- \frac{dC}{dt} + \delta S \right) \sin \delta t. \tag{6.158}$$

From Eq. 6.152,

$$\frac{dR_1}{dt} = - \frac{\omega_1 R_3 \cos \delta t}{2} + \frac{S \cos \delta t}{T_2} - \frac{C \sin \delta t}{T_2}. \tag{6.159}$$

Since $\cos \delta$ and $\sin \delta$ are linearly independent functions, the only way that Eqs. 6.158 and 6.159 can both be true is for the coefficients of these functions to be equal in both:

$$\frac{dS}{dt} + \delta C = - \frac{\omega_1 R_3}{2} + \frac{S}{T_2} \tag{6.160}$$

and

$$- \left(- \frac{dC}{dt} + \delta S \right) = - \frac{C}{T_2}. \tag{6.161}$$

Equations 6.160 and 6.161 could also have been obtained from Eqs. 6.153 and 6.156.

Equations 6.155 and 6.156 may be substituted into Eq. 6.154. Then

$$\frac{dR_3}{dt} = \frac{\omega_1 S}{2} - \left(\frac{R_3 - R_3^e}{T_1} \right). \tag{6.162}$$

6.9 The ensemble-averaged magnetization

Equations 6.160 to 6.162, together with all the changes of variables and transformations of coordinate systems that have been performed, contain the answers to all the questions that could possibly be asked about an ensemble of spin-$\frac{1}{2}$ particles. For example, the x, y, and z components of magnetization of the sample will be calculated. If N' is the number of spins per unit volume, the magnetization is given by

$$\mathbf{M} = N'(\langle \overline{P_x} \rangle \hat{x} + \langle \overline{P_y} \rangle \hat{y} + \langle \overline{P_z} \rangle \hat{z}). \tag{6.163}$$

Equation 5.41 may be used to calculate $\langle \overline{P_y} \rangle$:

$$\langle \overline{P_y} \rangle = \mathrm{Tr} \left\{ \begin{bmatrix} \rho_{11} & \rho_{12} \\ \rho_{21} & \rho_{22} \end{bmatrix} \begin{bmatrix} (\mathsf{p}_y)_{11} & (\mathsf{p}_y)_{12} \\ (\mathsf{p}_y)_{21} & (\mathsf{p}_y)_{22} \end{bmatrix} \right\}$$

$$= \rho_{11}(\mathsf{p}_y)_{11} + \rho_{12}(\mathsf{p}_y)_{21} + \rho_{21}(\mathsf{p}_y)_{12} + \rho_{22}(\mathsf{p}_y)_{22}. \tag{6.164}$$

Since

$$\mathsf{p}_y = \gamma \mathsf{S}_y, \tag{6.165}$$

and the matrix elements of S_y are available in Eqs. 6.102 and 6.103,

$$\langle \overline{P_y} \rangle = \frac{i\gamma\hbar(\rho_{12} - \rho_{21})}{2}. \tag{6.166}$$

From Eqs. 6.127 and 6.128,

$$\langle \overline{P_y} \rangle = \frac{i\gamma\hbar \left[\rho_{12}^{\dagger} \exp(i\omega_0 t) - \rho_{21}^{\dagger} \exp(-i\omega_0 t) \right]}{2}. \tag{6.167}$$

From Eqs. 6.140 and 6.141,

$$\langle \overline{P_y} \rangle = \frac{-\gamma\hbar(R_1 \cos\omega_0 t + R_2 \sin\omega_0 t)}{2}. \tag{6.168}$$

From Eqs. 6.155 and 6.156,

$$\langle \overline{P_y} \rangle = -\frac{\gamma\hbar \left[S(\cos\delta\cos\omega_0 t - \sin\delta\sin\omega_0 t) + C(\sin\delta\cos\omega_0 t + \cos\delta\sin\omega_0 t) \right]}{2}. \tag{6.169}$$

Using trigonometric identities and Eq. 6.157 yields

$$\langle \overline{P_y} \rangle = \frac{-\gamma\hbar(S\cos\omega t + C\sin\omega t)}{2}. \tag{6.170}$$

Similarly,

$$\langle \overline{P_x} \rangle = \frac{\gamma \hbar (- S \sin \omega t + C \cos \omega t)}{2} \tag{6.171}$$

and

$$\langle \overline{P_z} \rangle = \frac{\gamma \hbar R_3}{2}. \tag{6.172}$$

The components of the expectation value of the magnetic dipole moment presented in Eqs. 6.170 to 6.172 can be compared with the components of the magnetic field that have produced these expectation values (see Eqs. 6.114, 6.117, and 6.118) in order to make a physical interpretation of the quantities S and C. The field $H_1(t)$ corresponds, as has been stated previously, to an electromagnetic wave propagating in the z direction and polarized so that the magnetic field oscillations occur exclusively in the xy plane. As was stated in Chapter 4, a plane-polarized wave may be thought of as consisting of two counterrotating circularly polarized waves of equal amplitude $H_1^0/2$, as shown in Figure 4.9. Because the magnetogyric ratio of the spin-$\frac{1}{2}$ particle has a definite algebraic sign (assumed to be positive in this example), the Larmor precession of the magnetic moments occurs in only one sense (i.e., counterclockwise) about the z axis. Therefore only one circularly polarized component of H_1 can effectively "chase" the spins around. In the rotating coordinate system introduced by transformations given in Eqs. 6.127 and 6.128, the magnetization vector (Eq. 6.163) and the appropriate component of H_1 move very slowly. The former exerts a torque upon the latter, doing rotational work, and transfers energy from the electromagnetic field to the ensemble of spins. The other rotating component of H_1 oscillates in this frame at very nearly twice the Larmor frequency, producing only a small jiggling motion (sometimes called *zitterbewegung*) in the tip of the precessing magnetization vector, and is neglected. C is proportional to the component of magnetization in phase with the driving field; S is proportional to the component in quadrature with the same; and R_3 is a measure of the remaining z component of magnetization, which changes only slowly in time in both the laboratory and rotating coordinate systems. Equations 6.160 to 6.162, when multiplied on both sides by $N'\gamma \hbar/2$ to give the quantities that appear there in the units of magnetization, were first derived by Felix Bloch[3] and are called the *Bloch equations* in his honor.

According to the conventional notation,

$$u \equiv \frac{N'\gamma\hbar C}{2} , \tag{6.173}$$

$$v \equiv -\frac{N'\gamma\hbar S}{2} , \tag{6.174}$$

$$M_z \equiv \frac{N'\gamma\hbar R_3}{2} , \tag{6.175}$$

and

$$M_0 \equiv \frac{N'\gamma\hbar R_3^e}{2} . \tag{6.176}$$

Then Eqs. 6.160 to 6.162 become

$$\frac{du}{dt} = -\delta v - \frac{u}{T_2} , \tag{6.177}$$

$$\frac{dv}{dt} = \delta u + \frac{\omega_1 M_z}{2} - \frac{v}{T_2} , \tag{6.178}$$

and

$$\frac{dM_z}{dt} = -\frac{\omega_1 v}{2} - \left(\frac{M_z - M_0}{T_1}\right). \tag{6.179}$$

Also, from Eqs. 6.163 and 6.170 to 6.175,

$$\mathbf{M}(t) = M_z \hat{z} + (v \sin \omega t + u \cos \omega t)\hat{x}$$
$$+ (v \cos \omega t - u \sin \omega t)\hat{y}. \tag{6.180}$$

The effect of the second coordinate rotation in Eqs. 6.155 and 6.156 was to transform the problem into a reference frame rotating at the frequency ω rather than ω_0 (interaction representation). The quantities M_z, u, and v are the components of the magnetization vector which lie along the x', y', and z axes fixed in that rotating frame. In the same frame, the "correct" circularly polarized component of the electromagnetic wave is represented by a vector of constant length $H_1/2$ oriented along the x' axis. This

physical interpretation will facilitate the solution to the Bloch equations
6.177 to 6.179 in several cases of interest.

6.10   Solutions to the Bloch equations

Suppose that the ensemble sits for a time much longer than the relaxation
time $T_1 > T_2$, in the absence of an rf field. The absence of an rf field
means that $\omega_1 = 0$, and δ (not being defined) may be taken as zero without
any loss of generality. The only terms that survive on the right-hand side of
Eqs. 6.177 to 6.179 are the damping terms due to relaxation. The solutions
are as follows:

$$u(t) = u(t') \exp\left[\frac{-(t-t')}{T_2}\right], \tag{6.181}$$

$$v(t) = v(t') \exp\left[\frac{-(t-t')}{T_2}\right], \tag{6.182}$$

and

$$M_z(t) - M_0 = [M_z(t') - M_0] \exp\left[\frac{-(t-t')}{T_1}\right]. \tag{6.183}$$

The values of the constants $u(t')$, $v(t')$, and $M_z(t')$ are not known, but that
is not important because the system has sat so long that $t - t' \to \infty$. The
exponential terms therefore damp out the right-hand sides of Eqs. 6.181 to
6.183, giving the results

$$u = 0, \tag{6.184}$$

$$v = 0, \tag{6.185}$$

and

$$M_z = M_0. \tag{6.186}$$

Equations 6.184 to 6.186 are the conditions for equilibrium for an ensemble of magnetic two-level systems.

Next, suppose that an rf field $H_1(t)$ is turned on suddenly at time $t = 0$,
and the behavior of the ensemble is examined at times very much shorter
than T_1 and T_2, so that the relaxation will not yet have affected the
magnetization. Furthermore, let the field oscillate at exact resonance with
the Larmor frequency of the sample,

$$\omega = \omega_0. \tag{6.187}$$

The Bloch equations become

$$\frac{du}{dt} = 0, \tag{6.188}$$

$$\frac{dv}{dt} = \frac{\omega_1 M_z}{2}, \tag{6.189}$$

and

$$\frac{dM_z}{dt} = -\frac{\omega_1 v}{2}. \tag{6.190}$$

Equation 6.188 can be solved immediately:

$$u(t) = u(0) = 0. \tag{6.191}$$

The second equality in Eq. 6.191 comes from Eq. 6.184. To solve Eqs. 6.188 and 6.190, it is necessary to differentiate one with respect to time and substitute the other:

$$\frac{d^2v}{dt^2} = +\frac{\omega_1}{2}\frac{dM_z}{dt} = +\frac{\omega_1}{2}\left(-\frac{\omega_1}{2}\right)v \tag{6.192}$$

and

$$\frac{d^2M_z}{dt^2} = -\frac{\omega_1}{2}\frac{dv}{dt} = -\frac{\omega_1}{2}\left(+\frac{\omega_1}{2}\right)M_z. \tag{6.193}$$

This uncouples the two equations. The solutions to Eqs. 6.192 and 6.193 are

$$v = A_1 \sin\left(\frac{\omega_1 t}{2}\right) + A_2 \cos\left(\frac{\omega_1 t}{2}\right) \tag{6.194}$$

and

$$M_z = B_1 \sin\left(\frac{\omega_1 t}{2}\right) + B_2 \cos\left(\frac{\omega_1 t}{2}\right). \tag{6.195}$$

The relationships among the coefficients A_1, A_2, B_1, and B_2 can be discovered by substituting Eqs. 6.194 and 6.195 into the original Eqs. 6.189

and 6.190:

$$\omega_1 A_1 \cos\left(\frac{\omega_1 t}{2}\right) - \omega_1 A_2 \sin\left(\frac{\omega_1 t}{2}\right) = \omega_1 B_1 \sin\left(\frac{\omega_1 t}{2}\right)$$

$$+ \omega_1 B_2 \cos\left(\frac{\omega_1 t}{2}\right). \quad (6.196)$$

Since the cosine and sine functions are independent of one another, Eq. 6.196 can be satisfied only if

$$A_1 = B_2 \quad (6.197)$$

and

$$A_2 = - B_1. \quad (6.198)$$

Now, Eqs. 6.197 and 6.198 may be substituted into Eqs. 6.194 and 6.195, and the boundary conditions used in Eqs. 6.184 to 6.186 to find

$$v(0) = A_1 \sin(0) + A_2 \cos(0) = 0 \quad (6.199)$$

and

$$M_z(0) = - A_2 \sin(0) + A_1 \cos(0) = M_0. \quad (6.200)$$

Therefore

$$A_2 = 0 \quad (6.201)$$

and

$$A_1 = M_0. \quad (6.202)$$

Finally, combining Eqs. 6.194, 6.195, 6.197, 6.201, and 6.202 yields

$$v = M_0 \sin\left(\frac{\omega_1 t}{2}\right) \quad (6.203)$$

and

$$M_z = M_0 \cos\left(\frac{\omega_1 t}{2}\right). \quad (6.204)$$

Here is the physical interpretation for Eqs. 6.203 and 6.204. In the frame rotating at $\omega=\omega_0$ at equilibrium, the spins do not precess about z. But a magnetic field is defined in terms of the torque it exerts upon the magnetic dipole moment, and an object having angular momentum that experiences a torque *must* precess. It follows that in the rotating frame there *is* no field $H_0\hat{z}$; it has been transformed away. When H_1 is turned on, half of it appears as a vector of fixed orientation along the x' axis. Since this is the only magnetic field present in the rotating frame at exact resonance, the magnetization **M** of magnitude M_0, initially aligned·with the z axis by relaxation processes, begins to precess around it. The precession of **M** around the field $H_1^0\hat{x}'/2$ occurs in a clockwise direction about the x' axis in the $y'z'$ plane. The frequency with which **M** precesses about H_1 in the rotating frame is $\gamma H_1^0/2$. In the laboratory frame, of course, v precesses about the z axis at the frequency $\gamma H_0 \gg \gamma H_1^0/2$ (see Figure 6.7). (Note the similarity to Figure 4.4.) Since an oscillating or rotating dipole radiates electromagnetic waves, the sample will begin to "broadcast" a radio frequency signal in the laboratory. The amplitude of the radiated waves will be proportional to the square of v, the magnitude of the oscillating component of the magnetization. What has just been stated in words can

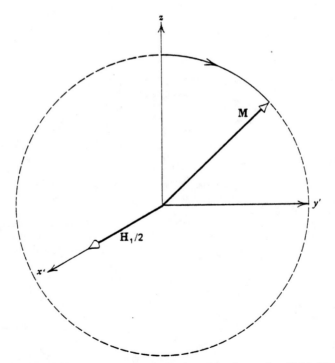

Figure 6.7. Precession of the magnetization **M** about the field $H_1/2$ in the rotating coordinate system.

be expressed mathematically by substituting Eqs. 6.191, 6.203, and 6.204 into Eq. 6.180:

$$M(t) = M_0\left[\cos\left(\frac{\omega_1 t}{2}\right)\hat{z} + \sin\left(\frac{\omega_1 t}{2}\right)\sin\omega t\,\hat{x}\right.$$
$$\left. + \sin\left(\frac{\omega_1 t}{2}\right)\cos\omega t\,\hat{y}\right]. \tag{6.205}$$

Note that the torque exerted by H_1 produces a slow motion of the magnetization in a direction that is perpendicular to the fast motion produced by the torque due to H_0. In the classical theory of gyroscopes, a slow wobble of the gyroscope axis perpendicular to the fast precessional motion is called a *nutation* (see Figure 6.8). (Note the similarity to Figure 4.12a.) In the case of the ensemble of spin-1/2 gyromagnets, the "wobbles" eventually damp out because of relaxation terms heretofore neglected; for this reason, the response of the sample to the abrupt switching on of H_1 is called the *transient nutation effect*. It was first observed by H. C. Torrey[4] for nuclear spins.

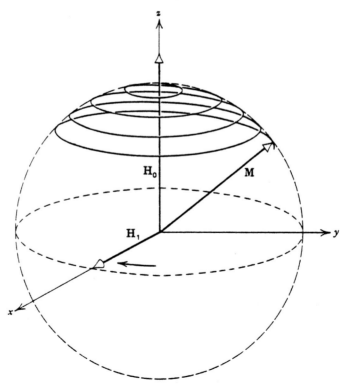

Figure 6.8. Simultaneous precession of the magnetization M about the fields H_0 and H_1 in the laboratory coordinate system.

6.11   Absorption and stimulated emission: free-induction decay

The magnetic energy density of the ensemble can be computed by means of

$$\mathcal{E} = -\mathbf{M} \cdot \mathbf{H}. \tag{6.206}$$

Equation 6.206 is analogous to Eq. 6.115. Using Eq. 6.205 for $\mathbf{M}$ and Eq. 6.114 for $\mathbf{H}$, one finds

$$\mathcal{E} = -M_0 \left[\sin\left(\frac{\omega_1 t}{2}\right) \sin\omega t \, H_1^0 \cos\omega t + \cos\left(\frac{\omega_1 t}{2}\right) H_0 \right]. \tag{6.207}$$

Because H_1^0 is very much smaller than H_0, the first term in parentheses on the right-hand side of Eq. 6.207 can be neglected:

$$\mathcal{E} \cong -M_0 H_0 \cos\left(\frac{\omega_1 t}{2}\right). \tag{6.208}$$

If the relaxation times are sufficiently long,

$$T_1, T_2 \gg \frac{1}{\omega_1}. \tag{6.209}$$

The $\cos(\omega_1 t/2)$ term will undergo many excursions between $+1$ and -1 before damping becomes important. During the first half of such a cycle,

$$0 < \frac{\omega_1 t}{2} < \pi. \tag{6.210}$$

During the interval in Eq. 6.210, the magnetic energy of the ensemble of spin systems is increasing. Therefore the energy in the radiation field is suffering a corresponding decrease in order that the total energy may be conserved. The process corresponds to *absorption*. During the next half cycle,

$$\pi < \frac{\omega_1 t}{2} < 2\pi, \tag{6.211}$$

energy flows back out of the sample into the radiation field. This process is called *stimulated emission*. Since one half of a cosine function is exactly like the other, it is seen that the "cross sections" for absorption and stimulated emission are equal. This fact was first deduced by Einstein on thermodynamic grounds, but the simple geometric picture based on the dynamics of the interaction process presented above makes the result very obvious. An experiment that "sees" the transient nutation effect, then, actually observes "photons" crawling into the quantum systems and out again over and over, until relaxation sets in. The amount of time required for either process can be calculated from

$$\frac{\omega_1 t}{2} = \pi. \tag{6.212}$$

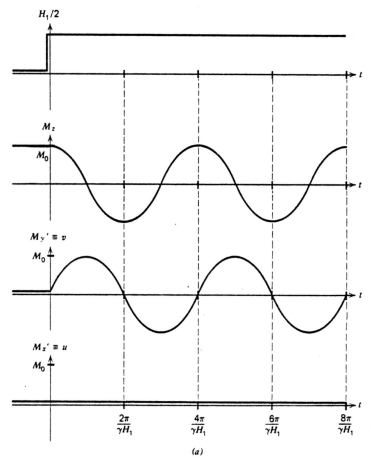

Figure 6.9. (a) Relationship between H_1 and M_x', M_y', and M_z in the transient nutation effect. (b) The first experimental observation of transient nutations by H. C. Torrey [*Phys. Rev.* **75**, 1326, and **76**, 1059 (1949)]. Shown is Fig. 4 from the latter paper: Proton resonance (v-mode signal) in glycerine at exact resonance ($\delta = 0$), $H_1^0 = 0.17 \times 10^{-4}$ T (tesla), $\omega_0/2\pi = 9.0$ MHz. The horizontal axis runs from 0 to 10 μs. Note the damping of the oscillations due to relaxation, corresponding to $T_1 \sim T_2 = 11$ μs; this phenomenon will be described in detail in Chapter 8.

The relationship between H_1 and M during transient nutations is shown schematically in Figure 6.9a; experimental results are displayed in Figure 6.9b. The question of how such an experiment would be performed will be deferred for the moment. Suppose that, at some time Υ during the course of a Torrey-type experiment,

$$0 < \Upsilon \ll T_1, T_2, \tag{6.213}$$

$H_1(t)$ was turned off as suddenly as it was turned on. This would mean that the system had been irradiated with a brief pulse of electromagnetic radiation. The Bloch equations (Eqs. 6.177 to 6.179) which apply during the subsequent time interval are

$$\frac{du}{dt} = -\frac{u}{T_2}, \tag{6.214}$$

$$\frac{dv}{dt} = -\frac{v}{T_2}, \tag{6.215}$$

and

$$\frac{dM_z}{dt} = -\frac{M_z - M_0}{T_1}. \tag{6.216}$$

Equations 6.214 to 6.216 are identical with those used at the start of the discussion of the values of u, v, and M_z obtained at thermodynamic equilibrium; the solutions are given by Eqs. 6.181 to 6.183 with $t' = \Upsilon$. The difference in this case is that it is desired to examine the behavior of u, v, and M_z before $t \to \infty$, and therefore the values of the parameters $u(\Upsilon)$, $v(\Upsilon)$, and $M_z(\Upsilon)$ must be computed. These may be obtained from Eqs. 6.191, 6.203, and 6.204. Substituting them into Eqs. 6.181 to 6.183, one finds that

$$u(t) = 0, \tag{6.217}$$

$$v(t) = M_0 \sin\left(\frac{\omega_1 \Upsilon}{2}\right) \exp\left[-\frac{(t-\Upsilon)}{T_2}\right], \tag{6.218}$$

and

$$M_z(t) = M_0 \left\{ 1 + \left[\cos\left(\frac{\omega_1 \Upsilon}{2}\right) - 1 \right] \exp\left[-\frac{(t-\Upsilon)}{T_1}\right] \right\}. \tag{6.219}$$

By properly choosing the amplitude H_1^0, one can obtain

$$\frac{\omega_1 \Upsilon}{2} = \frac{\pi}{2}. \tag{6.220}$$

which has the effect of putting the systems of the ensemble into superposition states exactly halfway "between" α and β and therefore tips the magnetization vector completely into the xy plane (spin sideways). An expression for the resulting magnetization can be found by substituting Eqs. 6.217 to 6.219 into 6.180, as before. The result is

$$M(t) = M_0 \left(\left\{ 1 - \exp\left[-\frac{(t-T)}{T_1} \right] \right\} \hat{z} \right.$$

$$\left. + \sin \omega t \, \exp\left[-\frac{(t-T)}{T_2} \right] \hat{x} + \cos \omega t \, \exp\left[-\frac{(t-T)}{T_2} \right] \hat{y} \right).$$

$$(6.221)$$

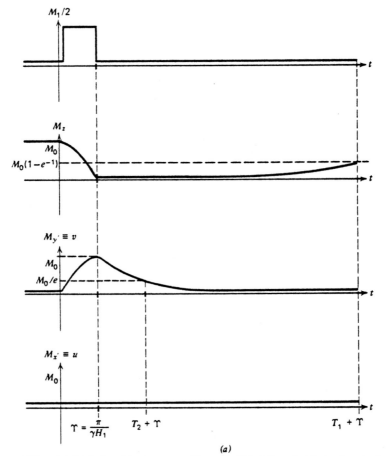

(a)

Figure 6.10. *(a)* Relationship between H_1 and M'_x, M'_y and M_z in free-induction decay.

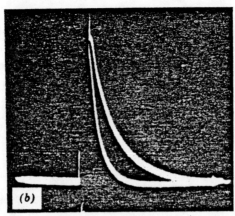

(b) The first experimental observation of free-induction decay by E. L. Hahn [*Phys. Rev.* 77, 297 (1950), Fig. 1]. The time constant for the decay, T_m, is a combination of the true relaxation time, T_2, and the inverse width of the distribution of Larmor frequencies, T_2^*; $1/T_m = 1/T_2 + 1/T_2^*$. The quantum systems are protons in water excited at exact resonance ($\delta = 0$) by means of a 90° pulse (not shown). The oscillogram is a double exposure; the longer decay corresponds to a T_2 of 1.8 ms, the shorter to 0.4 ms, and $T_2^* = 0.46$ ms for both. The relaxation time was adjusted by adding varying amounts of unpaired electron spins [Fe^{3+} ions from $Fe(NO_3)_3$].

Note that the x and y components of magnetization die away exponentially in a characteristic time T_2; the z component of magnetization, however, grows exponentially back to its equilibrium value in a time T_1. Because the xy magnetization induced originally by H_1 is no longer being driven by that field, the behavior of a sample after irradiation by a brief intense electromagnetic pulse is called *free-induction decay*. It was first observed by E. Hahn,[5] in an ensemble of nuclear spins. The relationship between H_1 and M during free-induction decay is shown schematically in Figure 6.10a; experimental results are displayed in Figure 6.10b.

6.12   The crossed-coil nuclear magnetic resonance spectrometer

It is now appropriate to discuss methods of detection of magnetic resonance signals. For nuclear spins, an instrument called a *crossed-coil spectrometer* is commonly employed. In this instrument, as well as in the beam apparatus described in Chapter 4, the radio frequency is transmitted to the sample by means of Helmholtz coils, aligned so that H_1 is oriented along the x axis of the laboratory coordinate system. In the crossed-coil spectrometer, a receiver coil is placed inside the transmitter coils and surrounds the sample. The receiver coil is mechanically aligned with its plane as nearly perpendicular to the y axis as possible. By adjusting field deflection "paddles" in a procedure called "balancing the probe," the transmitter and receiver coils are made magnetically orthogonal to one part per million. Oscillations of the magnetization of the sample along the y axis induce a voltage across the coil, just as the rotation of an armature of an electric generator produces a voltage across the surrounding induction coil in an electrical power plant. A drawing of this instrument appears in Figure 6.11.

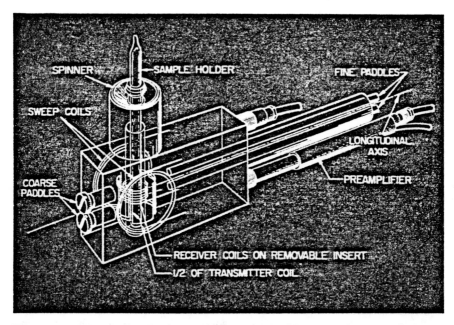

Figure 6.11. The crossed-coil nmr spectrometer. The part shown (called the probe) fits between the pole faces of a large magnet (not shown). The field of the large magnet is parallel to that produced by the sweep coils, and the two together constitute H_0. A low-amplitude, low-frequency, sawtooth-shaped current signal is applied through the lowest cable to the sweep coils. This causes the output of the receiver coil to periodically produce the slow-passage signal (u or v). This signal passes through the preamplifier, then to an rf detector, and then to the vertical deflection plates of an oscilloscope. (The horizontal plates are driven by the sweep generator.) An rf transmitter supplies a signal at the frequency ω through the uppermost cable to the transmitter coil, which then produces H_1. The spinner averages out the spatial inhomogeneities in H_0. Photograph courtesy of Norman S. Bhacca. This drawing is a negative print of Fig. 3 on p. 58 of *NMR and EPR Spectroscopy* (Pergamon Press, London, 1960), by Varian Associates.

The amplitude of the oscillations in the voltage signal is directly proportional to the magnitude of M_y and has the same frequency. Generally, the electronics introduce a shift in the phase of the detected voltage relative to H_1:

$$V \propto v \cos(\phi + \omega t) - u \sin(\phi + \omega t). \tag{6.222}$$

This voltage is "mixed" with a reference signal derived from the same crystal-controlled oscillator that supplied H_1; the output of the mixer is proportional to the product of the inputs:

$$V_{out} \propto V \cdot V_{ref}$$

$$\propto H_1^0 \cos \omega t \left[v \cos(\phi + \omega t) - u \sin(\phi + \omega t) \right]$$

$$= \frac{H_1^0}{2} \left\{ v[\cos(\phi + 2\omega t) + \cos \phi] \right.$$

$$\left. - u[\sin(\phi + 2\omega t) + \sin \phi] \right\}. \tag{6.223}$$

The output signal is then "detected" by passing it through an electronic element with a response time too slow to respond to oscillations as fast as ω:

$$V_{det} \propto H_1^0 (v \cos \phi - u \sin \phi). \tag{6.224}$$

Because the magnitude of ϕ is controllable by the experimenter, the detected signal may be adjusted to be proportional to either u or v alone (e.g., by choosing $\phi = 3\pi/2$ or $\phi = 0$, respectively) or to any desired combination thereof according to Eq. 6.224. An oscilloscope or a strip-chart recorder may be used to display V_{det}, as desired.

This electronic gadgetry is called collectively a *phase-sensitive heterodyne detector*. It would also be possible to utilize a *homodyne detector*; this name means that the signal is its own reference in the mixer:

$$V_{out} \propto V \cdot V_{ref}$$

$$\propto v^2 \cos^2(\phi + \omega t) + u^2 \sin^2(\phi + \omega t)$$

$$- 2uv \cos(\phi + \omega t) \sin(\phi + \omega t)$$

$$= \frac{v^2}{2} \left\{ 1 + \cos[2(\phi + \omega t)] \right\}$$

$$+ \frac{u^2}{2} \left\{ 1 - \cos[2(\phi + \omega t)] \right\}$$

$$- uv \sin[2(\phi + \omega t)]. \tag{6.225}$$

In this case, after the high-frequency components are averaged to zero in the detector portion of the apparatus, the resultant signal is

$$V_{det} \propto u^2 + v^2. \tag{6.226}$$

Note that phase information is not obtainable from homodyne detection: Eq. 6.226 is independent of ϕ. The signal is always proportional to the square of the magnetization, and hence to the total power radiated by the sample; it is the *photon density*, one might say. It can be shown that photomultipliers and other detectors used in conventional spectroscopy effectively produce a homodyne signal as they are ordinarily employed.

More can be said about the photon picture of the detection process. Because the receiver coil is oriented to "see" magnetic oscillations along the y axis, it will pick up photons propagating along any direction in the xz plane. The transmitter coil, on the other hand, broadcasts in the yz plane. The intersection of these two planes is the z axis. The probability that the propagation vector of a transmitted photon lies exactly along that axis is small because the radiation is distributed isotropically in the yz plane. This is the reason why, in a properly balanced probe from which the sample has been removed, the transmitter can be operated at full power and yet no detectable amount of rf radiation will enter the receiver coil. This is exactly the opposite of what one would expect in an absorption spectrometer, in which the signal detected is of maximum intensity in the absence of the sample. In such an instrument, the sample is placed between the source and the detector on the optic axis. The interaction of radiation and matter in the sample has the effect of removing photons from the incident beam and *reducing* the intensity of the radiation received by the detection system. Therefore the crossed-coil nmr spectrometer is not an absorption spectrometer and must be an *emission* spectrometer.

There are two kinds of emission, spontaneous and stimulated. One feature of stimulated emission noted by Einstein is that a stimulated photon always propagates in the same direction as the photon that does the stimulating. In other words, the beam of electromagnetic radiation produced by stimulated emission from matter is always collinear with the beam that is incident upon the sample. But, because of the geometry of a crossed-coil nmr spectrometer, the receiver coil detects only radiation propagating at right angles to the incident beam. Therefore the receiver coil cannot see either the incident photons or the photons stimulated by the incident beam. This means that the emission detected in a crossed-coil nmr spectrometer is spontaneous emission.

The geometrical arguments given in the preceding paragraph can be supplemented by temporal ones. If the light source is turned on abruptly in an absorption spectrometer, the signal appears with maximum intensity immediately. (There is actually a small delay due to the fact that perhaps 100 ps is required for the incident light to propagate from the source to the detector, but this can be neglected completely in nmr experiments.) Stimulated emission also appears immediately (although not necessarily at its maximum intensity). The signal in an absorption spectrometer ceases the instant the incident beam is turned off. Stimulated emission also disappears at the same instant that the exciting beam is extinguished. By way of contrast, in an nmr experiment, when the incident H_1 field is turned on the signal starts from zero and gradually builds to its maximum value as $\sin(\omega_1 t/2)$—see Eq. 6.205 and remember that the signal is proportional to M_y. After the exciting electromagnetic radiation is turned off, the signal does not disappear instantaneously; instead, M_y decays exponentially with a time constant T_2, which may be as long as several seconds. This can be seen from Eq. 6.221.

It has therefore been proved, by both geometric and temporal arguments, that the signal produced in a crossed-coil nmr spectrometer is due to spontaneous emission. But this spontaneous emission is very peculiar. A branch of conventional spectroscopy is devoted to the measurement of fluorescent lifetimes, an area of study that is superficially very similar to the study of free-induction decay in nuclear magnetic resonance. In both cases a more or less exponential decay of luminescent intensity following the pulse is observed. If one calculates the intensity of spontaneous fluorescence to be expected from a nuclear spin system (which may be done by calculating the Einstein A coefficient), one finds that the signal should be so feeble as to be unobservable. Furthermore, the fluorescent lifetime (the time constant for the exponential decay) is simply the time required for the population difference between initial and final states to return to the value expected for a Boltzmann distribution at the temperature of the sample. This is the time T_1. In fact, the intensity of the signal is *not* undetectably low, and the decay constant is T_2, which may be several orders of magnitude less than T_1—see Eq. 6.221 and again remember that the *signal* is M_y. The reason for this paradoxical behavior of the free induction is that the spontaneous emission detected in a crossed-coil nmr spectrometer is coherence brightened, as discussed in Chapter 4. (Some of the ideas presented in this section were published previously by the author.[6])

6.13   Steady-state magnetization: Curie's law

Now steady-state solutions to the Bloch equations will be discussed. These are appropriate for calculating the appearance of the ordinary nmr spectrum familiar to analytical chemists. In this case the field H_1 is so weak that energy is removed from the ensemble by relaxation as fast as it can be supplied by the absorption of electromagnetic radiation. Therefore

$$\frac{du}{dt} = \frac{dv}{dt} = \frac{dM_z}{dt} = 0. \tag{6.227}$$

Equations 6.177 to 6.179 become merely linear algebraic equations rather than differential equations and can be written in matrix form:

$$\begin{bmatrix} 0 \\ 0 \\ (M_0/T_1) \end{bmatrix} = \begin{bmatrix} +(1/T_2) & +\delta & 0 \\ -\delta & +(1/T_2) & -(\omega_1/2) \\ 0 & +(\omega_1/2) & +(1/T_2) \end{bmatrix} \begin{bmatrix} u \\ v \\ M_z \end{bmatrix}. \tag{6.228}$$

The solution to the system of equations represented by Eq. 6.228 can be found by standard methods (e.g., using determinants):

$$u = \frac{\delta T_2[-(\omega_1/2)]M_0}{\P} \tag{6.229}$$

$$v = -\frac{(\omega_1/2)M_0}{\P}, \tag{6.230}$$

$$M_z = \frac{\left[1+(\delta T_2)^2\right]M_0}{\P}, \tag{6.231}$$

where

$$\P \equiv 1 + \left(-\frac{\omega_1}{2}T_1\right)\left(-\frac{\omega_1}{2}T_2\right) + (\delta T_2)^2. \tag{6.232}$$

The calculation of M_0 from Eqs. 6.176, 6.142, 5.47, 5.48, 6.90, and 6.91 is straightforward:

$$\begin{aligned} M_0 &= \frac{N'\gamma\hbar R_3^e}{2} \\ &= \frac{N'\gamma\hbar(\rho_{11}^e - \rho_{22}^e)}{2} \\ &= \frac{N'\gamma\hbar}{2}\left[\frac{\exp(-\mathcal{E}_1/k_0 T) - \exp(-\mathcal{E}_2/k_0 T)}{\exp(-\mathcal{E}_1/k_0 T) + \exp(-\mathcal{E}_2/k_0 T)}\right] \\ &= \frac{N'\gamma\hbar}{2}\tanh\left(\frac{\hbar\omega_0}{2k_0 T}\right). \end{aligned} \tag{6.233}$$

Finally, by substituting Eqs. 6.229 to 6.233 into Eq. 6.180, one may obtain

$$\mathbf{M}(t) = \frac{N'\gamma\hbar\tanh(\hbar\omega_0/2k_0T)}{2\left[1+(\omega_1^2/4)T_1T_2+\delta^2T_2^2\right]}\left\{-\frac{\omega_1T_2}{2}\left[(\sin\omega t+\delta T_2\cos\omega t)\hat{x}\right.\right.$$

$$\left.\left.+(\cos\omega t-\delta T_2\sin\omega t)\hat{y}\right]+(1+\delta^2T_2^2)\hat{z}\right\}. \quad (6.234)$$

Several features of this equation deserve special mention. First, note that the amplitude of the magnetization is proportional to the number of spin-$\frac{1}{2}$ particles in the ensemble. Since the radiated power is proportional to the square of the amplitude, it is also proportional to the square of the number of radiators. This quadratic dependence of the radiant intensity on the number of quantum systems is a feature of coherent spontaneous emission, as has been previously stated. Second, it may be seen that the magnetization is proportional to the magnitude of the magnetic dipole moment of a representative spin, $\gamma\hbar/2$. Third, it may be noted that the magnetization is proportional to the fractional excess of population in the ground state at equilibrium, $\tanh(\hbar\omega_0/2k_0T)$. The usual situation in magnetic resonance spectroscopy is that $\hbar\omega_0/k_0T \ll 1$ for ordinary temperatures. Therefore

$$\tanh\left(\frac{\hbar\omega_0}{2k_0T}\right) \simeq \frac{\hbar\omega_0}{2k_0T}. \quad (6.235)$$

Remember that ω_0 is proportional to H_0. In the absence of an oscillating field, H_1, Eq. 6.235 implies that the equilibrium magnetization of a sample is inversely proportional to the temperature—this is called *Curie's law of paramagnetism*[7] (see Figure 6.12). Nuclear paramagnetism is so weak that the detection of nmr signals requires very sensitive electronics. The fourth feature of note in Eq. 6.234 is that the sizes of both the x and the y components of magnetization are proportional to ω_1, which in turn, it should be remembered, is proportional to the strength of the rf field H_1^0 for values of $\omega_1T_2 \ll 1$. If the field is made too intense, however, the $\omega_1^2T_1T_2$ term in the denominator causes all three components of magnetization to diminish. This phenomenon, called *saturation*, is due to the fact that, at high power levels, photons are absorbed at such a rate that relaxation cannot keep up. The population difference between the two energy levels, small to begin with, is reduced still further until absorption and stimulated emission become equally likely and no net energy transfer between sample and radiation field is possible. Under these conditions, the Beer-Bouguer-Lambert law discussed in Chapter 1 cannot describe the absorptivity. This is so because an implicit assumption in Beer's law is that each chromophore has returned to its ground state before the next photon arrives, making the absorption coefficient independent of the illuminating intensity.

The value of H_1^0 that is optimum for detecting magnetic resonance is determined from

$$\frac{d}{dH_1^0}\left[\frac{H_1^0}{1+\delta^2 T_2+\gamma^2(H_1^0)^2 T_1 T_2/4}\right]\doteq 0. \qquad (6.236)$$

The solution is

$$H_1^0=\frac{2}{\gamma}\sqrt{(1/T_1 T_2)+\delta^2(T_2/T_1)}\; . \qquad (6.237)$$

At exact resonance between the Larmor precession and the oscillating frequency of the field, Eq. 6.237 states that the largest signal is produced when the time required for a photon to crawl into a quantum system is equal to the geometric mean of the relaxation times. The reader must be cautioned, however, that the word "optimum" has been used here to mean "largest." It will be seen shortly that for high-resolution work a much

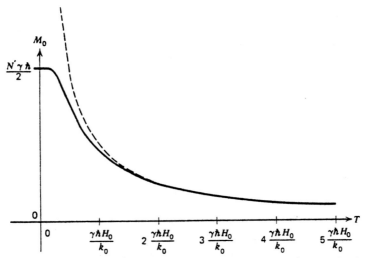

Figure 6.12. The temperature dependence of the equilibrium magnetization, M_0. The solid curve is the exact solution (from Eq. 6.233 of the text). The dotted curve is the Curie's law approximation from Eq. 6.235. Note that the two are practically indistinguishable for $T>2\gamma\hbar H_0/k_0$. Under typical conditions in nuclear magnetic resonance (protons in water, using magnetic field $H_0=1$ T at 300 K), $2\gamma\hbar H_0/k_0 \approx 4\times 10^{-3}$ K.

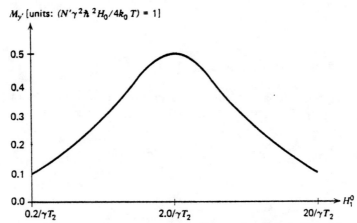

M_y [units: $(N'\gamma^2\hbar^2 H_0/4k_0 T) = 1$]

0.5

0.4

0.3

0.2

0.1

0.0

$0.2/\gamma T_2$ $2.0/\gamma T_2$ $20/\gamma T_2$ H_1^0

Figure 6.13.   The intensity dependence of the signal magnetization $M_y' = v$. It has been assumed that the spin systems are at exact resonance ($\gamma H_0 = \omega$) and that the relaxation times are equal ($T_1 = T_2$). Note that the location of the maximum is given correctly by Eq. 6.237 of the text. If mks units are used for M, $(N'\gamma^2\hbar^2 H_0/4k_0 T) \approx 0.3$ A m^{-1} in a typical case for nuclear magnetic resonance (protons in water, using a magnetic field $H_0 = 1$ T at 300 K). Also for protons, $1/\gamma T_2 \approx 4 \times 10^{-6}$ T ($\sim$40 mG) if $T_2 = 10^{-3}$ s.

smaller H_1^0 than that given in Eq. 6.237 should be employed. The dependence of the signal intensity upon H_1^0 is shown graphically in Figure 6.13.

6.14   Conventional nuclear magnetic resonance spectroscopy: slow passage

The fifth feature of Eq. 6.234 that should be examined is the dependence of M_x, M_y, and M_z on the frequency difference, δ. First, notice that for very large values of $|\delta|$ both M_x and M_y go to zero and M_z approaches M_0. Physically, this means that, if one is trying to drive an oscillator which has a natural frequency of ω_0, one ought to choose a driver that oscillates at very nearly the same frequency, $\omega \approx \omega_0$. There are two principal methods of observing the resonance. One is to slowly change ω, the frequency of the rf oscillator, keeping the magnetic field H_0 constant. The other is to keep ω constant and slowly vary the Larmor frequency by changing the magnetic field H_0. Since the response of the system depends only on the difference $\delta \equiv \omega - \omega_0$, the two methods produce results that are essentially identical.

By adjusting the phase of the detection system, one may obtain either the u-mode signal,

$$u_{\text{det}} \propto \frac{-\delta T_2}{1 + (\omega_1^2/4)T_1 T_2 + \delta^2 T_2^2}, \qquad (6.238)$$

or the v-mode signal,

$$v_{det} \propto \frac{1}{1 + (\omega_1^2/4) T_1 T_2 + \delta^2 T_2^2}. \tag{6.239}$$

It is convenient to factor out the saturation term from the resonance denominator on the right-hand sides of Eqs. 6.238 and 6.239;

$$1 + \frac{\omega_1^2}{4} T_1 T_2 + \delta^2 T_2^2 = \left(1 + \frac{\omega_1^2}{4} T_1 T_2\right)\left[1 + \delta^2 (T_2')^2\right], \tag{6.240}$$

where

$$T_2' \equiv T_2 \left(1 + \frac{\omega_1^2}{4} T_1 T_2\right)^{-1/2}. \tag{6.241}$$

If the u-mode signal is fed to the vertical deflection plates of an oscilloscope and the signal that drives δ to the horizontal plates, the resultant trace on the screen will be shown by the dashed curve in Figure 6.14. If the v mode is selected instead, the oscilloscope trace will look like the solid curve in Figure 6.14. For $\omega_1^2 T_1 T_2 \ll 1$, the amplitude of the v-mode signal will be 1 and the full width between half-amplitude points [i.e., $2\Delta\omega \equiv \delta(v_{det} = \frac{1}{2}) - \delta(v_{det} = -\frac{1}{2})$] will be $2/T_2$.

The effect of saturation on the line shape is twofold. The first effect, as has been mentioned, is that the amplitude is diminished by the factor $[1 + (\omega_1^2/4) T_1 T_2]$. The second effect of saturation is a broadening of the lines by a factor of $[1 + (\omega_1^2/4) T_1 T_2]^{1/2}$. The broadening (sometimes called power-broadening) may be thought of as being due to the uncertainty relation,

$$\Delta\mathcal{E} \, \Delta t \cong \hbar. \tag{6.242}$$

By substituting $\Delta\mathcal{E} = \hbar\Delta\omega$ and $\Delta t = T_2'$, one achieves the relationship just described for a bell-shaped curve of the v type. Such a curve is called a *Lorentzian line shape function*. If T_2 may be thought of as the "lifetime" of a freely oscillating quantum system, T_2' is to be regarded as the lifetime of a driven oscillator. The radiation field produces stimulated emission that increases the decay rate from the excited states of the quantum systems. It should be remembered that the relaxation time T_2 is, properly speaking, the lifetime of the phase memory of the ensemble, which may be less than the actual state lifetime. Phase interruption processes will be discussed in more detail in Chapter 7.

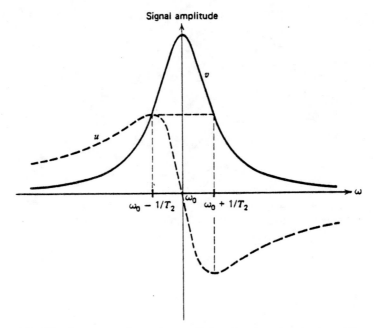

Figure 6.14. The frequency dependence of the signal magnetization $M_x' \equiv u$ and $M_y' \equiv v$. The signal amplitude is in arbitrary units, and the frequency ω is in rad s^{-1}. Notice that the half width at half height is $1/T_2$.

It is important to remember the relationship between the magnetization and the driving fields, which was discussed in Chapter 3. Note that Eq. 6.118 is analogous to Eq. 3.54:

$$H_1(t) = \text{Re}\left[H_1^0 \exp(-i\omega t) \right]. \tag{6.243}$$

It has been assumed already that H_1^0 is real (see Eqs. 6.123 and 6.124) and therefore analogous to $|E_0| \exp[i(\phi + \omega\alpha_0 z)]$ with $\phi + \omega\alpha_0 z = 0$. From Eq. 3.57, discarding all but the terms of interest, one obtains

$$\mu_0 \text{Re}(M) = \text{Re}\left[\chi H_1^0 \exp(-i\omega t) \right] \tag{6.244}$$

if the z component of magnetization is neglected. For the x and y components, Eq. 6.244 may be expressed in tensor (matrix) form:

$$\mu_0 \text{Re}\begin{pmatrix} M_x \\ M_y \end{pmatrix} = \text{Re}\left[\begin{pmatrix} \chi_{xx} & \chi_{xy} \\ \chi_{yx} & \chi_{yy} \end{pmatrix} \begin{pmatrix} H_1^0 \exp(-i\omega t) \\ 0 \end{pmatrix} \right]. \tag{6.245}$$

Using Eq. 3.27 in 6.245, one obtains two equations analogous to Eq. 2.115:

$$\mu_0 \text{Re}(M_x) = \text{Re}\left[(\chi'_{xx} + i\chi''_{xx})H_1^0 \exp(-i\omega t)\right]$$

$$= H_1^0(\chi'_{xx} \cos \omega t + \chi''_{xx} \sin \omega t) \qquad (6.246)$$

and

$$\mu_0 \text{Re}(M_y) = \text{Re}\left[(\chi'_{yx} + i\chi''_{yx})H_1^0 \exp(-i\omega t)\right]$$

$$= H_1^0(\chi'_{yx} \cos \omega t + \chi''_{yx} \sin \omega t). \qquad (6.247)$$

Equations 6.246 and 6.247 may be compared with Eq. 6.234 term by term to find (remember that H_1^0 is the magnetic induction here, not the field)

$$\chi_{xx} = -\frac{\mu_0 N' \gamma^2 \hbar T_2 \tanh(\hbar\omega_0/2k_0 T)}{4\left[1 + \gamma^2(H_1^0/2)^2 T_1 T_2 + \delta^2 T_2^2\right]}(\delta T_2 + i) \qquad (6.248)$$

and

$$\chi_{yx} = -\frac{\mu_0 N' \gamma^2 \hbar T_2 \tanh(\hbar\omega_0/2k_0 T)}{4\left[1 + \gamma^2(H_1^0/2)^2 T_1 T_2 + \delta^2 T_2^2\right]}(1 - i\delta T_2). \qquad (6.249)$$

It has already been explained why the susceptibility is anisotropic; H_1 can be thought of as two circularly polarized waves of equal amplitude $H_1^0/2$, only one of which rotates in the proper sense to have a long-term effect on the magnetic moments. As soon as the static magnetization M_0 is torqued away from the z axis by the H_1 field, it is carried around at the frequency ω_0 by the Larmor precession of the spins. This naturally results in a magnetization that is also circularly polarized. Hence both x and y components are present, even though they are lacking for the H_1 field itself. It will be shown in Chapter 7 that, in laser experiments, left-hand circularly polarized light and right-hand circularly polarized light are ordinarily equally effective in interacting with the sample. In such cases, waves of both senses of circular polarization are induced in the material, and their y components cancel vectorially, resulting in an overall isotropic susceptibility of $2\chi_{xx}$.

In Chapter 3 it was proved that the real part of the susceptibility gives rise to a change in the phase velocity of light waves. The amount of change varies with frequency. It may be seen from Eq. 6.24 that this phenomenon is associated with the *u* mode (the *x'* component of magnetization in the rotating coordinate system). The v mode is produced by the imaginary part of the susceptibility; it lies along the y' axis in the rotating frame and, as will be remembered from Chapter 3, is associated with the absorption of energy from the beam by the sample. The vector sum of u and v in the rotating frame shifts as one sweeps through resonance with the quantum transitions. At large values of δ, u is much larger than v so that the light wave passing through the medium is slowed (or, for $\delta > 0$, accelerated) without being attenuated. The phase relationship between a driving field and the response it induces in matter was shown schematically in Figure 3.8.

A graphical display of the magnitudes of u and v as a function of δ is shown in Figure 6.14. This is analogous to the case of transparent materials like water and glass in the visible region of the spectrum. In the neighborhood of $\delta = \pm 1/T_2'$, the magnitudes of u and v are comparable; their vector sum has swung 45° away from $H_1^0/2$ (the x' axis). At exact resonance, u disappears completely; the absorption is a maximum, and the phase velocity of light is the same as it would be if the transition were not taking place at all.

It can also be seen (from Eqs. 6.248 and 6.249) that the susceptibility depends on the magnitude of H_1^0, and therefore the relationship between **M** and **H** is nonlinear. This prevents the Kramers-Kronig relations from being valid except in the limit $H_1^0 \ll 1/\gamma\sqrt{T_1 T_2}$.

Historically, the first experimental detection of electron[8] and nuclear[9] resonances used the slow-passage technique.

6.15   Equivalence of transient and steady-state methods

In this book, the primary emphasis will be placed on the description of the transient response of an ensemble of quantum systems to a brief, intense pulse of coherent light, rather than on the steady-state solutions to the Bloch equations usually emphasized in conventional nmr spectroscopy. It should be noted that for each type of steady-state experiment one can find an equivalent transient one. For example, the unsaturated slow-passage spectrum in Eq. 6.234 is simply the Fourier transform of the free-induction decay signal given by Eqs. 6.218 and 6.220.[10] Also, the slow-passage spectrum of a sample that is strongly saturated by additional irradiation at the center frequency of the line is the Fourier transform of the transient nutation signal.[11]

Relaxation times may be measured by either type of experiment. For example, T_2 is the inverse of the half width of the v-mode spectrum between half-amplitude points; it is also the $1/e$ decay time of the free-induction tail following a $\pi/2$ pulse. If one saturates the slow-passage spectrum with an intense field at fixed frequency to the point at which the signal vanishes, one can be sure that the z component of magnetization is also zero. After the saturating field is turned off, the z component will recover with a time constant T_1. Subsequent repeated rapid scans of the spectrum with a weak frequency-swept field will reveal a gradual return of the signal to its initial strength, because the M_x and M_y components are proportional to M_z. In this way, one can determine T_1.[12]

As for transient methods, it already has been mentioned that T_2 can be determined directly from the free-induction decay signal following a $\pi/2$ pulse. One can also determine T_1 by applying a π pulse. Before the π pulse, the sample is at equilibrium and therefore has a magnetization $M_0\hat{x}$. After the π pulse, the magnetization will be $-M_0\hat{x}$. (All pulses are presumed to be very brief in comparison with either T_1 or T_2.) As the sample sits in the heat bath, it will relax; the magnetization vector will shrink along the negative branch of the axis, pass through zero, and then regain its equilibrium value exponentially in a time T_1. How far this relaxation has proceeded after a given time interval t' can be determined by measuring the length of the magnetization vector at that time. This measurement may be performed by applying a $\pi/2$ pulse to the sample; whatever M_z happens to be, it will be tipped into the xy plane and will generate a signal, which will then decay in a time T_2. The initial amplitude of this signal will be equal to that of M_z just before the $\pi/2$ pulse was applied. If one then waits for a time much longer than T_1, the sample will completely recover to equilibrium and the experiment can be repeated, this time using a different value of t'. By plotting the initial signal amplitudes versus pulse separation t', the entire decay process can be mapped out and T_1 determined. The signal produced following the $\pi/2$ pulse is displayed versus t' in Figure 6.15.

6.16 Spin echoes

The most dramatic transient coherence effect in all magnetic resonance spectroscopy is the phenomenon of spin echoes, also discovered by Hahn.[13] To explain this elegant experiment, it is necessary to discuss the difference between a homogeneous and an inhomogeneous broadening of spectral lines. "Homogeneous" contains the prefix *homo*, meaning "same." An ensemble of quantum systems all of which have exactly the same Hamiltonian will have a spectrum which looks just like that of a single system. All systems will have spectral lines with the same center frequencies, the same intensities, and the same breadths. These individual lines will all fall on top of one another, so that irradiation of the ensemble with light of a given frequency will produce the same response for each system.

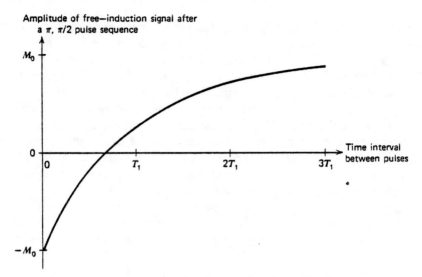

Figure 6.15.   The determination of T_1 by a series of π, $\pi/2$ pulse sequences.

The line shape function presented algebraically in Eq. 6.234 and drawn in Figure 6.14 is appropriate for such a quantum-mechanically "pure" ensemble.

In an ensemble giving rise to an inhomogeneously broadened line, there exists a *distribution* of Hamiltonians. In nmr spectroscopy, the usual source of the inhomogeneity is a nonuniform magnetic field H_0. Each region of the sample sees a slightly different field from all of the others; associated with each value of H_0 is a particular Larmor precession frequency. If ω, the frequency of the radio wave, is swept through resonance, the spins that see a slightly weaker field than the average will have a slightly slower precession and consequently will come into resonance at a rather low value of ω. As ω is gradually increased, more and more spins will come into resonance until ω equals the "most popular" (modal) precession frequency in the sample. Ordinarily, the mean value of ω_0 is also the modal frequency because the inhomogeneity in H_0 is usually distributed symmetrically about the mean, $\overline{H_0}$. As ω is increased beyond that point, fewer and fewer spins are in exact resonance, until finally ω exceeds the Larmor frequency for even the most strongly magnetized quantum systems.

The resultant spectral line may be regarded as the sum of the homogeneously broadened lines due to all regions of the sample, and the intensity of each such homogeneously broadened component is proportional to the number of spins in that region. Since the magnetic field distribution is continuous, the homogeneously broadened components will overlap and blur together, forming one broad line. The overall line shape will be given mathematically by the convolution integral of the homogeneous line shape with the distribution function for H_0 within the sample. The homogeneously broadened components of an inhomogeneously broadened line are shown schematically in Figure 6.16a.

One way to discover whether or not a given line is inhomogeneously broadened is by means of a steady-state experiment. If one irradiates the sample with a very intense monochromatic beam of light somewhere in the neighborhood of the line's center, one will of course saturate the sample. If the line is homogeneously broadened, each system in the ensemble will be saturated to the same degree (with an efficiency that decreases with increasing $|\delta|$), and consequently the entire spectrum will broaden and diminish in intensity (a fact that one can discover by rapidly scanning through the line with a weak field after the saturating field has been extinguished). If, however, the line is inhomogeneously broadened, there will be exact resonance with only a few of the systems of the ensemble, that is, those with Larmor frequencies very close to ω. All of the other spins will be saturated to a much lesser extent because they are so far off resonance; see Eq. 6.237. A subsequent weak field scan will reveal a dip in the profile of the spectral line in the neighborhood of ω where the saturation is strongest; the rest of the line will also be reduced in intensity, but to a much lesser extent. The width of the hole "eaten" or "burned" into the line will be of the order of $2/T_2'$, and, if H_1 is removed, it will "heal" in a time $\cong T_1$.[12] See Figure 6.16b. The overall width of an inhomogeneously broadened line will be roughly the sum of the widths of the two distribution functions that were "convolved" in the making of it, and is sometimes expressed by the notation $2/T_m$, $1/T_m \cong 1/T_2 + 1/T_2^*$. The Hahn spin echo experiment is the transient equivalent of hole burning because it also enables one to measure the "true" (homogeneous) relaxation time T_2 in spite of the fact that the effective relaxation time is T_m.

The first step in producing a spin echo is the application of a $\pi/2$ pulse to the sample. In the case of the homogeneously broadened line discussed in connection with free-induction decay, the frequency of the H_1 pulse was adjusted to the exact center of the line ($\omega = \omega_0$) before applying it to the sample. In this way, in the rotating frame, where $H_1^0/2$ was stationary, the magnetization vector did not precess about the z axis. Because the line in this case is inhomogeneously broadened, an infinite number of different values of ω_0 are distributed symmetrically about some average value ω_0^0. It is therefore impossible to satisfy the condition $\omega = \omega_0^0$ for every dipole in the ensemble. Since spins having precession frequencies in the neighborhood of ω_0^0 are the most numerous, $\omega = \omega_0^0$ is chosen as the best possible compromise. After the pulse has terminated, the sample magnetization

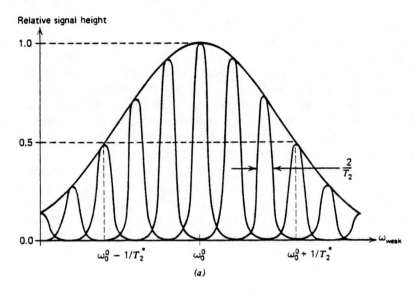

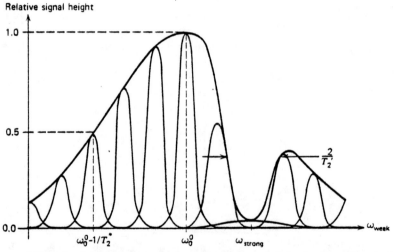

Figure 6.16. An inhomogeneously broadened line and its homogeneously broadened components: (a) unsaturated and scanned with a weak field, and (b) saturated with a strong field at ω_{strong} near $\omega_0^0 + 1/T_2^*$, then scanned with a weak field.

vector of length M_0 is found along the y' axis in the rotating frame. But this condition persists for only an instant; the macroscopic magnetization vector is, after all, merely the vector sum of the microscopic magnetic moment vectors of the individual spinning particles. Each of these has its own Larmor precession frequency, ω_0—some less than the average ω_0^0, and some greater, as has been stated. Therefore they cannot all remain stationary in a frame rotating at ω_0. The magnetic moments of spins precessing more slowly than ω_0 begin to fall back in the counterclockwise direction in the rotating frame; those that precess more rapidly begin to gain, on the average, and move around in the clockwise direction. Only the few that precess at exactly the center frequency, ω_0, remain pointed along the y' axis. The magnetization vector becomes "unstuck"; the individual spins leak from it in both directions until, eventually, the magnetic moments are distributed uniformly in the $x'y'$ plane. The vector sum of the moments begins diminishing from its initial value M_0 as soon as the individual components start to fan out and eventually goes completely to zero. The decay of the $x'y'$ component of magnetization occurs exponentially, with a time constant related to the inverse of the magnitude of the spread of Larmor frequencies present in the initial distribution, that is, in a time T_2^* (see Figure 6.17).

It may be seen from the above description that these microscopic magnetic moments are the "soldiers" described in Chapter 5 (see Figure 5.5), and the H_1 pulse is the "drill sergeant." In the laboratory frame, the drill sergeant makes all of the soldiers precess in step about H_0. As soon as he ceases counting cadence, however, each soldier precesses to the beat of

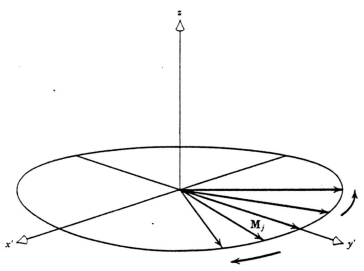

Figure 6.17. Free-induction decay due to the dephasing of isochromats ($\mathbf{M}_j$) of an inhomogeneously broadened line, in a coordinate system rotating at the frequency of its center (ω_0^0).

his own internal "drummer." As a natural consequence of this individu-
alism, all semblance of a proper military formation soon disappears. The
only modification of the analogy suggested in Chapter 5 is that now the
soldiers must parade on a circular track.

The next step in the process is to call the sergeant out of retirement and
have him issue the command, "To the rear! March!" to the soldiers. This is
accomplished by applying a π pulse to the sample after a time t':

$$T_2 \gg t' \gg T_2^*. \tag{6.250}$$

The appropriate circularly polarized component of the wave associated
with the second pulse will occur along the x'' axis of the rotating
coordinate system. Both pulses can be created by a single oscillator that
operates continuously. The radio frequency is normally prevented from
reaching the transmitter coils by means of an electronic shutter called a
gate. When it is desired to irradiate the sample, the gate is opened for the
appropriate interval. If a gated oscillator is used, all pulses will occur along
the same axis in the rotating frame ($x'' = x'$).

The effect of the π pulse will be to invert the y' coordinate of each
individual magnetic moment, e.g.,

$$\langle p_{y'}(t > t') \rangle_j = -\langle p_{y'}(t < t') \rangle_j, \qquad \text{for all } j. \tag{6.251}$$

If one imagines a sphere of radius $\gamma\hbar/2$ aligned with the x' axis, the tip of
the certain component of each magnetic moment vector will be located
somewhere on a great circle (e.g., the 0° and 180° lines of longitude) at the
start of the pulse. During the pulse, each microscopic vector will travel to
the opposite meridian along a parallel of latitude. In particular, the spins
that precess about the z axis at the frequency ω_0^0 initially parallel to the y'
axis will travel along the equator and end up pointing in the negative y'
direction. The drill sergeant again retires (the H_1 pulse has been com-
pleted), and each soldier resumes marching to his internal cadence (each
spin precesses at its characteristic Larmor frequency, ω_0). The spins that
precess slower than the average continue to slip in the counterclockwise
direction in the rotating frame, and those that precess faster than ω_0^0
continue to move in a clockwise direction. Before the π pulse, these
motions caused the spins to get further and further out of "formation."
Now, however, the same motions bring the spins closer and closer together
toward the $-y'$ axis, where the spins precessing at exactly ω_0^0 await them.
The amount of time required to bring all of the spins back together is
exactly the same as that which elapsed while they were coming apart,
namely, t'. The macroscopic vector sum of the microscopic moments then
grows exponentially from zero back to its initial value, M_0, this time along

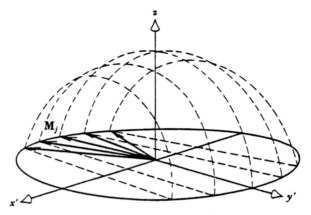

Figure 6.18. Formation of a spin echo due to refocusing of isochromats (M_j) along the $-y'$ axis by means of a 180° pulse applied along the $+x'$ axis.

the $-y'$ axis, with the same time constant T_2^*. See Figure 6.18.

This is the reason why the process was described as a "rear march" command. Picture the soldiers starting in a single rank, following the $\pi/2$ pulse and starting to straggle out as the fast ($\omega_0 > \omega_0^0$) marchers get ahead of the slow ($\omega_0 < \omega_0^0$) ones. For simplicity, let us imagine three soldiers marching at cadences of 0.8, 1.0, and 1.2 Hz, respectively, each with strides of 2 meters per cycle. At the end of $t' = 1$ min, their distances from the starting line will be 96, 120, and 144 m, respectively (complete dephasing). After the "rear march" command is given, each reverses direction and heads back to the starting point. But, again, the slow walker will march only 96 m in the next minute; the middle one, 120 m; and the fast one, 144 m. Therefore, at $t = 2t'$, they will be all in a single rank again, at the same position on the parade field, but facing in the opposite direction.

After the spins have recollected themselves along the $-y'$ axis, they will immediately begin to come apart again. The macroscopic magnetization will again decay exponentially to zero with the same time constant, T_2^*. This spontaneous recovery and subsequent decay of the $x'y'$ components of magnetization is called a "spin echo." The peak magnitude of the echo will not be exactly the same as the initial magnetization following the $\pi/2$ pulse, however. The echo amplitude will, in fact, be somewhat less than M_0 because of the fact that the parade field is not perfectly level; some of the soldiers will have stumbled slightly or bumped into one another in the time interval $2t'$. Such phase interruption processes are the military analogy to "true" T_2 processes, which produce uncontrollable and irreversible dephasing of the magnetic moment vector in the $x'y'$ plane. Soldiers that have stumbled or bumped, just like spins that have undergone transverse relaxation, will no longer be on exactly the same schedule that they would have followed on an ideal parade ground, and will show up either too early or too late to contribute their portion of the echo. For $T_2 \gg T_2^*$, the echo will have an amplitude only very slightly less than M_0 if the condition in Eq. 6.250 holds. This experiment can be repeated for various values of t'; a plot of the echo amplitude versus t' will enable one to determine the time constant for irreversible (homogeneous) dephasing—the true T_2.

The relationship between H_1 and M during a spin echo is shown schematically in Figure 6.19; experimental results are presented in Figures 6.20a and 6.20b. The $\pi/2$, π pulse sequence for the determination of T_2 is a natural companion to the π, $\pi/2$ pulse sequence for the determination of T_1 described in section 6.15, but the two differ in an important way.

In the determination of T_1, one *must* let a time $t \gg T_1$ elapse between pulse pairs. In the determination of T_2, an alternative system is possible; one may apply the pulse sequence $\pi/2(0), \pi(t'), \pi(3t'), \pi(5t'), \ldots$. The symbol in parentheses after each pulse designation is the time when the pulse in question must be applied—"rear march" may be given a number of times to the same sample without waiting for a return to equilibrium. The successive echoes that are produced by this (at times $2t'$, $4t'$, $6t'$, etc.) become weaker and weaker, their amplitudes being $M_0 \exp(-2t'/T_2)$, $M_0 \exp(-4t'/T_2)$, ... The pulse sequence described above was invented by Carr and Purcell,[14] who used it to study self-diffusion in liquids (diffusion in an inhomogeneous H_0 field produces an irreversible dephasing and hence adds to the $1/T_2$ term in the exponential decay of the echo amplitudes).

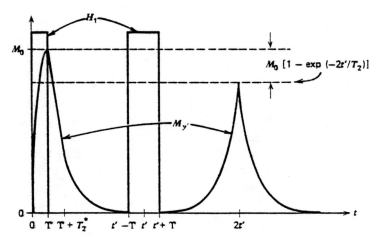

Figure 6.19. The determination of T_2 by means of a $\pi/2$, π pulse sequence.

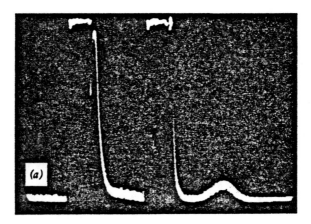

Figure 6.20. (a) The first observation of spin echoes by E. L. Hahn [*Phys. Rev.* **80**, 580 (1950), Fig. 11]. The chromophores are protons in paraffin; the echo lasts for 14 μs. The rf pulses, about 25 μs wide, cause some blocking of the rf amplifier used in the detection system. (b) The first observation of electron spin echoes. The sample consisted of a solution of Na in NH_3. The transition was at exact resonance with the radiation field ($\delta = 0$), $\omega_0/2\pi = 17.4$ MHz ($H_0 = 6.2 \times 10^{-5}$ T). Each major division on the horizontal axis represents 1 μs. The 90° rf burst starts with the left edge of the oscillogram reticle and actually lasts 0.3 μs, although in this photo it appears to be prolonged to about 1.5 μs by residual ringing of the tuned pickup coil. As the 180° burst is moved to the right, the echo moves twice as far to the right. The signal is displayed without rf detection, with a sweep so fast that the actual oscillations at 17.4 MHz may be discerned. By way of contrast, only the envelope is displayed in (a), above. This photograph is a negative print of Fig. 5 in the paper by R. J. Blume [*Phys. Rev.* **109**, 1867 (1958)].

The subjects presented in this chapter by no means exhaust the list of coherent transient effects that have been observed by ingenious experimentalists working in the fields of epr and nmr spectroscopy, but should give some idea of the power of these methods. It should be mentioned that the standard reference work on nuclear magnetic resonance is the book by Abragam;[15] a comprehensive work on electron spin resonance by Poole is also available.[16]

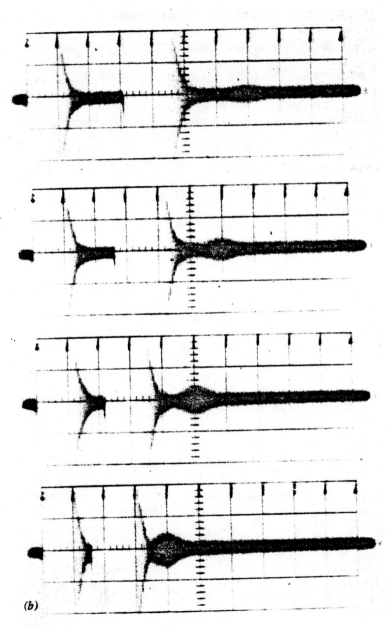

(b)

Figure 6.20. (b) (Continued)

6.17 References

1. W. Pauli, "Zur Quantenmechanik des magnetischen Elektrons," *Z. Phys.* **43**, 601 (1927).

2. R. H. Dicke, "Coherence in spontaneous radiation processes," *Phys. Rev.* **93**, 99 (1954).

3. F. Bloch, "Nuclear induction," *Phys. Rev.* **70**, 460 (1946).

4. H. C. Torrey, "Transient nutations in nuclear magnetic resonance," *Phys. Rev.* **76**, 1059 (1949).

5. E. L. Hahn, "Nuclear induction due to free Larmor precession," *Phys. Rev.* **77**, 297 (1950).

6. J. D. Macomber, "How does a crossed-coil NMR spectrometer work?", *Spectrosc. Lett.* **1**, 131 (1968); see also *Spectrosc. Lett.* **1**, 265 (1968).

7. Pierre Curie, *Propriétés Magnétiques des Corps a Diverses Températures* (Gauthier-Villars, Paris, 1895), Chap. III, pp. 47–66: "Corps faiblement magnétiques."

8. a. E. K. Zavoisky, "Paramagnetic relaxation of liquid solutions for perpendicular fields," *J. Phys. USSR* **9**, 211 (1945).
   b. E. K. Zavoisky, "Spin-magnetic resonance in paramagnetics," *J. Phys. USSR* **9**, 245 (1945).
   c. E. K. Zavoisky, "Spin-magnetic resonance in the decimetre-wave region," *J. Phys. USSR* **10**, 197 (1946).

9. a. E. M. Purcell, H. C. Torrey, and R. V. Pound, "Resonance absorption by nuclear magnetic moments in a solid," *Phys. Rev.* **69**, 37 (1946).
   b. F. Bloch, W. W. Hansen, and M. Packard, "Nuclear induction," *Phys. Rev.* **69**, 127 (1946).

10. I. J. Lowe and R. E. Norberg, "Free-induction decays in solids," *Phys. Rev.* **107**, 46 (1957).

11. J. D. Macomber, "Saturation and the transient nutation effect," *Appl. Phys. Lett.* **13**, 5 (1968).

12. N. Bloembergen, *Nuclear Magnetic Relaxation* (W. A. Benjamin, New York, 1961).

13. E. L. Hahn, "Spin echoes," *Phys. Rev.* **80**, 580 (1950).

14. H. Y. Carr and E. M. Purcell, "Effects of diffusion on free precession in nuclear magnetic resonance experiments," *Phys. Rev.* **94**, 630 (1954).

15. A. Abragam, *The Principles of Nuclear Magnetism* (Oxford University Press, London, 1961).

16. C. P. Poole, Jr., *Electron Spin Resonance* (Interscience Publishers, New York, 1967).

6.18 Problems

6.1
a. Prove that $[S^2, S_y] = 0$.
b. Calculate $[S_+, S_-]$.

6.2   A matrix is Hermitian if it is equal to its Hermitian adjoint. Show that the matrices $[S_x]$, $[S_y]$, $[S_z]$, and $[S^2]$ are Hermitian for a spin $s = \frac{1}{2}$ particle, but $[S_+]$ and $[S_-]$ are not.

6.3   For a spin $s = 1$ particle the eigenkets are $|2, 1\rangle$, $|2, 0\rangle$, and $|2, -1\rangle$. Calculate the results of operating with S_+ and S_- upon these kets, using Eq. 6.81.

6.4   The operator that represents the component of angular momentum along the axis oriented at (θ, Ω) is

$$S_{u_1}(\theta, \Omega) = S_x \sin\theta \cos\Omega + S_y \sin\theta \sin\Omega + S_z \cos\theta.$$

Show that the ket

$$|(\theta, \Omega)\rangle = e^{ib} \cos\left(\frac{\theta}{2}\right)\alpha + e^{i(b+\Omega)} \sin\left(\frac{\theta}{2}\right)\beta$$

is an eigenket of $S_{u_1}(\theta, \Omega)$.

6.5   Plot M_x, M_y, and M_z as functions of t for the nutation effect (use Eq. 6.205). Use $M_0 = 1$ A m^{-1}, $\gamma/2\pi = 42$ MHz T^{-1}, $H_0 = 14$ mT, $H_1 = 1.4$ mT, and $\omega = \omega_0$. Let t run from 0 to 20 μs. Label the time axes to show where absorption and stimulated emission occur.

6.6   Plot M_x, M_y, and M_z as functions of t for free-induction decay (use Eq. 6.221). Use $M_0 = 1$ A m^{-1}, $\gamma/2\pi = 42$ MHz T^{-1}, $H_0 = 14$ mT, $T_2 = 5$ μs, and $\omega = \omega_0$. Let t run from 0 to 20 μs.

6.7   Calculate the Curie's law paramagnetism (Eqs. 6.233 and 6.235) due to protons in water at 300 K. Use $\gamma/2\pi = 42$ MHz T^{-1}, $d = 1.0 \times 10^3$ kg m^{-3}, M (gram-molecular weight) $= 0.018$ kg mol^{-1}, and $H_0 = 1.0$ T.

6.8

a.   Calculate the value of H_1^0 (teslas) that produces the maximum signal from a sample of protons ($\gamma/2\pi = 42$ MHz T^{-1}) in which the relaxation times are $T_1 = T_2 = 1$ s. Assume that the H$_1$ field is in exact resonance with the Larmor precession of the spins (Eq. 6.237).

b.   Calculate the effective relaxation time T_2' for such a system from Eq. 6.241.

c.   Calculate Im(χ_{xx}) from Eq. 6.429 at 300 K, assuming exact resonance. What are the units?

d.   Calculate the Beer's law absorption coefficient corresponding to the χ in Problem 6.8c, using relationships found in Chapter 3.

e.   Evaluate the integral

$$I(\omega) = \frac{M_0}{2\pi} \int_0^\infty \exp\left(\frac{-t}{T_2^*}\right) \exp(i\omega t)\, dt.$$

7 Generalization to all spectroscopic transitions

7.1 The gyroscopic model of the interaction process

The promises made in Chapters 4 and 5 will be fulfilled in this chapter. In the earlier chapters assertions were made about the dynamics of the interactions between matter and radiation that lead to spectroscopic transitions. These assertions were proved for the cases of nuclear and electron magnetic resonance in Chapter 6. The theory used in the magnetic resonance case will now be generalized to cover rotational, vibrational, and electronic transitions. Relaxation processes applicable to microwave, infrared, and optical spectroscopy will be discussed, as will the optical analogs of coherent transient effects first observed in nuclear magnetic resonance. The first step will be to establish the applicability of the gyroscopic model of the interaction process to electric dipole transitions.

A review of the gyroscopic model of a magnetic dipole transition is in order. The magnetic field, discussed in Chapter 3, is defined in terms of the torque that it exerts upon a magnetic dipole moment (**H** is the induction):

$$\mathbf{T} = \mathbf{p}_M \times \mathbf{H}. \tag{7.1}$$

In classical mechanics, there is a circular equivalent of Newton's force law: the torque is equal to the rate of change of the angular momentum,

$$\mathbf{T} = \frac{d\mathbf{S}}{dt}. \tag{7.2}$$

Equation 7.2 is the fundamental law governing the behavior of gyroscopes. Combining Eqs. 7.1 and 7.2, one finds that

$$\frac{d\mathbf{S}}{dt} = \mathbf{p}_M \times \mathbf{H}. \tag{7.3}$$

If both sides of Eq. 7.3 are multiplied by the magnetogyric ratio, γ, using the relationship between angular momentum and the magnetic moment in

Eq. 6.84, it may be seen that

$$\frac{d\mathbf{p}_M}{dt} = \mathbf{p}_M \times (\gamma \mathbf{H}).$$ (7.4)

The relationships expressed in Eq. 7.4 are illustrated in Figure 7.1.

From the definition of the cross product (expressed, e.g., in Eq. 6.5), Eq. 7.4 can be written component by component:

$$\frac{dp_x}{dt} = p_y \gamma H_z - p_z \gamma H_y,$$ (7.5)

$$\frac{dp_y}{dt} = p_z \gamma H_x - p_x \gamma H_z,$$ (7.6)

and

$$\frac{dp_z}{dt} = p_x \gamma H_y - p_y \gamma H_x.$$ (7.7)

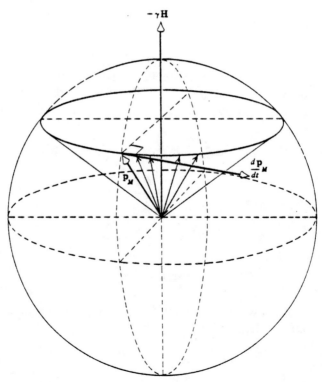

Figure 7.1.   Vector representation of the gyroscope equation for a magnetic dipole transition.

Suppose that p_x, p_y, and p_z are replaced by their expectation values, representing the projection of the "certain component" of the magnetic moment of an individual quantum system along the three coordinate axes in the rotating frame (see Eqs. 6.163 and 6.173 to 6.175):

$$N'\langle p_x \rangle = u, \tag{7.8}$$

$$N'\langle p_y \rangle = v, \tag{7.9}$$

and

$$N'\langle p_z \rangle = M_z, \tag{7.10}$$

where N' is the number of spins per unit volume. Also, in that rotating frame,

$$H_y = 0 \tag{7.11}$$

and

$$H_x = \frac{H_1^0}{2}, \tag{7.12}$$

where H_1^0 is the maximum magnetic amplitude of the electromagnetic wave. If both sides of Eqs. 7.5 to 7.7 are multiplied by N', and the equivalences expressed in Eqs. 7.8 to 7.12 are used, one obtains

$$\frac{du}{dt} = v\gamma H_z, \tag{7.13}$$

$$\frac{dv}{dt} = M_z \frac{\gamma H_1^0}{2} - u\gamma H_z, \tag{7.14}$$

and

$$\frac{dM_z}{dt} = -v\frac{\gamma H_1^0}{2}. \tag{7.15}$$

Next, the effective value of the z component of the magnetic field in the rotating frame is defined by

$$H_z = H_0 - \frac{\omega}{\gamma}. \tag{7.16}$$

Remembering the definitions of ω_0, ω_1, and δ from Eqs. 6.90, 6.131, and

6.157, one can use Eq. 7.16 to rewrite Eqs. 7.13 to 7.15:

$$\frac{du}{dt} = -\delta v, \tag{7.17}$$

$$\frac{dv}{dt} = \frac{\omega_1}{2} M_z + \delta u, \tag{7.18}$$

and

$$\frac{dM_z}{dt} = -\frac{\omega_1}{2} v. \tag{7.19}$$

Finally, if frictional damping terms are added to each of the three equations 7.17 to 7.19, the latter will become the Bloch equations 6.177 to 6.179. Note that Eq. 7.16 is consistent with the previous assertion that the magnetic field in the z direction vanishes at exact resonance in the rotating frame. The transformation to the new coordinate system causes H_0 to be cancelled out. Equation 7.16 gives the formula for the effective field in the more general off-resonance case as well.

The derivation just outlined is the basis of the contention, made first in Chapter 3, that the interaction between radiation and matter is of the nature of a torque. This torque is exerted by the field component $H_1^0/2$ in the rotating frame, acting on the magnetic moment (in the usual case, $M_0\hat{z}$). The torque produces a precession of this vector about $H_1^0/2$, changing the z component of magnetization, as was shown in Figure 6.8a. As a consequence of the fact that the magnitude of the z component is proportional to the energy of the ensemble, the rf field does work on the sample.

7.2   Electric-dipole-allowed transitions

The question raised in Section 4.3, was "This is all very well for magnetic resonance, but how can it apply to any other form of spectroscopy?" True, there is always a dipole moment vector (usually electric) associated with any transition, which may interact with a field vector (usually electric) associated with the light wave, and these quantities may be substituted for $\mathbf{p}_M$ and $\mathbf{H}$ in Eq. 7.1. But, as was stated in Chapter 4, the transition dipole moment almost never has a z component; it is confined to the xy plane. Also, the transition dipole moment is not necessarily proportional to an angular momentum vector. If not, why should the dipole precess about the field in the rotating frame? In other words, how are the analogs to Eqs. 7.2 and 7.3 to be obtained? Finally, the oscillation frequency of the transition dipole moment in magnetic resonance, the Larmor frequency, is due to precession of the spins about a large external magnetic field in the z direction. Where is an analog to H_0 to be found in the general spectroscopic case, and, without it, how is an equation of the form of Eq. 7.16 to be obtained?

Many of these difficulties are merely apparent, not genuine, problems. The fact that the symbol H_0 represents a genuine magnetic field measurable in the laboratory (say, by a Hall-effect magnetometer) has never been used. The role of H_0 was merely to provide an energy difference between the upper and lower stationary states connected by the transition. In the magnetic resonance case the energies of both states were provided by the Zeeman Hamiltonian; in other kinds of spectroscopy, the rotational, vibrational, and electronic Hamiltonians will provide the energies, and they will serve just as well. Also, the fact that the symbol M_z represents a genuine static component of magnetization measurable in the laboratory (say, by a Göuy balance) has never been used either—M_z is merely a measure of the difference in population between any two energy levels connected by a spectroscopic transition.

The truth of the above assertions may be seen by remembering from Chapter 5 that a proper description of the dynamics of spectroscopic transitions lies in the density matrix $[\rho_{jk}]$ (or in the $[D_{jk}]$ matrices of which $[\rho_{jk}]$ is the sum). The necessity and sufficiency of the density matrix description were established long before magnetic resonance was specifically discussed. For example, ω_0 was introduced in Eq. 2.68 as the beat frequency between the waves representing the superposed stationary states without calling it the Larmor frequency.

The treatment presented in Chapter 5 assumed that the matrix representing H_1 (the term in the Hamiltonian responsible for producing the transitions) is totally off-diagonal. This happy circumstance occurs quite naturally in magnetic resonance, where the various terms in the Hamiltonian are proportional to the Pauli spin matrices. But it was also described in Chapter 5 how any perturbation capable of producing transitions can be written in totally off-diagonal form by a suitable adjustment in the definitions of H_0 and H_1.

The off-diagonal matrix elements of the dipole moment operator in the general spectroscopic case are no longer simply $\gamma\langle S_x\rangle_{12}$ and $\gamma\langle S_x\rangle_{21}$, but are the more general $\langle p_x\rangle_{12}$ and $\langle p_x\rangle_{21}$. These latter can be calculated and will serve the same function in the equations of motion of the density matrix that the $\gamma\langle S_x\rangle$ did. The oscillations of $\langle \mathbf{p}(t)\rangle$ can be calculated from the density matrix according to the general rule, Eq. 5.19. These oscillations will occur in the xy plane as before; their ensemble average will then represent a polarization wave $\mathbf{P}$ propagating along the z axis parallel to the

E wave that induced it.

It has just been shown why the physically observable effects of an oscillating electromagnetic field on an ensemble of two-level quantum systems will be the same regardless of the nature of the quantum transitions. One might think that at least the nice, simple picture of the interaction process in terms of a field-vector torque on a gyroscopic dipole in the rotating frame could not be used for electric dipole transitions. In fact, even that picture may be retained.

Suppose, for an electric (or even magnetic) dipole transition in the general case, the transition dipole moment, $(p_x)_{12}$, is calculated using the standard methods of quantum mechanics. If this electric dipole moment had been produced by the rotation of a spherical magnetic ball (more properly, the intrinsic spin of a point magnetic monopole), $(p_x)_{12}$ would be proportional to the x component of angular momentum of the ball. If the intrinsic spin of the ball were $s = \frac{1}{2}$, the angular momentum matrix element would be $\hbar/2$, just as it is for a spinning electron, proton, or neutron. The constant of proportionality should probably be called the "electrogyric ratio" by analogy with the magnetic case, and it might even be assigned the same symbol, γ. An effective γ can be calculated from

$$\gamma = \frac{2(p_x)_{12}}{\hbar}, \tag{7.20}$$

even though the physical origin of $(p_x)_{12}$ may have nothing directly to do with angular momentum about the x axis. A "pseudopolarization" vector can then be defined:

$$p = \frac{\gamma\hbar(\rho_{11} - \rho_{22})\hat{z}}{2} + \langle \overline{p_x} \rangle \hat{x} + \langle \overline{p_y} \rangle \hat{y}. \tag{7.21}$$

If Eq. 7.21 is multiplied by N', the number of quantum systems per unit volume, it becomes

$$P = \frac{\gamma\hbar(N_1 - N_2)\hat{z}}{2} + P_x\hat{x} + P_y\hat{y}. \tag{7.22}$$

The components of the pseudopolarization vector are shown in Figure 7.2.

It should be remembered that only P_x and P_y represent genuine electromagetic properties of the system. In contrast, the "pseudo" (false) component P_z has been introduced only to make the behavior of the quantum systems describable by means of the gyroscopic model.

To accompany Eq. 7.22, there also must be an expression for a "pseudo-electric" field vector. This quantity must be defined so as to produce the

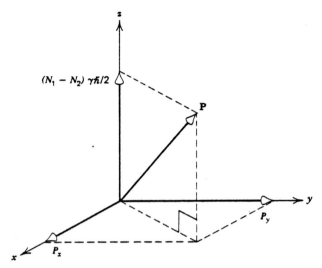

Figure 7.2. Vector representation of the pseudopolarization vector for an electric dipole transition.

correct expression for the energy density of the system (see Eq. 6.206):

$$\mathcal{E} = -\mathbf{P} \cdot \mathbf{E}$$
$$= -(P_x E_x + P_y E_y + P_z E_z). \tag{7.23}$$

The x and y components will cause no problem in finding an adequate definition for $\mathbf{E}$ for two reasons. First, they ordinarily contribute only a small part of the total energy for the ensemble. Second, these components are not "pseudo" and are therefore well defined.

The reasoning used to select an appropriate expression for E_z is as follows. One has from the definitions of $\mathcal{E}_1$ and $\mathcal{E}_2$,

$$\mathcal{E} \cong N_1 \mathcal{E}_1 + N_2 \mathcal{E}_2. \tag{7.24}$$

Also, since

$$\mathcal{E} \cong -P_z E_z, \tag{7.25}$$

a relation exists between $\mathcal{E}$ in Eq. 7.24 and P_z, given in Eq. 7.22:

$$N_1 \mathcal{E}_1 + N_2 \mathcal{E}_2 = \frac{\gamma \hbar (N_1 - N_2) E_z}{2}. \tag{7.26}$$

In the magnetic resonance case there was a genuine field $H_z = H_0$ instead of E_z, and, similarly, a genuine M_z instead of P_z. The magnetic energy was given by

$$\mathcal{E}_2 = -\mathcal{E}_1 = \frac{\gamma\hbar}{2}H_z. \tag{7.27}$$

The first equality in Eq. 7.27 can be satisfied in any two-level system by defining the zero of energy to lie exactly halfway between the energies of the two levels. The symbol H_z may be replaced by E_z in Eq. 7.27. The two equalities expressed therein then may be combined and solved for E_z:

$$E_z = \frac{\mathcal{E}_2 - \mathcal{E}_1}{\gamma\hbar}. \tag{7.28}$$

The pseudoelectric field then becomes

$$E = \left(\frac{\mathcal{E}_2 - \mathcal{E}_1}{\gamma\hbar}\right)\hat{z} + E_x\hat{x} + E_y\hat{y}. \tag{7.29}$$

The components of the pseudoelectric field vector are shown in Figure 7.3. Note that, when the dot product between Eqs. 7.22 and 7.29 is formed, the effective electrogyric ratio cancels out of the resulting expression.

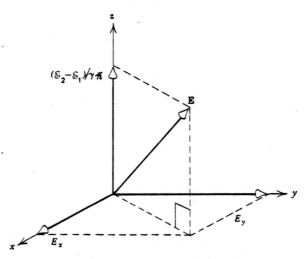

Figure 7.3. Vector representation of the pseudoelectric field vector for an electric dipole transition.

When Eqs. 7.22 and 7.29 are used to describe the interaction between radiation and matter in the course of an electric-dipole-allowed spectroscopic transition, they give results identical with those formally derived by means of the density matrix. In other words,

$$\frac{d\mathbf{P}}{dt} = \mathbf{P} \times (\gamma\mathbf{E}). \qquad (7.30)$$

This equation, by analogy with Eq. 7.4, provides an accurate description of the dynamic behavior of the ensemble of quantum systems. The relationships expressed in Eq. 7.30 are shown in Figure 7.4. The use of the gyroscopic model to describe electric-dipole-allowed transitions was pioneered by the authors listed in Chapter 1 (see especially references 7 through 10 in that chapter).

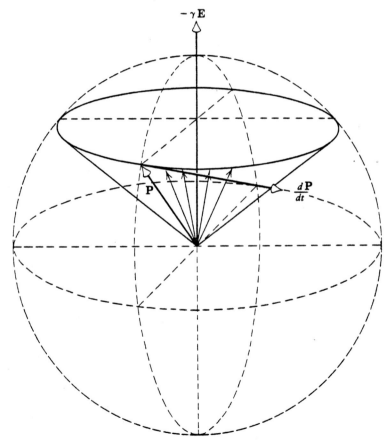

Figure 7.4. Vector representation of the gyroscope equation for an electric dipole transition.

Why should there be a formal connection between the pseudoelectric field and pseudopolarization vectors of the type described by Eq. 7.30? The reader who suspects that this remarkable equation is not just a happy accident, but is rather a manifestation of some deeper underlying principle, is correct. The Pauli spin matrices arise naturally out of group theory as a symmetry property underlying a broad range of physical phenomena. For example, one can give an "isospin" description of the relationship between fundamental particles in which the proton plays the part of "spin up," and the neutron, that of "spin down". Fain and Khanin[1] have shown that one can define an "energy space" analogous to "spin space" and "isospin space," in which any transition between two states of differing energy can be formally and rigorously described. Equation 7.30 is simply a special case of the energy-spin formalism, appropriate whenever the transition is brought about by means of an oscillating electromagnetic field.

7.3 Relaxation and its effect on line widths

It is to be remembered, however, that to make the description valid for times long in comparison with the relaxation times, damping terms must be added to Eq. 7.30. The same symbols as those used in magnetic resonance may be adopted for the rates of these processes, and they may be given generally the same physical interpretations. In other words, $1/T_2$ is the rate at which off-diagonal elements of the density matrix decay, through loss of phase coherence among the dipoles of the various quantum systems of the ensemble (e.g., during free-induction decay). Also, $1/T_1$ is the rate at which the population difference between the two quantum states connected by the transition returns to its equilibrium value, through flow of energy from the ensemble to the surrounding heat bath.

In the case of a sample consisting of a dilute gas, a very simple and clear description of the mechanism of some of these relaxation processes can be given. At low temperatures and pressures, the atoms, ions, or molecules of the gas move very slowly and seldom bump into one another or the walls of the container. In many such cases, the principal relaxation mechanism for excited systems is spontaneous emission. The "heat bath" for such systems is constituted by the walls of the container upon which the radiation is incident and which can be described as a black body at a given temperature T. Because the heat capacity of these walls is very large compared to that of the sample, T does not change during the course of the experiment. The precise time lapse between excitation and spontaneous emission cannot be predicted, of course, because this is a random process. However, one may imagine that radiation begins immediately after excitation and persists for a time $T_1 = 1/A_E$ (A_E is the Einstein coefficient) with a symmetric intensity profile (the exponential free-induction decay result will be similar). The fact that the emitted wave train has an envelope of finite width means that the light is not "pure." Completely monochromatic light must be a perfect sine wave, having a fixed frequency and constant amplitude, with no beginning or ending. One may think of a wave train of finite duration as being composed of a large number of sine waves, each having a different frequency and a different amplitude. In this particular case, the wave train has a dominant (most important) frequency, ω_0, also called the "carrier frequency." This means that the constituent sine waves having frequencies close to ω_0 will have the largest amplitudes; sine waves with higher and lower frequencies will not contribute very much to the sum. There exists a relationship between the phases of these waves, such that they interfere with one another constructively in the interval of time between t_0, the start of the spontaneous emission process, and $t_0 + T_1$. Because they have different frequencies, however, they must interfere destructively elsewhere along the t axis, and a wave train of finite duration results. The addition of sine waves to form a packet is shown in Figure 7.5.

The mathematical technique of Fourier analysis enables one to compute the amplitudes of the sine waves constituting a finite wave train as a function of their frequencies, if the algebraic form of the wave envelope is known. The Fourier analysis of an exponentially decaying envelope produces an amplitude versus frequency curve that is Lorentzian in shape, is centered at ω_0, and has a half width (at half height) equal to the reciprocal of the decay constant. In other words, the Fourier transform of the free-induction decay signal is the unsaturated slow-passage emission spectrum of the sample, as stated previously. In this case, because no other decay mechanism is possible, the length of the wave train is simply related to the longitudinal relaxation time, T_1. Therefore the inverse width of the spectral line, T_2, is equal to T_1 for a cold dilute gas. (This need not be true, however, if there are extra degrees of freedom internal to the quantum system which can soak up an appreciable fraction of the excitation energy before spontaneous emission occurs.) Another way of looking at this situation is to think of T_2 in terms of its other definition, as being the coherence decay time of a radiating ensemble of quantum systems. If the ensemble were excited coherently, the subsequent spontaneous emission would be coherent. All of the transition dipole moments would oscillate in phase, with amplitudes proportional to the product of the coefficients of superposition, $c_1 c_2^*$. These amplitudes would die away exponentially with a time constant T_1 because of the decay of c_2, which occurs as the sample populations relax back to their equilibrium distribution. Therefore the off-diagonal elements of the microscopic radiators will cease to oscillate in phase because the quantum systems themselves will have ceased to radiate.

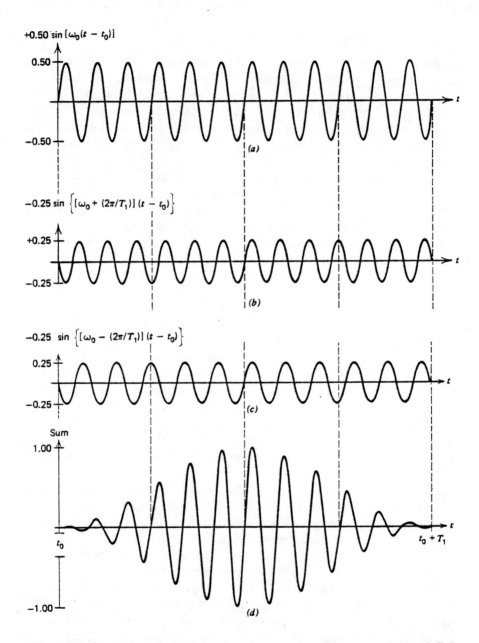

Figure 7.5. A wave train of finite duration, expressed as a sum of three infinite wave trains of different frequencies. Note that the frequency spread (half width of spectral distribution at half height) is $2\pi/T_1$. In any physically realizable case, many more frequencies would be involved, but the spectral half width would be about the same.

249

7.4   Phase interruption and pressure broadening

If the gas is isothermally compressed, the density of quantum systems will increase until at some point the mean time between collisions of gas molecules will approach T_1. A collision between two members of the ensemble will not result in a net change in the excitation energy of the ensemble, so that T_1 will be (to the first approximation) unaffected by the increase in density. On the other hand, T_2 will be affected; the reason is as follows.

First, imagine that one of the two gas atoms, ions, or molecules has only recently been excited and has just commenced to radiate an exponentially decaying wave train of light with a carrier frequency ω_0 and a definite value of the phase constant §. Assume that the other gas particle is unexcited. Because the systems are identical, when they collide there is some possibility that the excitation energy will be transferred from one to the other, much as a baton is passed between two runners in a relay race. In this case, the first system ceases to radiate as its wave train is abruptly terminated. Radiation of the second system commences at the same time and continues until all the energy has been transferred to the heat bath. The total time required for the ensemble to lose the excitation energy is still very nearly T_1, but it has been split between two wave trains of duration $T_2 < T_1$. These trains, being shorter in length, differ from a perfect sine wave in a more pronounced fashion than the one that would have been emitted if the collision had not occurred. The envelope of each of the phase-interrupted wave packets must damp down to zero along the axis more abruptly than was previously the case. A wider distribution of frequencies must be included in the mixtures that comprise both packets in order to produce more rapid destructive interference. Consequently, Fourier analysis produces a Lorentzian spectrum with a breadth greater than $1/T_1$. The transverse relaxation time is now the mean time between collisions rather than the lifetime determined solely by spontaneous emission. These facts are illustrated in Figure 7.6.

Because energy was transferred from one quantum system to the other within the ensemble in the picture presented above, magnetic resonance spectroscopists sometimes call T_2 the "spin-spin" relaxation time. This is to be contrasted with T_1, the "spin-lattice" relaxation time. Actual transfer of energy during the collision process is not necessary, however. Imagine two colliding systems again, but this time both of them are in the act of radiating, with phase constants $§_1$ and $§_2$. During the act of collision, the oscillating electric or magnetic dipole moments of the two particles will exert forces on one another, which will have the effect of momentarily retarding one oscillation and accelerating the other. This, in turn, will

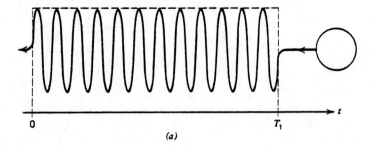

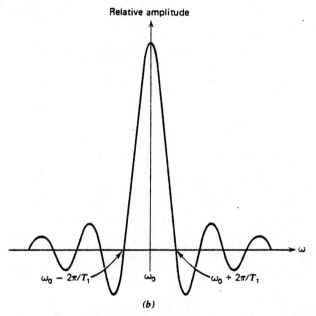

Figure 7.6. Spin-spin relaxation. (*a*) An atom (size greatly exaggerated) radiating a finite wave train without interruption. (*b*) Fourier transform of the finite wave train in (*a*). The square of this curve is customarily called the spectrum.

produce a change in both §₁ and §₂, by an amount that depends on the details of the dynamics of the collision process. Since the various types of collisions are presumed to occur in a random and unpredictable way in a gas at mechanical equilibrium, the phases of the oscillations will be just as random during collisions of this type as if energy had actually been transferred. Both systems will resume radiating as they separate from one another after the collision, but the "damage will be done"; their wave trains will have been interrupted.

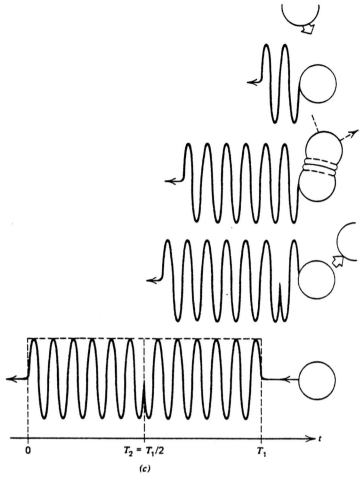

$$T_2 = T_1/2 \qquad\qquad T_1$$

(c)

Figure 7.6 (*Continued*) (*c*) An atom radiating a finite wave train of the same overall length as in (*a*). At the top, another atom approaches. In the next picture, the atoms collide, producing a phase shift of 180° at $t = T_2 = T_1/2$. In the third picture, the colliding atom departs. At the bottom, the atom ceases radiating.

In an ensemble of identical particles, one cannot ordinarily distinguish between collisions in which energy is exchanged and collisions in which a mere phase interruption has occurred. One therefore cannot distinguish between the two corresponding T_2 mechanisms. Finally, it is also possible to view the line broadening due to phase interruption as an effect of the uncertainty principle, as illustrated in Figure 7.7.

What will be the effect of collisions on the free-induction decay follow-

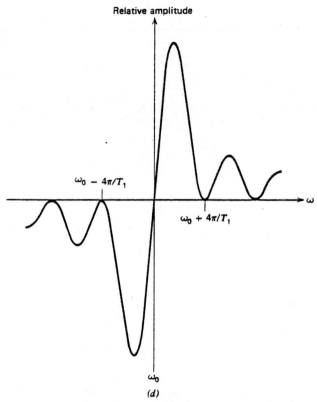

Figure 7.6 (*Continued*)   (*d*) Fourier transform of the finite wave train in (*c*). Note that the first zeros of the amplitude which bound the bulk of the spectrum are twice as far away from the origin as they are in (*b*).

ing coherent excitation? Either type of T_2 process described above will jostle the microscopic dipole moment vectors out of their proper positions in the rotating frame, so that they will not get back together properly after a 2π pulse. The analogy with soldiers bumping into one another on a parade field, introduced in Chapter 5 and amplified in Chapter 6, is very apt in the case of a gaseous sample. Fluorescence spectra obtained from gases (excited by means of incoherent radiation) are also affected by T_2 processes. Increases in the widths of special lines due to molecular collisions are called "pressure broadening" in conventional spectroscopy. Since each member of the ensemble is equally likely to collide with another, each radiated wave train is shortened by the same amount on the average; pressure broadening is therefore homogeneous, and the reciprocal of the half widths of the lines are true T_2's.

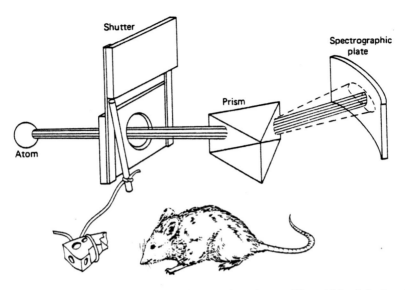

Figure 7.7. Broadening of a spectral band with a shutter. The width of the band is $\Delta t \sim 1/T_1$ if the shutter is not used; if the shutter is open for a time T_2, $T_2 < T_1$, the width of the band is $\Delta t \sim 1/T_2$ (dotted lines). This may be considered to be due to the effect of the uncertainty principle, $\Delta E \Delta t \sim \hbar$, on the attempt to measure the energy of the photon, $\hbar \omega$. The shutter is of the author's own design.

7.5 Other relaxation processes in gases and solids

At any temperature above absolute zero the molecules of a gas are in motion. At mechanical equilibrium, the directions of molecular motion are distributed at random and the speeds are given by the Maxwell–Boltzmann formula. All but a few of the quantum systems will therefore possess some nonzero component of velocity along the line of sight (e.g., parallel or antiparallel to the optic axis of the spectrometer). Each such component will produce a Doppler shift in the frequency of the radiation emitted into the detector by those atoms, ions, or molecules which move appropriately. At sufficiently high temperatures, these Doppler shifts begin to exceed $1/T_2$ and therefore broaden the line. For rotational and vibrational transitions, the spectral line widths of most molecules at room temperature are largely determined by the Doppler effect. Lines associated with electronic transitions in atoms and ions in the gas phase are also frequently Doppler broadened. Molecules, on the other hand, have so many degrees of freedom that the widths of spectral lines produced by their electronic transitions are often dominated by other broadening mechanisms. Since at any other one given time each radiating species has its own particular velocity, and therefore its own particular Doppler shift, this type of broadening is called T_2^* or *inhomogeneous*. It is sometimes also called *temperature broadening*. See Figure 7.8 for the influence of temperature on line width; the relationship between T_2 and T_2^* was given in Figure 6.16a.

In condensed phases it is not possible to decide a priori what the dominant broadening mechanism will be, because the processes that are effective in producing relaxation depend so critically on the nature of the quantum transition and the local environments of the chromophores. The two energy levels that give rise to the R lines of ruby, for example, are due to electronic states of the chromic ion which would be degenerate in the gas phase. When small amounts of Cr_2O_3 are doped into Al_2O_3 to make a ruby crystal, the Cr^{3+} ions enter sites where the local symmetry is less than spherical. The geometrical asymmetry gives rise to an electromagnetic asymmetry, and the associated fields exert forces on the electrons of the chromic ion. The result of these forces is to produce a distortion of the stationary-state electronic eigenfunctions and a change in their energies. One such change removes the degeneracy between the states giving rise to the R lines of ruby (a process called *crystal field splitting*). There being no such thing as a perfect crystal, however, each ruby sample has within it a certain amount of strain. This strain produces slight changes in the dimensions of the Al_2O_3 lattice, which are not the same in every unit cell. The amount of the distortion of the electronic wavefunction produced at

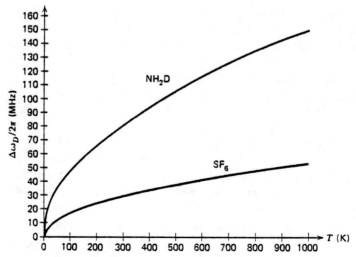

Figure 7.8. Doppler widths as a function of temperature for NH_2D and SF_6, of their absorption bands at $\lambda = 10.6$ μm ($\omega_0/2\pi = 2.83 \times 10^{13}$ Hz).

any given site depends on the unit cell dimensions at that location. Therefore inhomogeneous crystal strains give rise to inhomogeneous broadening of the spectral lines associated with the transitions between these levels. Homogeneous broadening of the R lines in ruby is a complex process, involving in part a magnetic interaction between the electron spin of chromium and the nuclear spin of aluminum in adjacent lattice sites. Spontaneous emission and radiationless relaxation both contribute to T_1.

7.6 Optical analogs to magnetic resonance phenomena

One of the principal differences between magnetic resonance and other kinds of spectroscopy concerns the sign of the magnetogyric or electrogyric ratio. The various m_s energy levels of a spinning particle are completely nondegenerate in the presence of an external magnetic field H_0, and the sign of the associated γ is a fixed property of each type of nucleus. For this reason, an ensemble of identical spinning particles always absorbs one circularly polarized component of the incident wave and, to all intents and purposes, ignores the other. By way of contrast, at least one of the energy levels associated with transitions between rotational, vibrational, and electronic states is ordinarily degenerate. For this reason, usually at least two different transitions are excited by the same incident electromagnetic wave. It is also ordinarily true that both of these transitions are associated with dipole moments having the same size but rotating in opposite directions. Therefore both circularly polarized components of the exciting wave will correspondingly be of equal amplitude, phased together in such a way that the components normal to the plane of polarization of the exciting wave always cancel vectorially. The overall susceptibility in such cases is therefore isotropic, unlike that of a spinning magnet.

The existence of the constituent circularly polarized components can be proved by removing the degeneracy of the corresponding quantum states, usually by applying an external electric or magnetic field to the sample. This will produce Stark or Zeeman splitting, respectively, of the spectral lines. If the emitted light is analyzed by means of a spectrograph, the light associated with each member of the split pair of lines is found to be circularly polarized, and the senses of polarization of the two lines are opposite. (This refers to light emitted parallel to the direction of the applied field—the normal Stark or Zeeman effect. The so-called anomalous splitting observed in light emitted perpendicularly to the field direction is more complicated.) As the perturbing field is reduced in intensity, the splitting diminishes. Finally, at zero field, the two spectrally split components coalesce in frequency, and the resulting line has no circularly polarized nature. The Zeeman effect as a function of field strength is illustrated in Figure 7.9.

The equations below are the analogs of those derived for magnetization produced in magnetic resonance experiments, using the same density matrix treatment. They apply to a single circularly polarized component of the polarization wave induced by coherent irradiation of an ensemble of two level-systems undergoing electric-dipole-allowed transitions:

$$\frac{dP_{x'}}{dt} = -\delta P_{y'} - \frac{P_{x'}}{T_2}, \tag{7.31}$$

$$\frac{dP_{y'}}{dt} = \delta P_{x'} + \frac{\gamma E_1^0}{2} P_z - \frac{P_{y'}}{T_2}, \tag{7.32}$$

$$\frac{dP_z}{dt} = -\frac{\gamma E_1^0}{2} P_{y'} - \frac{P_z - P_0}{T_1}. \tag{7.33}$$

Equations 7.31 to 7.33 are the optical analogs to the Bloch equations 6.177 to 6.179. The definition of P_0 is analogous to that of M_0 (Eq. 6.176):

$$P_0 = \frac{N'\gamma\hbar}{2} \tanh\left(\frac{\gamma\hbar E_z}{2k_0 T}\right). \tag{7.34}$$

The definition of E_z used above was given in Eq. 7.28. Remember that y' and x' are the coordinate axes in the frame rotating at ω, the frequency of the light wave.

Equations 7.31 to 7.33 can be solved under the appropriate limiting conditions to provide a description of optical transient phenomena. For example, the optical analog to the Torrey effect exists, and may be described exactly for times short in comparison with T_1 and T_2 by means of an equation analogous to Eq. 6.205:

$$\mathbf{P}(t) = P_0\left[\sin\left(\frac{\gamma E_1^0 t}{2}\right) \sin\omega t \,\hat{x} + \sin\left(\frac{\gamma E_1^0 t}{2}\right) \cos\omega t \,\hat{y} + \cos\left(\frac{\gamma E_1^0 t}{2}\right)\hat{z}\right].$$

$$\tag{7.35}$$

Oscillograms showing optical transient nutations are presented in Figure 7.10.

The optical analog to free-induction decay exists, as in Eq. 6.221. After a

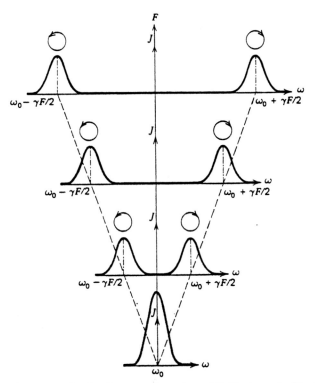

Figure 7.9. Zeeman or Stark effect as a function of field strength. The field F may be either magnetic or electric, γ the magneto- or electrogyric ratio, and ω_0 is the frequency of the unpolarized emission at $F=0$ (bottom curve). For $F>0$, the spectral line of irradiance J splits into two circularly polarized components of opposite helicity, symmetrically spaced about ω_0 (upper curves). Note that the spacing is proportional to F.

$\pi/2$ pulse of duration Υ:

$$\mathbf{P}(t) = P_0 \left\{ \sin \omega t \, \exp\left(-\frac{t-\Upsilon}{T_2}\right) \hat{x} \right.$$

$$+ \cos \omega t \, \exp\left(-\frac{t-\Upsilon}{T_2}\right) \hat{y}$$

$$\left. + \left[1 - \exp\left(-\frac{t-\Upsilon}{T_1}\right)\right] \hat{z} \right\}. \qquad (7.36)$$

Oscillograms showing microwave-induced free-induction decay are given in Figure 7.11.

Finally, the steady-state spectrum of the coherent spontaneous emission

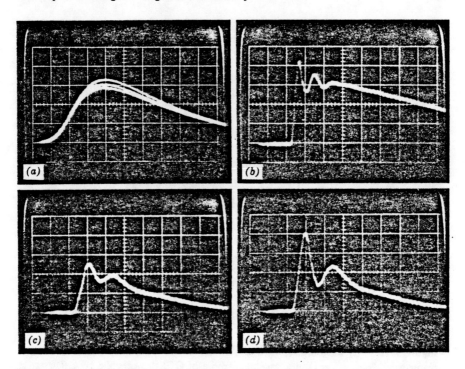

Figure 7.10. First observation of the optical transient nutation effect, by G. B. Hocker and C. L. Tang [*Phys. Rev.* **184**, 356 (1969), Fig. 1]. The sample was SF_6 gas, and the two quantum states connected by the transition have different amounts of vibrational energy in the mode conventionally designated as ν_3. The Q branch for the band $(0,0,0,0,0,0)$ (all six modes with $v=0$)→$(0,0,1,0,0,0)$ lies at $\omega_0/2\pi = 2.841 \times 10^{14}$ Hz; the Q branch for the "hot band" $(0,0,0,0,0,1)$ →$(0,0,1,0,0,1)$ lies at $\omega_0/2\pi = 2.838 \times 10^{14}$ Hz. Since the operating frequency of the CO_2 laser is $\omega/2\pi = 2.830 \times 10^{13}$ Hz, lines from the P branches of these SF_6 bands are responsible for the interaction. Horizontal scale is 50 ns per division. (*a*) Multiple traces of pulses without SF_6 in cell. Peak intensity could be varied from ~35 to 6 MW m^{-2}. (*b*) Output through cell for high-intensity pulse. $P_{SF_6} = 0.16$ torr. Vertical scale is 6.65 MW m^{-2} division. (*c*) Output through cell for a low-intensity pulse. $P_{SF_6} = 0.12$ torr. Vertical scale is 3.33 MW m^{-2} division. (*d*) Same as (*c*) except that detector was moved slightly across the beam.

from the sample can be expressed in an equation analogous to Eq. 6.234:

$$
\mathbf{P}(t) = P_0\Big\{ \big(\gamma E_1^0 T_2/2\big)\big[(\sin\omega t + \delta T_2\cos\omega t)\hat{x}
$$

$$
+ (\cos\omega t - \delta T_2\sin\omega t)\hat{y}\big] + \big(1+\delta^2 T_2^2\big)\hat{z}\Big\}
$$

$$
\div \Big\{ 1 + \Big[\gamma^2\big(E_1^0\big)^2 T_2^2/4\Big]T_1 T_2 + \delta^2 T_2^2\Big\} \tag{7.37}
$$

Figure 7.11. (*a*) Free-induction decay in the microwave region due to a rotation transition ($J = 0$ to $J = 1$) in a gaseous sample of OCS^{32} molecules [Fig. 1 from Hill et al., *Phys. Rev. Lett.* **18**, 105 (1967)]. The radiation field was provided by a more or less conventional microwave source producing pulses 100 ns→1 μs in duration, 10 W peak power in the neighborhood of the resonance frequency $\omega_0/2\pi = 12.162972$ GHz. Horizontal scale = 2 μs cm^{-1}, pressure = 3×10^{-3} torr. (*b*) Same as (*a*), but with $\sim 10^{-10}$ W of cw oscillations at $\delta = 500$ kHz added. Time scale = 0.5 μs cm^{-1}; pressure = 20×10^{-3} torr.

The effect of having systems with both positive and negative magnetogyric ratios present in equal numbers in the sample can be expressed by calculating the susceptibility tensor for each type of transition separately and adding the two values together.[2]

Define **F** (which may be either **E** or **H**, depending on whether the transitions are electric- or magnetic-dipole-allowed) by the relation

$$\mathbf{F}(t) = (F_y \hat{y} + F_x \hat{x}) \exp(-i\omega t). \tag{7.38}$$

The quantities F_y and F_x are complex scalars, presumed to be time independent.

The magnitude of the generalized "certain component" of the transition dipole, either electric or magnetic, is defined by

$$p \equiv \frac{\gamma \hbar}{2} . \tag{7.39}$$

The resonance denominator for the elements of the susceptibility tensor, including saturation under the combined influence of the two field components, is

$$\P \equiv 1 + \delta^2 T_2^2 + \frac{T_1 T_2 p^2 (|F_y|^2 + |F_x|^2)}{\hbar^2} . \tag{7.40}$$

Another parameter, o, must be introduced to describe the combination of the two field components:

$$o = \frac{2 T_1 T_2 p^2 |F_y| |F_x| \sin(\phi_x - \phi_y)}{\P \hbar^2} . \tag{7.41}$$

In Eqs. 7.40 and 7.41, the complex amplitudes have been expressed by their magnitudes and phases according to

$$F_y = |F_y| \exp(i\phi_y) \tag{7.42}$$

and

$$F_x = |F_x| \exp(i\phi_x). \tag{7.43}$$

The magnetic susceptibility is found to be

$$\chi = \mu_0 \frac{N' p_M^2 T_2 \tanh(\hbar \omega_0 / 2 k_0 T)}{\hbar \P_M (1 - o_M^2)} \left[\begin{pmatrix} \delta T_2 & -o_M \\ o_M & \delta T_2 \end{pmatrix} + i \begin{pmatrix} 1 & \delta T_2 o_M \\ -\delta T_2 o_M & 1 \end{pmatrix} \right]. \tag{7.44}$$

(See Eq. 6.245 for an identification of the tensor elements.)

To define the electric susceptibility, in addition to reinterpreting the symbols p and F, one must divide by the electric permittivity of the surrounding medium. The reason for including the permittivity in the numerator but the permeability in the denominator may be found from the difference in definitions between $\mathbf{P}$ and $\mathbf{M}$ (see Eqs. 3.15 and 3.21). Therefore

$$\eta = \frac{N' p_E^2 T_2 \tanh(\hbar \omega_0 / 2 k_0 T)}{\epsilon_0 \hbar \P_E (1 - o_E^2)} \left[\begin{pmatrix} \delta T_2 & -o_E \\ o_E & \delta T_2 \end{pmatrix} + i \begin{pmatrix} 1 & \delta T_2 o_E \\ -\delta T_2 o_E & 1 \end{pmatrix} \right]. \tag{7.45}$$

For linearly polarized light, $\phi_x = \phi_y$ and $o = 0$ (see Eq. 7.41). The susceptibilities in Eqs. 7.44 and 7.45 become isotropic in this case. It is also easy to show that the intrinsic anisotropies of χ and η are unobservable if the incident light is circularly polarized, unpolarized, or incoherent, the three cases that are of greatest interest.[2]

7.7   Photon echoes: qualitative discussion

In the case of nuclear magnetic resonance, the wavelength of the exciting radiation is ordinarily very large compared to the dimensions of the sample. For this reason, it is appropriate to ignore the phase modulation of the wave by the propagation factor $\exp(i\omega z/c)$; the sample is assumed to occupy the point $(0, 0, 0)$. In electron spin resonance, on the other hand, the wavelength of the exciting radiation is sufficiently short ($\simeq 1$cm) so that one may be able to observe propagation effects. These have been observed in ferromagnetic and antiferromagnetic resonance, but apparently not yet in paramagnetic samples.[3] By way of contrast, the usual conditions existing whenever rotational, vibrational, and electronic transitions are excited produce propagation effects because the associated wavelengths are ordinarily much smaller than the sample dimensions. It is of course possible to produce standing waves of very short length in a macroscopic optical cavity; a laser is an example of such a system. The result is to produce a time-independent spatial modulation of the field amplitudes (and therefore saturation parameters), periodic in $2\pi z/\lambda$, which in some cases can be ignored.

Aside from the exceptions enumerated in the preceding paragraphs, transient coherent effects in magnetic resonance ordinarily do not propagate, but their optical analogs do. This fact was utilized in a very clever way by Kurnit, Abella, and Hartmann[4] (KAH), the group that first observed photon echoes.

The first step in producing the echo is to supply the sample with two pulses, the first $\pi/2$ and the second π, separated by a time interval t'. The duration of the pulses should be less than T_2^*, and t' should be greater than T_2^* but less than T_2. The pulses should be at exact resonance with the two levels in the sample that must interact with them.

Unfortunately, all of these requirements pose problems. A necessary temperature difference between the ruby crystals used as the laser material and as the sample produces a difference between their resonant frequencies, ω and ω_0. Fortunately, there are two R lines in the ruby spectrum, and KAH were able to utilize one of these lines to produce the laser light and the other to act as the absorber at the frequency $\omega = \omega_0$. Another difficulty is that the required delay between pulses, t', is so short that the laser could not be repumped to threshold in the interval. The problems of synchronization of two different lasers on that time scale are also formidable.

Therefore KAH used a single pulse from a single laser and split it into two, employing a partially reflecting-partially transmitting mirror (beam splitter) located at an angle with the optic axis. A delay of one of the beams was produced by causing the light to bounce back and forth between a pair of mirrors located a fixed distance apart. The axis of this mirror pair could be adjusted so that the angle of incidence of the laser pulse on the first mirror varied. The number of round-trip bounces of the pulse before it "walked off" the mirror pair depended on the angle of incidence, so that this part of the apparatus functioned as a variable delay line. Each 300 mm of additional beam path lengthened t' by 1 ns. Because it is very difficult to control a ruby laser, it is unlikely that either pulse corresponded exactly to $\pi/2$ or π. This is not very important, however, since the only advantage to that particular pulse sequence is that the echo amplitude is a maximum and bears a simple relationship to P_0. In general, any pair of pulses separated by t' will produce *some* echo at $t = 2t'$.

The next problem to be solved was that of saturation of the detectors used to record the arrival of the pulse. If an intense beam hits a detector at a time t', that detector will not recover immediately. If a weak pulse (e.g., an echo) arrives before recovery is complete, that pulse might not be recorded. (This problem also plagued early workers in pulsed nuclear magnetic resonance.) This difficulty was overcome by a trick based on the fact that optical coherent transients propagate. The first and second pulses were caused to be incident on the sample at slightly different directions of propagation. Under these conditions, the transmitted pulses, together with any sample luminescence produced in the direction of the beam, could be recorded on separate detectors located at some distance beyond the exit face of the sample.

The most important reason for irradiating the sample at two different angles was that under these circumstances the echo produced propagated in yet a third direction. If the first pulse was incident at an angle with respect to the optic axis $\theta = 0$ at a time $t = 0$, and the second pulse was incident at $\theta = \varphi$ and $t = t'$, the echo emerged at $\theta = 2\varphi$ and $t = 2t'$. The use of different angles of incidence not only avoided detector saturation but also eliminated the possibility that an echo signal might have been a spurious reflection occurring somewhere in the optical train, rather than a true echo.

The experimental setup used to produce photon echoes is presented in Figure 7.12a.

7.8   Angle of echo propagation using the gyroscopic model

Abella, Kurnit, and Hartmann gave a very elegant but highly abstract explanation of the reason for the emergence of the echo at 2φ in their first long paper.[4b] The reader is invited to compare that proof with the one given below, presented by the same authors in a subsequent work.[4d] The later explanation will be seen to be an excellent advertisement for the utility of the gyroscopic model of spectroscopic transitions.

Suppose that the electric field vector associated with the $\pi/2$ pulse is applied in such a way that $\mathbf{E}_1$ makes an angle α_1 with the x' axis in the rotating frame. The pseudopolarization vector will therefore be rotated into the $x'y'$ plane in such a way that $\mathbf{P}$ will make an angle $\S_1 = \alpha_1 + \pi/2$ with the x' axis. This is shown in Figure 7.13a. Because of dephasing processes, the microscopic dipoles $\mathbf{p}_M$ of which $\mathbf{P}$ is composed begin to spread out in the $x'y'$ plane with a characteristic rate $\sim 1/T_2^*$. Some will remain at the angle $\alpha_1 + \pi/2$ because their resonance frequencies ω_0^0 are identical with ω, the rotational frequency of the coordinate system. Other dipoles move either clockwise (f) or counterclockwise (s) away from $\alpha_1 + \pi/2$, as shown in Figure 7.13b.

Suppose further that the electric field vector associated with the π pulse is applied along an axis that makes an angle α_2 with the x' axis in the rotating frame. This will have the effect of transferring the stationary microscopic dipoles from the axis making an angle of $\alpha_2 + (\Delta\S/2)$ with the x' axis to an axis that makes an angle of $\alpha_2 - (\Delta\S/2)$ with the x' axis, as shown in Figure 7.13c. Since $\alpha_2 + (\Delta\S/2)$ is equal to $\alpha_1 + \pi/2$,

$$\Delta\S = 2(\alpha_1 - \alpha_2) + \pi. \tag{7.46}$$

It is easy to see from the location of the vectors labeled f and s that all of the microscopic dipoles will come back together at the new location of the

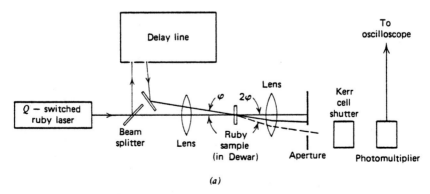

(a)

Figure 7.12. First observation of photon echoes. (a) Experimental arrangement shown is Fig. 2 from the first paper by Kurnit et al., [*Phys. Rev. Lett.* **13**, 567 (1964)]. A Q-switch is a device that causes a laser to produce an intense brief pulse.

stationary dipole, so that the pseudopolarization vector associated with the echo will make an angle of

$$\S_3 = 2\alpha_2 - \alpha_1 - \frac{\pi}{2} \tag{7.47}$$

with the x' axis.

What is the relationship between the angles α_1, α_2, and $\S_3$ and the

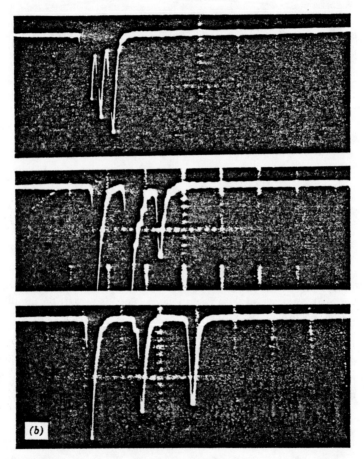

Figure 7.12 (*Continued*) (*b*) Oscilloscope photographs of the output from the photomultiplier shown in (*a*), given as Fig. 10 in *Phys. Rev.* **141**, 391 (1966). *R* lines of ruby at nearly exact resonance ($\delta = 0$), $E_1^0 \sim 1.2 \times 10^4$ V m^{-1}, $\omega_0/2\pi = 432$ THz (10^{12} Hz). Pulse durations $\Upsilon \sim 10$ ns (10^{-9} s), $\varphi \sim 3°$. Time increases to right at 100 ns division. The first two pulses are due to scattered light from excitation pulses. The third pulse is from the photon echo.

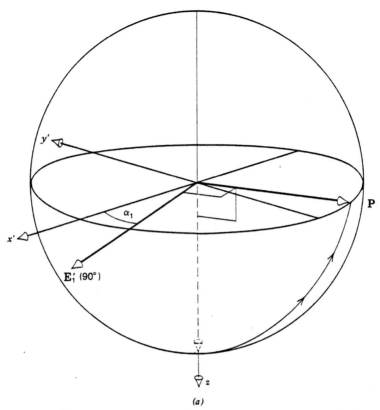

(a)

Figure 7.13. Echo production by propagating waves, viewed in rotating coordinate system. *(a)* The first laser pulse, E_1', rotates the pseudopolarization vector through an angle of 90°. The angle α_1 depends in part on the direction of propagation of the pulse in the laboratory.

direction of propagation of the associated pulses in the laboratory frame of reference? These angles are the time-independent parts of the phases of the three oscillating fields;

$$\mathbf{E}_1\left(\frac{\pi}{2}\right) = \hat{k}_1 E_{11}^0 \cos(\omega t + \alpha_1), \tag{7.48}$$

$$\mathbf{E}_1(\pi) = \hat{k}_2 E_{12}^0 \cos(\omega t + \alpha_2), \tag{7.49}$$

and

$$\mathbf{P}(\text{echo}) = \hat{k}_3 P_0 \cos(\omega t + \S_3). \tag{7.50}$$

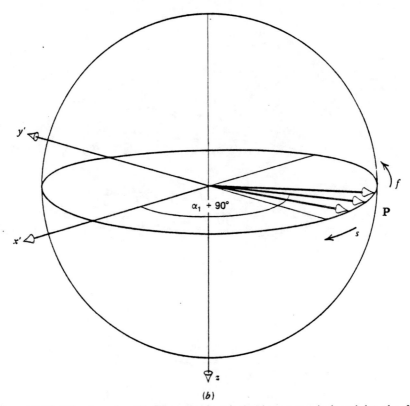

(b)

Figure 7.13 (*Continued*) (*b*) The pseudopolarization wave induced by the first laser pulse decays because of inhomogeneous dephasing. The vector marked f precesses faster than the average in the laboratory pseudoelectric field, E_z. The vector marked s precesses slower than the average. The vector between f and s precesses at the average frequency and is therefore stationary in the rotating frame.

In Chapter 8, it will be shown that

$$\alpha_1 = \mathbf{k}_1 \cdot \mathbf{r} + \phi_1, \tag{7.51}$$

$$\alpha_2 = \mathbf{k}_2 \cdot \mathbf{r} + \phi_2, \tag{7.52}$$

and

$$\S_3 = \mathbf{k}_3 \cdot \mathbf{r} + \phi_3. \tag{7.53}$$

Therefore, by combining Eqs. 7.51 to 7.53 with Eq. 7.47, one can find

$$\mathbf{k}_3 \cdot \mathbf{r} + \phi_3 = (\mathbf{k}_2 \cdot \mathbf{r} + \phi_2) - (\mathbf{k}_1 \cdot \mathbf{r} + \phi_1) - \frac{\pi}{2}. \tag{7.54}$$

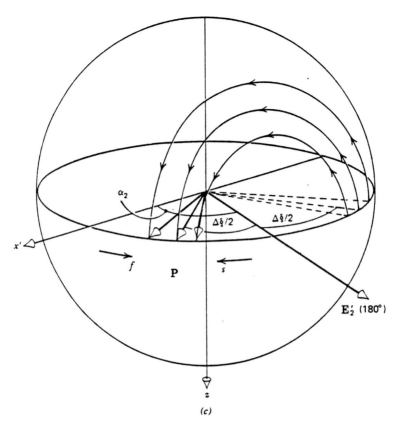

(c)

Figure 7.13 (*Continued*) (*c*) The second laser pulse, E_1', rotates the pseudopolarization vector through an angle of 180°. The angle α_2 depends in part on the direction of propagation of the pulse in the laboratory. It is easy to see that the vectors will come together again. The angle $\Delta\S$ between the initial and final locations of **P** is related to the direction of propagation of the echo in the laboratory.

The terms that contain no dependence on **r** can be equated independently

$$\phi_3 = 2\phi_2 - \phi_1 - \frac{\pi}{2}. \tag{7.55}$$

The **r**-dependent terms yield the relationship

$$\mathbf{k}_3 \cdot \mathbf{r} = (2\mathbf{k}_2 - \mathbf{k}_1) \cdot \mathbf{r}. \tag{7.56}$$

The information contained in Eq. 7.56 will be sufficient to calculate the angles between the propagation vectors. Let

$$\mathbf{k}_1 = k_1 \hat{z}, \tag{7.57}$$

$$\mathbf{k}_2 = k_2(\cos\varphi\hat{z} + \sin\varphi\hat{x}). \tag{7.58}$$

and

$$\mathbf{k}_3 = k_3(\cos\theta\,\hat{z} + \sin\theta\,\hat{x}). \qquad (7.59)$$

Then, from Eq. 7.56,

$$\mathbf{k}_3 = (2k_2\cos\varphi - k_1)\hat{z} - 2k_2\sin\varphi\hat{x}. \qquad (7.60)$$

Therefore, comparing Eq. (7.59) with (7.60) term by term, one obtains

$$\frac{\sin\theta}{\cos\theta} = \frac{2k_2\sin\varphi}{2k_2\cos\varphi - k_1}. \qquad (7.61)$$

The sines and cosines that appear in Eq. 7.61 can be expanded in a power series:

$$\frac{\theta - (\theta^3/3!) + \cdots}{1 - (\theta^2/2!) + \cdots} = \frac{2\left[\varphi - (\varphi^3/3!) + \cdots\right]}{2\left[1 - (\varphi^2/2!) + \cdots\right] - (k_1/k_2)}. \qquad (7.62)$$

If φ and θ are small angles, and if

$$k_1 = k_2, \qquad (7.63)$$

Eq. 7.62 yields

$$\theta = 2\varphi + \frac{13\varphi^3}{3} + \cdots. \qquad (7.64)$$

7.9 Mathematical analysis of $\pi/2$, π echoes

A mathematical description can be given of the free-induction decay of the signal that follows a $\pi/2$ pulse at the center of an inhomogeneously broadened line. First, consider the behavior of an assembly of quantum systems, all with absorption lines centered a distance $\Delta\omega_j^0$ from the peak resonance frequency, ω_0^0. This assembly is sometimes called an *isochromat*. The behavior of the macroscopic polarization vector due to this particular isochromat in the rotating frame will be given by the Bloch equations 7.31 to 7.33. If $t = 0$ is chosen to be the time when the $\pi/2$ pulse terminates, for all $t > 0$, $E_1^0 = 0$. Also, it must be assumed that inhomogeneous (reversible) dephasing is a faster process than homogeneous (irreversible) dephasing, if one hopes to observe an echo. Therefore all terms proportional to $1/T_2$

and $1/T_1$ may be neglected. The results are as follows:

$$\frac{dP^j_{x'}}{dt} = -\Delta\omega^0_j P^j_{y'}, \tag{7.65}$$

$$\frac{dP^j_{y'}}{dt} = \Delta\omega^0_j P^j_{x'}, \tag{7.66}$$

and

$$\frac{dP^j_z}{dt} = 0. \tag{7.67}$$

The boundary conditions after a $\pi/2$ pulse are as follows:

$$P^j_{x'}(0) = 0, \tag{7.68}$$

$$P^j_{y'}(0) = P^j_0, \tag{7.69}$$

and

$$P^j_z(0) = 0. \tag{7.70}$$

Therefore the solutions to Eqs. 7.65 to 7.67 are as follows:

$$P^j_{x'}(t) = -P^j_0 \sin(\Delta\omega^0_j t), \tag{7.71}$$

$$P^j_{y'}(t) = P^j_0 \cos(\Delta\omega^0_j t), \tag{7.72}$$

and

$$P^j_z(t) = 0, \tag{7.73}$$

for all $t > 0$.

To calculate the polarization of the entire sample, one must sum Eqs. 7.71 to 7.73 over all the isochromats:

$$P_{x'} = \sum_j P^j_{x'}(t) \cong -P_0 \int_{-\infty}^{\infty} \sin(\Delta\omega^0 t) f(\Delta\omega^0) d(\Delta\omega^0), \tag{7.74}$$

$$P_{y'} = \sum_j P^j_{y'}(t) \cong P_0 \int_{-\infty}^{\infty} \cos(\Delta\omega^0 t) f(\Delta\omega^0) d(\Delta\omega^0), \tag{7.75}$$

and

$$P_z = \sum_j P_z^j(t) = 0. \tag{7.76}$$

In Eqs. 7.74 to 7.76, $f(\Delta\omega^0)$ is the normalized line shape function centered at $\Delta\omega^0 = 0$:

$$f_{\max}(u) = f(0), \tag{7.77}$$

$$f_{\min}(u) = f(\pm\infty), \tag{7.78}$$

and

$$\int_{-\infty}^{\infty} f(u)\,du = 1. \tag{7.79}$$

Ordinarily, $f(u)$ is a Gaussian function of u. However, in the interest of mathematical simplicity, a Lorentzian will be used instead:

$$f(u) = \frac{T_2^*}{\pi\left[1 + u^2(T_2^*)^2\right]}. \tag{7.80}$$

The reader may verify that $f(u)$ defined in this way satisfies Eqs. 7.77 to 7.79. (The substitution $uT_2^* = \tan w$ will prove useful.) When Eq. 7.89 is substituted into Eqs. 7.74 and 7.75, it is found that $P_{x'}$ is merely the Fourier sine transform of the Lorentzian line shape function, and $P_{y'}$ is the cosine transform. Note that $f(u)$ in Eq. 7.80 is an even function of u and that $\sin ut$ is odd. For this reason, the integral on the right-hand side of Eq. 7.74 is zero:

$$P_{x'} = 0. \tag{7.81}$$

Equation 7.81 would be true even if a Gaussian or any other symmetric line shape function had been used instead of a Lorentzian. The geometric vector model of the dephasing process also makes Eq. 7.81 obvious. The cosine transform on the right-hand side of Eq. 7.75 can be found in standard tables:[5]

$$P_{y'} = P_0 \exp(-t/T_2^*). \tag{7.82}$$

If a π pulse is applied at time $t = t'$, all of the components of $\mathbf{P}_j$ are transformed in accordance with the following:

$$P^j_{x'}\left(t' + \frac{\Upsilon}{2}\right) = P^j_{x'}\left(t' - \frac{\Upsilon}{2}\right), \tag{7.83}$$

$$P^j_{y'}\left(t' + \frac{\Upsilon}{2}\right)\Upsilon = -P^j_{y'}\left(t' - \frac{\Upsilon}{2}\right), \tag{7.84}$$

and

$$P^j_z\left(t' + \frac{\Upsilon}{2}\right) = -P^j_z\left(t' - \frac{\Upsilon}{2}\right). \tag{7.85}$$

Equations 7.83 to 7.85 may be used in the limit that the pulse width, Υ, goes to zero. Now the same Bloch equations 7.65 to 7.67 are solved with the new boundary conditions, Eqs. 7.83 to 7.85:

$$P^j_{x'}(t) = -P^j_0\left\{\sin\left(\Delta\omega^0_j t'\right)\cos\left[\Delta\omega^0_j(t - t')\right]\right.$$
$$\left. -\cos\left(\Delta\omega^0_j t'\right)\sin\left[\Delta\omega^0_j(t - t')\right]\right\}, \tag{7.86}$$

$$P^j_{y'}(t) = -P^j_0\left\{\cos\left(\Delta\omega^0_j t'\right)\cos\left[\Delta\omega^0_j(t - t')\right]\right.$$
$$\left. +\sin\left(\Delta\omega^0_j t'\right)\sin\left[\Delta\omega^0_j(t - t')\right]\right\}, \tag{7.87}$$

and

$$P^j_z(t) = 0. \tag{7.88}$$

Equations 7.86 to 7.88 are good for all $t > t'$. They may be used to compute the total $P_{x'}$, $P_{y'}$, and P_z, in a fashion analogous to that expressed by Eqs. 7.74 to 7.76:

$$P_{x'} = -P_0\int_{-\infty}^{\infty}\sin\left[\Delta\omega^0(2t' - t)\right]f(\Delta\omega^0)d(\Delta\omega^0) = 0, \tag{7.89}$$

$$P_{y'} = -P_0\int_{-\infty}^{\infty}\cos\left[\Delta\omega^0(2t' - t)\right]f(\Delta\omega^0)d(\Delta\omega^0), \tag{7.90}$$

and

$$P_z = 0. \tag{7.91}$$

From Eq. 7.90,

$$P_{y'} = -P_0\exp\left(-\frac{|t - 2t'|}{T_2^*}\right). \tag{7.92}$$

This may be compared with the form of the echoes actually observed: see Figures 7.12*b* and 7.14.

7.10   Self-induced transparency: qualitative discussion

One very interesting example of the importance of the fact that photon echoes propagate but spin echoes ordinarily do not is provided by the self-induced transparency effect. Consider the utter futility of a 2π pulse in magnetic resonance spectroscopy. The system first absorbs and then emits the rf radiation (largely by stimulated emission, although some coherent spontaneous emission is produced and provides the signal), undergoing no net change. The same might be said of a 4π, 6π,..., pulse as well. However, if one can produce just such a pulse for an optical (rotational, vibrational, electronic) transition, the result is no longer trivial or uninteresting.

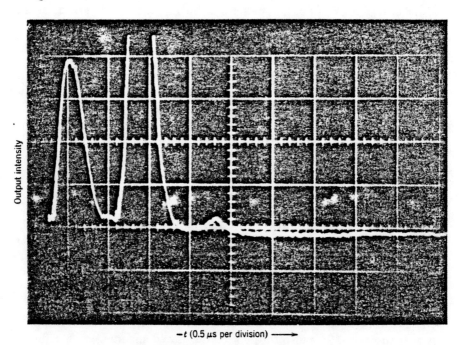

$-t$ (0.5 µs per division) ⟶

Figure 7.14.   Infrared echoes in gaseous SF_6 excited by a CO_2 laser [Fig. 1 from *Phys. Rev. Lett.* **20**, 1087 (1968), by C. K. N. Patel and R. E. Slusher]. The quantum systems and the excitation source were described previously in the caption to Figure 7.10. Shown is a typical oscilloscope trace of output pulses from SF_6 cell at $P_{SF_6} \cong 0.015$ torr. The first two pulses are transmitted CO_2 laser pulses, and the third is the photon echo. The second laser pulse is off scale by a factor of about 4.

Suppose that the spectroscopic sample is shaped into a cylinder of such a length that it is essentially opaque at the frequency ω_0; that is to say, the sample is to be much longer than the reciprocal of the Beer's law absorption coefficient. If an ordinary light wave at the frequency ω_0 is directed into one end of the sample so that it travels along the cylinder axis, its intensity will damp to practically zero long before the light rays have approached the opposite (exit) face. If, however, this ordinary light source is replaced by an intense coherent pulse of sufficient brevity so that it succeeds in producing a rotation of the pseudopolarization vector through an angle of 2π before relaxation sets in, there will be no net absorption of energy by the sample.

Imagine the sample to consist of a horizontal stack of differentially thin disks normal to the cylinder axis. The leading edge of the pulse will be strongly absorbed by the quantum system in each lamina. The trailing edge of the pulse will then produce stimulated emission and will force all of the energy back out of the matter into the radiation field. The pulse then passes into the next lamina, where the process is repeated. In this way, the burst of electromagnetic radiation chews its way through the sample, and finally exits, having suffered no net energy loss. Any time that light passes through a material without suffering a reduction in intensity thereby, the material is said to be transparent. Therefore a completely opaque sample has been rendered completely transparent! The point is that the radiation field itself created this situation, and for this reason the phenomenon is called "self-induced transparency." It was first predicted and observed by McCall and Hahn.[6] A mechanical analog to self-induced transparency is shown in Figure 7.15.

There are several interesting features of a propagating 2π pulse. In the first place, it is probably not proper to call it a "light pulse." This term implies that at every instant of time, most of the pulse energy is in the form of electromagnetic radiation. By way of contrast, the 2π pulse is a mixed excitation, in the sense that the energy is shared between the quantum systems and the radiation field. The allocation of energy between these two reservoirs depends on the characteristics of the sample. In particular, the larger the Beer's law absorption coefficient, the larger is the fraction of the energy properly assigned to the quantum systems. For this reason, the propagation of a 2π pulse through matter is accompanied by a reduction in the velocity of the disturbance. Insofar as the disturbance is purely light, it ought to propagate at the velocity $c_0 = 1/\sqrt{\epsilon_0 \mu_0}$. But if, on the other hand, the energy of the excitation spends 50% of its time residing in the (essentially motionless) quantum system of the sample, the velocity will drop to $c/2$. (This fact will be proved in Chapter 8.) In principle, there is no lower limit to the velocity. In practice, of course, one dares not permit the energy to reside in any one atom, ion, or molecule as long as T_2. If one

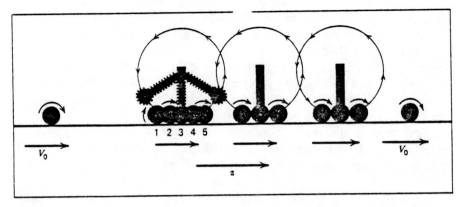

Figure 7.15. Mechanical analog to self-induced transparency. Pendulum row (sample) is struck by rolling ball (light pulse), which gives most of its energy to first pendulum ball and slows down. Pendulum turns 360° and spanks rolling ball on backside. Second impact restores energy to rolling ball, and it moves in original direction. Process can repeat along pendulum row. The drawing was taken from *Phys. Today* **20**, 47 (August 1967).

were to permit any relaxation, the trailing edge of the pulse would not be able to recover fully the energy delivered to the sample by the leading edge, and the pulse would eventually be damped out. Reductions to velocities of the order of $10^{-3}c_0$ have been observed in the laboratory.

What happens if the initial pulse does not correspond exactly to the formula $2n\pi$? If the pulse is *less* than 2π, it will eventually be totally absorbed. If it is greater than 2π (but less than 4π), it is attenuated until it corresponds exactly to a 2π pulse, which then propagates without loss. If it corresponds to more than 4π, the pulse eventually breaks up into a train of 2π pulses, and all the extra energy is absorbed. So far, it has been assumed that the pulse propagates as a plane wave—in other words, that the intensity of a beam propagating in the z direction is independent of x and y. In practice, laser beams are most intense in the neighborhood of the optic axis and die away to zero intensity rather quickly as one's observation post is moved away from the origin of the xy plane. The simplest beam profiles are those produced by a laser firing in what is called a TEM_{00} mode. The beam profile in such cases is very nearly Gaussian:

$$J(x, y) = J(0,0)\exp\left[\frac{-(x^2+y^2)}{a_G^2}\right]. \qquad (7.93)$$

Not infrequently, the diameter of the sample is much greater than a_G. This means that, even though the 2π pulse condition is satisfied for any given bundle of rays (e.g., those in the neighborhood of the region $x^2 + y^2 = r^2$), it is not satisfied for any other bundles. Therefore the portion of the beam in the region $x^2 + y^2 > r^2$ is stripped off from the core, and attenuated to zero intensity. The portions in the region $x^2 + y^2 < r^2$ exceed the 2π condition and are damped until (ideally) a cylindrical beam profile is attained.

A clever variant of the self-induced transparency effect enables one to save the entire Gaussian beam. This is called "zero π pulse propagation". At first thought, this seems to be a silly idea; surely a pulse that produces rotation through the angle $2n\pi$ with $n = 0$ must be no pulse at all! This is not, however, the case. Suppose that one begins irradiation with a pulse having a Gaussian (or any other) intensity distribution. Suppose further that the intensity at the center corresponds to, say, a $\pi/7$ pulse. At some distance off the axis, another ray corresponds to a $2\pi/31$ pulse. At the midpoint of the pulse, then, a quantum system in the path of the central ray will have its pseudodipole rotated clockwise in the rotating frame through an angle of $\pi/14$. The off-axis ray will have produced a rotation of $\pi/62$ in the pseudodipole in another quantum system at this time. Suppose now that one suddenly shifts the phase of the E_1 wave by 180°. In the rotating frame, this phase shift will have the effect of reversing the direction of the electric field from $(E_1^0/2)\hat{x}'$ to $(-E_1^0/2)\hat{x}'$. Since the pulse is symmetric, the second half will be exactly like the first. However, because the sign of the electrogyric ratio remains the same, the pseudodipole of the quantum system in the path of the central ray will rotate through $-\pi/14$, and that of the off-axis system, through $-\pi/62$. They will therefore both end up exactly along the z axis, their equilibrium position; all of their absorbed energy will have been returned to the radiation field. See Figure 7.16. A description of this technique can be found in the work of Grieneisen et al.[7]

Several different methods of producing the 180° phase shift have been employed. In one of them, an electro-optic phase shifter is inserted between the laser and the sample. By carefully synchronizing the electrical pulse that actuates the phase shifter with the firing of the laser, it is possible to switch on the phase shifter while the light filament is exactly halfway through. In another method, the laser pulse is split into two parts by a partially reflecting mirror. One half is directly incident on the sample. The other is bounced around with totally reflecting mirrors and tacked onto the trailing edge of the first half pulse. By properly adjusting the mirror separations, the bounced half can be made to be exactly 180° out of phase with the first half.

7.11   Other coherent transient phenomena

In all experiments designed to observe optical analogs to coherent transient effects in magnetic resonance spectroscopy, one of the major

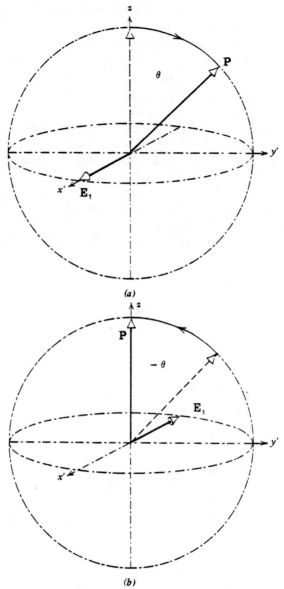

Figure 7.16. Zero π pulse propagation in the rotating frame. (*a*) During the first half of the pulse, the electric field vector of the light wave, $\mathbf{E}_1$, causes the pseudopolarization vector, $\mathbf{P}$, to rotate clockwise through the arbitrary angle θ in the $y'z$ plane. This corresponds to absorption of energy from the light wave by the sample. (*b*) During the second half of the pulse, the electric field vector of the light wave changes phase by 180° in the laboratory frame, which reverses its orientation in the rotating frame. This causes the pseudopolarization vector to reverse its direction of rotation in the $y'z$ plane, corresponding to stimulated emission. If the phase shift in $\mathbf{E}_1$ comes in the midpoint of a symmetric pulse, the rotation angle will be $-\theta$ and the sample will be returned to its initial state, with no net absorption of energy.

experimental difficulties has been control of the laser pulse. One would like to have the laser fire in a single TEM_{00} mode (no nodes in the electromagnetic wave in any plane that includes the axis of propagation), and yet control the intensity and duration of the pulse over wide ranges. Brewer and Shoemaker[8] have devised a technique for observing transient coherent phenomena that makes this possible. They use a laser that operates continuously. Such lasers can be made to be very stable and forced to fire in practically any desired mode. Brewer and Shoemaker use a gaseous sample having a transient frequency at some $\omega_0 \neq \omega$, but also one that can be shifted in frequency by means of the Stark effect (the Zeeman effect could also be used). The sample is placed between capacitor plates, by means of which the Stark field, E_s, may be applied. The pulse-forming network is then applied, not to the laser beam, but to the source of the Stark field. The laser is fired through the sample, which is ordinarily

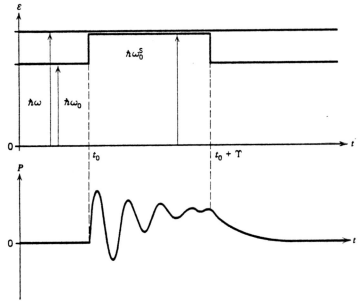

Figure 7.17. Stark-shifted coherent transients: theory. At the top, the energy difference $\hbar\omega_0$ between the quantum states is boosted into resonance with the laser beam $\hbar\omega$ at time t_0 by application of a Stark pulse. The Stark field is then switched off at time $t_0 + T$. At the bottom, the sample polarization is zero until the pulse is applied. At that point, transient nutations begin. Relaxation processes then set in, damping these oscillations toward the asymtotic saturation value of P. (The curve shown is actually the envelope of much more rapid oscillations at the frequency ω_0^s. The drawing is not to scale.) Finally when the Stark pulse is turned off, the sample begins to undergo free-induction decay; now, P is the envelope of oscillations at the unshifted frequency ω_0.

transparent at the frequency ω. The E_s pulse is then applied, causing the gaseous molecules to jump suddenly into resonance with the light beam, $\omega_0 \to \omega_0^s = \omega$. After the quantum systems have interacted with the light wave for the desired amount of time, the E_s pulse terminates. The Stark shift disappears, and the molecules hop back to their unperturbed frequencies, $\omega_0^s \to \omega_0 \neq \omega$. The laser beam is still on, of course, but it has ceased to interact with the sample just as if it had been switched off. The Stark-shift technique is displayed schematically in Figure 7.17; experimental results are shown in Figures 7.18 and 7.19.

The most useful feature of this technique, however, is not that the sample is pulsed rather than the laser. Even more important is the fact that one laser can be used to observe transients in a large variety of samples. Few quantum systems are likely to be found with an ω_0 exactly coincident with the ω for any given laser, and a varying ω is usually quite difficult. On the other hand, $\omega_0^s - \omega_0$ can be varied over a wide range by simply varying the intensity of the Stark field, E_s. One can usually find many quantum

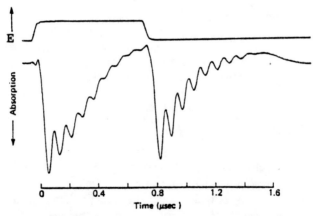

Figure 7.18. Stark-shifted coherent transients: experiments. Brewer and Shoemaker [*Phys. Rev.* **A6**, 2001 (1972), Fig. 4] performed essentially the same experiment as that diagrammed in Figure 7.17. However, they found it desirable to place one isochromat of the inhomogeneously broadened absorption band in resonance (by means of a dc Stark shift if necessary) at the outset, and then jump to the other side with an additional electric field pulse. In this case, the free-induction decay from the initial isochromat provides an exponentially diminishing base line for the transient nutations undergone by the second isochromat; when the pulse terminates, the same phenomena occur but with reversed roles for the two isochromats. The sample is gaseous NH_2D illuminated by means of a CO_2 laser; the transition is $(\nu_2, J, M) = (1, 5, 5) \to (0, 4, 4)$. The symbol ν_2 refers to the "umbrella" vibration.

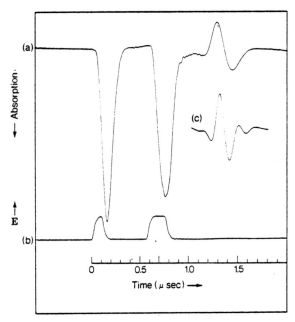

Figure 7.19. Photon echoes observed by the Stark-shifted technique. Drawing taken from *Phys. Rev. Lett.* **27**, 631 (1971), Fig. 2, by Brewer and Shoemaker. The sample is gaseous $^{13}CH_3F$ illuminated by means of a CO_2 laser. The pulses occur at the laser frequency, $\omega_0^S = \omega$, but the echo occurs at the unshifted value of $\omega_0 \neq \omega$. The echo signal is heterodyned with the laser signal by the detector, and the interference beat notes may be seen in (*a*) ($E_S = 3.5$ kV m^{-1}). The interference beats have a higher frequency in (*c*) because the Stark shift is larger ($E_S = 6.0$ kV m^{-1}).

systems with ω_0 close enough to ω so that the Stark effect can bring their transitions into resonance with the radiation field.

Laser-induced transient coherent phenomena have been observed for many different kinds of transitions; those between crystal-field-split electronic states, of course, and between vibrational levels of neutral molecules have been the most popular. In addition, these effects have been produced in a large number of systems without the aid of lasers. It has been mentioned already that they were first studied in nuclear magnetic and electron paramagnetic resonance; rf and microwave oscillators are intrinsically coherent sources suitable for these studies. After photon echoes were observed with ruby, a number of people recognized that a large number of systems other than paramagnetic electron spins could be made to produce transitions simply by using ordinary microwave oscillators. For example, echoes have been observed in ferromagnetic resonance, antiferromagnetic resonance, and molecular rotational transitions using these sources. Even cyclotron resonance echoes have been produced in this fashion. In the latter, ions in a plasma circulate around a magnetic field, $H_z\hat{z}$, creating macroscopic electric dipole moments oscillating in the xy plane. These will interact with microwave pulses to produce echoes that can be completely described by means of classical electromagnetic theory.

It has been shown in this chapter that the illumination of matter with an intense coherent beam of light produces many interesting transient phenomena. These phenomena are conveniently explained by the gyroscopic model of the interaction process developed for use in magnetic resonance. Transient coherent experiments are the most dramatic means available for studying the dynamics of spectroscopic transitions. Much of the work in this field before 1968 is described in a bibliography published by the author.[9] Some important, more recent papers have been listed as references.[4c, 6d, 7-8] In addition, two fine books on these subjects are available.[10]

7.12   References

1. V. M. Fain and Ya. I. Khanin, *Quantum Electronics*, Vol. 1 (1965), translated by H. S. H. Massey (M.I.T. Press, Cambridge, Mass., 1969), pp. 128–139.

2. J. D. Macomber, "Optical anisotropy induced by resonant absorption or amplification of radiation," *Appl. Opt.* **10**, 2506 (1971).

3. N. Bloembergen and S. Wang, "Relaxation effects in para- and ferromagnetic resonance," *Phys. Rev.* **93**, 72 (1954).

4. a. N. A. Kurnit, I. D. Abella, and S. R. Hartmann, "Observation of a photon echo," *Phys. Rev. Lett.* **13**, 567 (1964).
    b. I. D. Abella, N. A. Kurnit, and S. R. Hartmann, "Photon echoes," *Phys. Rev.* **141**, 391 (1966).
    c. S. R. Hartmann, "Photon echoes," *Sci. Am.* **218**, 32 (April 1968).
    d. N. A. Kurnit, I. D. Abella, and S. R. Hartmann, "Photon echoes in ruby," in *Physics of Quantum Electronics*, P. L. Kelly, B. Lax, and P. E. Tannenwald, Eds. (McGraw-Hill Book Company, New York, 1966), p. 267.

5. Anonymous, *Handbook of Chemistry and Physics*, 38th ed., C.D. Hodgman, Ed. (Chemical Rubber Publishing Company, Cleveland, Ohio, 1956), p. 275.

6. a. S. L. McCall and E. L. Hahn, "Self-induced transparency by pulsed coherent light," *Phys. Rev. Lett.* **18**, 908 (1967).
    b. Anonymous, *Sci. Am.* **216**, 57 (June 1967).
    c. Anonymous, *Phys. Today* **20**, 47 (August 1967).
    d. S. L. McCall and E. L. Hahn, "Self-induced transparency," *Phys. Rev.* **183**, 457 (1969).

7. H. P. Grieneisen, J. Goldhar, N. A. Kurnit, A. Javan, and H. R. Schlossberg, "Observation of the transparency of a resonant medium to zero-degree optical pulses," *Appl. Phys. Lett.* **21**, 559 (1972).

8. a. R. G. Brewer and R. L. Shoemaker, "Photon echo and optical nutation in molecules," *Phys. Rev. Lett.* **27**, 631 (1971).
    b. R. G. Brewer and R. L. Shoemaker, "Optical free induction decay," *Phys. Rev.* **A6**, 2001 (1972).
    c. Anonymous, *Phys. Today* **24**, 17 (December 1971).
    d. R. G. Brewer, "Nonlinear spectroscopy," *Science* **178**, 247 (1972).
9. J. D. Macomber, "A bibliography of transient effects in the resonant elastic response of matter to an intense light pulse," *IEEE J. Quantum Electron.* **QE-4**, 1 (1968).
10. a. M. Sargent, III, M. O. Scully, and W. E. Lamb, Jr., *Laser Physics* (Addison-Wesley Publishing Company, Reading, Mass., 1974).
    b. L. Allen and J. H. Eberly, *Optical Resonance and Two-Level Atoms* (Wiley-Interscience, New York, 1975).

7.13   Problems

7.1   For a transition described by $(p_x)_{12} = q_0 a_0$, calculate the electrogyric ratio (volt per meter·second) using Eq. 7.20.

7.2   Calculate $\langle \overline{p_z} \rangle$ for a gas at a pressure of 1 torr, assuming that each molecule carries one chromophore. Let the energy level separation be hc_0/λ, with $\lambda = 10.6$ μm, and let the ensemble be at thermal equilibrium with a heat bath at 300K. (Use Eq. 7.21 or 7.34/N'; express the answer in coulombs per meter.)

7.3   Calculate E_z for the system described in Problem 7.2. (Use Eq. 7.28; express the answer in volts per meter.)

7.4

a. Calculate ¶ (Eq. 7.40) for a wave that is linearly polarized in the xy plane at exact resonance with the two-level chromophores. Let $T_1 = T_2 = 1.0$ ns.

b. Show that the parameter $o = 0$ in this case (Eq. 7.41).

c. Calculate the electric susceptibility η by means of Eq. 7.45. What are the units?

d. Calculate the Beer's law absorption coefficient from formulas presented in Chapter 3.

7.5   Suppose that photon echoes are produced by means of colinear $\pi/2$ and π pulses polarized in planes that make angles of 0 and φ, respectively, with the xy plane. Show, by a reasoning process analogous to that used in

Section 7.8, that the plane of polarization of the echo will make an angle of $2\varphi_0$ with the xy plane.

7.6 Perform the integration on the right-hand side of Eq. 7.90, using a Gaussian for $f(\Delta\omega^\circ)$. Compare the result with that presented in Eq. 7.92.

7.7 Find a formula for the radius of a beam having a cylindrical profile that contains the same total power as the beam described in Eq. 7.93. Assume that the peak irradiances, $J(0,0)$, are the same for the two beams.

8 Propagation of light through two-level systems

8.1 General considerations

The propagation of a coherent electromagnetic wave through an absorbing (or amplifying) sample will be discussed in great detail in this chapter. The sample consists of an ensemble of quantum systems having two non-degenerate eigenstates in the neighborhood of resonance ($\Delta \mathcal{E} \cong \hbar\omega$). The transition responsible for the absorption or amplification is electric-dipole-allowed, and the relaxation of the ensemble is assumed to be adequately characterized by two relaxation times, T_1 and T_2. Other approximations and simplifications will be kept to a minimum and will be clearly identified as they are introduced. The treatment of this topic will be more mathematical than the presentations of most subjects considered previously.

In Chapter 7 the absorption length was defined as the reciprocal of the Beer's law coefficient, $\kappa N' \equiv \beta_0$. Samples that are much longer than the absorption length are termed "optically thick." Self-induced transparency is an example of a phenomenon that gains dramatic character only when it occurs in optically thick materials. By way of contrast, all the magnetic resonance phenomena discussed in Chapter 6 take place in samples that are optically thin. In optically thin samples, the description of the interaction between radiation and matter is greatly simplified by the fact that the exciting wave is essentially constant in amplitude and phase. In the rotating frame, this means that $(H_1^0/2)\hat{x}'$ may be considered a constant vector in both amplitude and orientation. It is obvious that in an optically thick sample H_1^0 diminishes while the wave is being attenuated by absorption and increases while the wave is being amplified by stimulated emission—H_1^0 will therefore depend on both z and t. It is not as obvious that the orientation of H_1^0 in the rotating frame will also depend in general on both of these variables. A change of orientation of H_1^0 in the rotating frame corresponds to a change of phase of $\mathbf{H}_1$ in the laboratory frame. In conclusion, a general treatment of the dynamics of the interaction between radiation and matter must allow for changes in phase and amplitude of the exciting wave.

Wittke and Warter[1] (WW) were the first to describe the propagation of light through an optically thick sample. They showed how the wave amplitude changed as the beam was amplified or absorbed. Arecchi and Bonifacio[2] (AB) generalized the treatment of WW to include changes in both the amplitude and the phase of the wave. The derivation presented in this chapter follows closely the work of AB.

8.2   Coupling the Bloch equations to the propagating wave

The Bloch equations are obtained from the density matrix, as has been described previously. It will be helpful to review the earlier derivation step by step, making the changes necessary to describe the propagation of a coherent light wave through an ensemble of two-level systems.

The density matrix is driven by the off-diagonal elements of the matrix representing the perturbation, $(H_1)_{12}$, in accordance with Eqs. 5.69 to 5.72. In magnetic resonance, the appropriate perturbation is an oscillating field $H_1(t)$ exerting a torque on the nuclear magnetic moment. The expression given for this field in Eq. 6.118 does not allow for propagation effects or phase shifts. Therefore the first step must be to find a more general expression for $(H_1)_{12}$:

$$(H_1)_{12} \equiv 2V^\dagger \cos(\alpha + \omega_0 t), \tag{8.1}$$

where

$$\alpha \equiv (\omega - \omega_0)t - kz + \phi(z, t). \tag{8.2}$$

The symbol k is the magnitude of the propagation vector introduced in Eq. 1.5.

The density matrix is transformed into a coordinate system rotating about the z axis with angular velocity ω_0, as before (see Eqs. 6.127 and 6.128). Again, just as before, the oscillations at ω_0 will beat with those of the driving field in $(H_1)_{12}$, and two kinds of terms will be obtained. One kind will represent oscillations at the very high frequency $2\omega_0$, which produce very little net effect on the elements of the density matrix, and will therefore be neglected. The other kind of term represents oscillations that vary only slowly with time and hence can have a major long-term effect on the response of the quantum systems to the light wave. The latter terms will be kept, just as before. The results are as follows:

$$\frac{\partial \rho_{22}}{\partial t} = \frac{-V^\dagger \left[\rho_{21}^\dagger (\cos\alpha + i\sin\alpha) - \rho_{12}^\dagger (\cos\alpha - i\sin\alpha) \right]}{i\hbar}$$

$$-\frac{\rho_{22} - \rho_{11}^e}{T_1}, \tag{8.3}$$

$$\frac{\partial \rho_{11}}{\partial t} = \frac{V^\dagger \left[\left(\rho_{21}^\dagger - \rho_{12}^\dagger\right) \cos \alpha / i + \left(\rho_{21}^\dagger + \rho_{12}^\dagger\right) \sin \alpha \right]}{\hbar}$$

$$- \frac{\rho_{11} - \rho_{11}^e}{T_1}, \tag{8.4}$$

$$\frac{\partial \rho_{12}^\dagger}{\partial t} = \frac{-V^\dagger (\cos \alpha + i \sin \alpha)(\rho_{11} - \rho_{22})}{i\hbar} - \frac{\rho_{12}^\dagger}{T_2}, \tag{8.5}$$

and

$$\frac{\partial \rho_{21}^\dagger}{\partial t} = \frac{-V^\dagger (\cos \alpha - i \sin \alpha)(\rho_{11} - \rho_{22})}{i\hbar} - \frac{\rho_{21}^\dagger}{T_2}. \tag{8.6}$$

The quantities R_1, R_2, and R_3 are defined in terms of the elements of the density matrix as in Eqs. 6.140 to 6.143. Then[‡]

$$\frac{\partial R_1}{\partial t} = \frac{2 V^\dagger R_3 \cos \alpha}{\hbar} - \frac{R_1}{T_2}, \tag{8.7}$$

$$\frac{\partial R_2}{\partial t} = \frac{-\left(2 V^\dagger R_3 \sin \alpha\right)}{\hbar} - \frac{R_2}{T_2}, \tag{8.8}$$

and

$$\frac{\partial R_3}{\partial t} = \frac{2 V^\dagger (-R_1 \cos \alpha + R_2 \sin \alpha)}{\hbar} - \frac{R_3 - R_3^e}{T_1}. \tag{8.9}$$

The symbol R_3^e is defined in Eq. 6.233.

Equations 8.7 to 8.9 should be compared with Eqs. 6.152 to 6.154. They are equivalent under the substitutions

$$\frac{2 V^\dagger}{\hbar} \rightarrow -\left(\frac{\omega_1}{2}\right), \tag{8.10}$$

and

$$\alpha \rightarrow (\omega - \omega_0) t. \tag{8.11}$$

[‡]The reader should be warned that (AB) $R_1 = $ (JDM) R_2, and (AB) $R_2 = -$ (JDM) R_1, where JDM = J. D. Macomber (this work).

The next step in the magnetic resonance case was to transform coordinates again, hopping from the frame rotating at the frequency ω_0 to one rotating at the frequency ω (the interaction representation). In the more general case treated in this chapter, a transformation will be made that is identical in apparent form and in spirit with the one made in magnetic resonance:

$$
\begin{bmatrix} R_1 \\ R_2 \\ R_3 \end{bmatrix} = \begin{bmatrix} \cos\alpha & \sin\alpha & 0 \\ -\sin\alpha & \cos\alpha & 0 \\ 0 & 0 & 1 \end{bmatrix} \begin{bmatrix} R_1' \\ R_2' \\ R_3' \end{bmatrix}. \tag{8.12}
$$

The difference comes about because α has a more complex time dependence than does $(\omega - \omega_0)t$. The new transformation is facilitated by generalizing the definition of the parameter δ presented in Eq. 6.157:

$$
\delta = \left(\frac{\partial\alpha}{\partial t} \right)_z. \tag{8.13}
$$

The expression for α given in Eq. 8.2 may be substituted into Eq. 8.13 to yield

$$
\delta = (\omega - \omega_0) + \left(\frac{\partial\phi}{\partial t} \right)_z. \tag{8.14}
$$

The second term on the right-hand side permits consideration of the dynamic effect of the interaction on the phase of the light wave. Throughout this discussion, partial derivatives with respect to time must be used because both z and t are independent variables. (In magnetic resonance, only t was an independent variable, so that ordinary derivatives sufficed.)

Differentiation of Eq. 8.12 with respect to time will produce expressions for $(\partial R_1/\partial t)$, $(\partial R_2/\partial t)$, and $(\partial R_3/\partial t)$ in terms of R_1', R_2', R_3', and δ. These expressions can be substituted into Eqs. 8.7 to 8.9, and terms containing the linearly independent functions $\sin\alpha$ and $\cos\alpha$ can be equated separately. A final substitution of Eq. 8.12 into the resulting formulas yields

$$
\frac{\partial R_3'}{\partial t} = \frac{\omega_1 R_1'}{2} - \frac{R_3' - R_3^e}{T_1}, \tag{8.15}
$$

$$
\frac{\partial R_2'}{\partial t} = \delta R_1' - \frac{R_2'}{T_2}, \tag{8.16}
$$

and

$$\frac{\partial R_1'}{\partial t} = -\delta R_2' + \frac{-\omega_1 R_3}{2} - \frac{R_1'}{T_2}. \tag{8.17}$$

Since Eqs. 8.15 to 8.17 are the equivalents of the equations of motion of the density matrix, they are the key to the calculation of any physically observable property of the ensemble.

In the magnetic resonance case, all three components of magnetization were calculated. Special emphasis was placed on M_y because the apparatus usually employed measured that component directly. The susceptibility was anisotropic because of the definite screw sense or handedness of the Larmor precession. It was shown later, in Chapter 7, that optical transitions ordinarily come in degenerate pairs, each with its own susceptibility tensor. When these two tensors are added together, the result is a scalar, or isotropic, susceptibility. However, it is possible to anticipate this result by proceeding directly to a polarization of the form

$$P(z,t) = N'\mathrm{Tr}\left\{ \begin{bmatrix} \rho_{11} & \rho_{12} \\ \rho_{21} & \rho_{22} \end{bmatrix} \begin{bmatrix} 0 & -p_E \\ -p_E & 0 \end{bmatrix} \right\}. \tag{8.18}$$

The dipole moment is represented by a real symmetric matrix and therefore corresponds to p_x. This, in effect, defines the plane of polarization of the E_1 wave; the electric field must oscillate along the $\hat{x}$ axis if the H_1 term in the Hamiltonian is to represent the dot product between **E** and p_E.

The elements of the p_E matrix are negative in Eq. 8.18 because

$$\frac{-\omega_1}{2} = \frac{p_E E_1^0}{\hbar}. \tag{8.19}$$

(Both sides of Eq. 8.19 are equal to the Λ of AB.) Since the energy of interaction between a dipole and a field is negative, the polarization must be proportional to $-p_E$ in order for $V^\dagger$ to have the correct algebraic sign.

Equation 8.18 may be used to calculate the polarization amplitude:

$$P(z,t) = -N'p_E(\rho_{12} + \rho_{21}). \tag{8.20}$$

Because the equations of motion of the density matrix have been transformed into the rotating frame and expressed in terms of the parameters R_1', R_2', and R_3', it is convenient to perform the same transformation upon

Eq. 8.20. The result is

$$P(z,t) = N'p_E[R_1' \sin(\alpha + \omega_0 t) - R_2' \cos(\alpha + \omega_0 t)] \tag{8.21}$$

Equation 8.21 is analogous to Eq. 6.168.

Arecchi and Bonifacio defined the variables C and S in a slightly different fashion from the one in Chapter 6. They wished to use these symbols to refer to components of the total macroscopic polarization, rather than the ensemble-averaged microscopic dipole moments. Therefore

$$C \equiv -N'p_E R_2', \tag{8.22}$$

$$S \equiv N'p_E R_1', \tag{8.23}$$

$$D \equiv N'R_3', \tag{8.24}$$

and

$$D_e \equiv N'R_3^e. \tag{8.25}$$

If both sides of the Bloch equations 8.15 to 8.17 are multiplied by $N'p_E$, the definitions above may be used to find

$$\frac{\partial S}{\partial t} = \delta C - \frac{\omega_1 p_E D}{2} - \frac{S}{T_2}, \tag{8.26}$$

$$\frac{\partial C}{\partial t} = \delta S - \frac{C}{T_2}, \tag{8.27}$$

and

$$p_E \left(\frac{\partial D}{\partial t} \right) = \frac{\omega_1 S}{2} - \frac{p_E (D - D_e)}{T_1}. \tag{8.28}$$

The only essential difference between Eqs. 8.26 to 8.28 and 6.177 to 6.179 (or 7.31 to 7.33) is that δ includes a phase term, $\partial \phi / \partial t$.

All of the above transformations and changes of variable are identical in spirit to ones made previously in the magnetic resonance case. The one further step taken by AB was to introduce dimensionless quantities:[‡]

[‡]Some of the symbols used by AB have already been assigned to other quantities in earlier chapters of this book. For this reason, there are some differences between Eqs. 8.89 to 8.36 and the AB paper.

$$\Xi \equiv \frac{S}{p_E D_e}, \tag{8.29}$$

$$\Pi \equiv \frac{-C}{p_E D_e}, \tag{8.30}$$

$$\Delta \equiv \frac{D}{D_e}, \tag{8.31}$$

$$\Theta \equiv \frac{-\omega_1 T_2}{2}, \tag{8.32}$$

$$g \equiv \frac{T_2}{T_1}, \tag{8.33}$$

$$\delta_0 \equiv (\omega - \omega_0) T_2, \tag{8.34}$$

$$\nu \equiv \frac{z}{c T_2}, \tag{8.35}$$

and

$$\tau \equiv \frac{t}{T_2} - \nu. \tag{8.36}$$

Very little need be said about the first seven of these definitions other than the fact that, in Eq. 8.35, c represents the speed of light in the medium surrounding the chromophoric quantum systems. This medium may or may not be a vacuum. The definition of τ in Eq. 8.36 is worthy of comment. The property represented by τ may be called a (reduced) retarded or local time. It is a measure of how much time has elapsed at the location z since the passage of the initial wave front (i.e., the wave front that crossed the plane $z = 0$ at the time $t = 0$). A representation of a pulse in terms of retarded time is shown in Figure 8.1.

As a result of the transformation described by Eqs. 8.29 to 8.36, the Bloch equations 8.26 to 8.28 become

$$\left(\frac{\partial \Xi}{\partial \tau}\right)_\nu = -\Xi + \Theta\Delta - \left[\delta_0 + \left(\frac{\partial \phi}{\partial \tau}\right)_\nu\right]\Pi, \tag{8.37}$$

$$\left(\frac{\partial \Pi}{\partial \tau}\right)_\nu = -\Pi + \left[\delta_0 + \left(\frac{\partial \phi}{\partial \tau}\right)_\nu\right]\Xi, \tag{8.38}$$

and

$$\left(\frac{\partial \Delta}{\partial \tau}\right)_\nu = -\Theta\Xi - g(\Delta - 1). \tag{8.39}$$

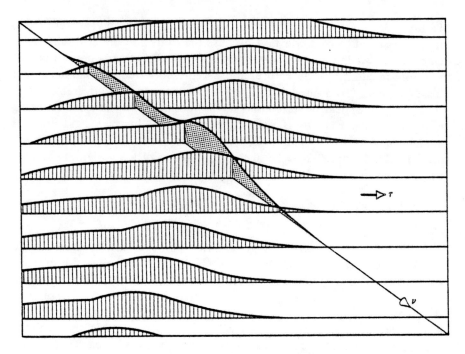

Figure 8.1.   Retarded time. An arbitrarily shaped light pulse propagates along the ν axis ($\nu \equiv z/cT_2$). At each point along the ν axis it is possible to construct a perpendicular τ axis $[\tau \equiv (t/T_2) - \nu]$ along which the pulse develops in time ($\tau > 0$ lies to the right).

Readers who wish to verify Eqs. 8.37 to 8.39 may find some helpful hints in Appendix A.1.

Equations 8.37 to 8.39 constitute a complete description of the time evolution of an ensemble of quantum systems under the influence of a coherent light wave.

8.3   The slowly varying envelope approximation

In Section 8.2 a mathematical description of the absorbing (or emitting) sample being driven by an electromagnetic field was presented. In this section the transport equations for that field must be derived. The wave equation for the temporal and spatial oscillations of E can be obtained from Maxwell's relations:[‡]

$$\frac{\partial^2 E_1}{\partial z^2} = \mu_0 \sigma \frac{\partial E_1}{\partial t} + \mu_0 \epsilon \frac{\partial^2 E_1}{\partial t^2} + \mu_0 \frac{\partial^2 P}{\partial t^2}. \tag{8.40}$$

[‡]Equation 8.40 represents the combination of Ohm's law with Eqs. 3.15 and 3.28.

In Eq. 8.40, μ_0 is the magnetic permeability of the medium. The permeability is presumed to be a constant because the transition under discussion is electric- (rather than magnetic-) dipole-allowed. The electric permittivity of the host medium is ϵ, as before, and σ represents frequency-independent losses of energy from the beam. These losses, due mostly to diffraction and scattering by optical imperfections in the sample, have the same damping effect upon the E wave as nonzero electrical conductivity has. For this reason, the symbol σ is employed to described them.

The polarization, P, may be expressed in terms of the variables C and S (introduced in Eqs. 8.22 and 8.23) by means of Eq. 8.21:[‡]

$$P(z,t) = C(z,t)\cos(\alpha + \omega_0 t) + S(z,t)\sin(\alpha + \omega_0 t). \qquad (8.41)$$

The next task is to differentiate P twice with respect to time and to substitute the resulting formula into Eq. 8.40. The differentiation process will generate a large number of terms because C, S, ϕ, and ωt (contained in $\alpha + \omega_0 t$) all depend on time. If every term is retained in the subsequent development of the theory, the calculations will become very complicated and laborious. Fortunately, many terms are so small that they can be neglected. To see that this is so, suppose that the system reaches a steady state. In that case, the amplitudes C and S, plus the phase ϕ, will no longer change with time at any given point in space, z. The term ωt, however, will produce 100% modulation of the field amplitude, E_1 (and will do so 10^{14} or 10^{15} times every second, if the interaction occurs in the optical region of the spectrum). In a dynamic or transient situation, C, S, and ϕ will also vary with time as does E_1. It is quite unlikely that any of the changes in C, S, and ϕ (which depend on the dynamics of the processes by means of which energy is exchanged between quantum systems and radiation fields) will occur as rapidly as 10^{14} or 10^{15} Hz.[§]

In the cases of greatest interest, therefore, the effect of the time dependence of S, C, and ϕ on the field E_1 will be to produce a slow change in the maximum amplitude and phase of the very rapid oscillation at the frequency ω. Changes in S and C will, in effect, delineate gentle curves,

---

[‡]Equation 8.41 is the same as Eq. 3.57.

[§]In order for there to be an appreciable change in C, S, or ϕ during a single optical cycle, the field intensity E_1 would have to be comparable in intensity to the field E_{atom} produced at the electron by the nucleus. Fields of this intensity can, in fact, be produced in laser beams; they cause frequency doubling and, in extreme cases, ionization and other forms of damage up to and including nuclear fusion in the samples. It was decided in Chapter 1 to omit discussion of such drastic optical processes on the grounds that phenomena of this type are not properly called spectroscopic. The only nonlinearities (in the dependences of amplitude of polarization on the amplitude of the incident beam) that will be considered are those that produce no changes in the frequency of the light beam.

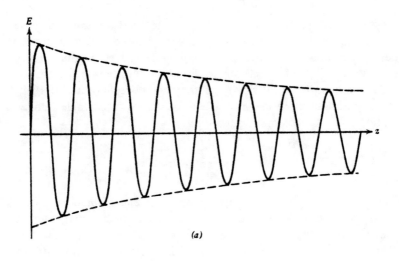

(a)

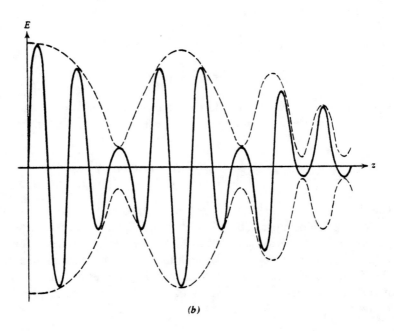

(b)

Figure 8.2. The slowly varying envelope approximation (SVEA). (a) The peak electric field amplitude (solid line) changes by less than 10% from one cycle of the wave to the next, satisfying the requirements of the SVEA. (b) The peak electric field amplitude changes by more than 10% from one cycle of the wave to the next; the SVEA does not hold. The "envelopes" in both cases are shown by dotted lines.

symmetrically placed on either side of the t axis, within which very rapid quasisinusoidal excursions of E_1 may be plotted—(see Figure 8.2). These gently curving boundaries are usually referred to as the *envelope* of the oscillations. Therefore, if the interaction between radiation and matter takes place sufficiently slowly so that no more than about 10% damping (or amplification) of the E_1 wave is produced in a single optical cycle, it will be a fair approximation to write

$$\frac{d^2P}{dt^2} \cong -\omega^2 P. \tag{8.42}$$

This is called the *slowly varying envelope approximation* (SVEA).[3] It is satisfied automatically in the usual situation in magnetic resonance spectroscopy, where it is equivalent to the statement that the Larmor precession frequency, ω_0, is greater than the transient nutation frequency, $\omega_1/2$. Alternatively, one may say that the static field H_0 is much larger than the oscillating field H_1.

The SVEA must also be applied to the E_1 terms in the wave equation. Equations 8.1 and 8.19 may be combined to yield

$$E_1 = E_1^0 \cos(\alpha + \omega_0 t). \tag{8.43}$$

The first time derivative on the right-hand side of Eq. 8.40 can be easily treated under the assumption that the losses represented by σ are small:

$$\left(\frac{\partial E_1}{\partial t}\right)_z \cong -\omega E_1^0 \sin(\alpha + \omega_0 t). \tag{8.44}$$

The problem in evaluating the second time derivative on the right-hand side of Eq. 8.40 is more subtle than that encountered in evaluating the first, because ϵ is ordinarily larger that σ. Consequently, contributions to the derivative that were neglected in obtaining Eq. 8.44 must now be retained. The details of the reasoning used in selecting the terms that can safely be discarded are presented in Appendix A.2. The resulting expression is as follows:

$$\left(\frac{\partial^2 E_1}{\partial t^2}\right)_z \cong -\omega^2 E_1^0 \cos(\alpha + \omega_0 t) - 2\omega \left(\frac{\partial E_1^0}{\partial t}\right)_z \sin(\alpha + \omega_0 t)$$

$$- 2\omega \left(\frac{\partial \phi}{\partial t}\right)_z E_1^0 \cos(\alpha + \omega_0 t). \tag{8.45}$$

Similar reasoning for the second derivative with respect to z gives

$$\left(\frac{\partial^2 E_1}{\partial z^2}\right)_t \cong -k^2 E_1^0 \cos(\alpha + \omega_0 t) + 2k\left(\frac{\partial E_1^0}{\partial z}\right)_t \sin(\alpha + \omega_0 t)$$

$$+ 2k\left(\frac{\partial \phi}{\partial z}\right)_t E_1^0 \cos(\alpha + \omega_0 t). \tag{8.46}$$

Equations 8.41, 8.42, 8.44, 8.45, and 8.46 provide expressions for all the terms that appear in Eq. 8.40. These terms are of two kinds—one kind is proportional to $\sin(\alpha + \omega_0 t)$; the other, to $\cos(\alpha + \omega_0 t)$. Since sine and cosine are linearly independent functions, Eq. 8.40 is really two equations, one for each of the two types of terms. The cosine equation will be satisfied if

$$-k^2 E_1^0 + 2k\left(\frac{\partial \phi}{\partial z}\right)_t E_1^0 = \mu_0 \epsilon\left[-\omega^2 E_1^0 - 2\omega\left(\frac{\partial \phi}{\partial t}\right)_z E_1^0\right] + \mu_0(-\omega^2 C). \tag{8.47}$$

The sine equations will be satisfied if

$$2k\left(\frac{\partial E_1^0}{\partial z}\right)_t = \mu_0 \sigma(-\omega E_1^0) + \mu_0 \epsilon\left[-2\omega\left(\frac{\partial E_1^0}{\partial t}\right)_z\right] + \mu_0(-\omega^2 S). \tag{8.48}$$

Next, the relationships $\mu_0 \epsilon = 1/c^2$ and $k = \omega/c$ given in Chapter 3 will be used as an aid in combining terms in Eqs. 8.47 and 8.48. The results are as follows:

$$E_1^0\left[c\left(\frac{\partial \phi}{\partial z}\right) - \frac{\partial \phi}{\partial t}\right] = \frac{\omega C}{2\epsilon}, \tag{8.49}$$

$$\left[c\left(\frac{\partial E_1^0}{\partial z}\right) + \frac{\partial E_1^0}{\partial t}\right] + \frac{\sigma E_1^0}{2\epsilon} = -\frac{\omega S}{2\epsilon}. \tag{8.50}$$

The next step is to transform Eqs. 8.49 and 8.50 from dependence on the variables z and t to dependence on ν and τ, as defined in Eqs. 8.35 and 8.36. The results are as follows:

$$E_1^0\left(\frac{\partial \phi}{\partial \nu}\right)_\tau = \frac{-\omega T_2 C}{2\epsilon} \tag{8.51}$$

and

$$\left(\frac{\partial E_1^0}{\partial \nu}\right)_\tau + \frac{\sigma T_2 E_1^0}{2\epsilon} = -\frac{\omega T_2 S}{2\epsilon}. \tag{8.52}$$

Again, the details are presented in Appendix A.

Finally, the dependent variables appearing in Eqs. 8.51 and 8.52 must be converted to dimensionless form. The necessary definitions are provided in Eqs. 8.19, 8.25, 8.29, and 8.30, plus the following:

$$\beta_0 \equiv \frac{-\omega p_E^2 D_e T_2}{\epsilon c \hbar}, \tag{8.53}$$

$$G \equiv \frac{\beta_0 c T_2}{2}, \tag{8.54}$$

and

$$L_0 \equiv \frac{\sigma T_2}{2\epsilon G}. \tag{8.55}$$

Equations 8.51 and 8.52 then become

$$\Theta\left(\frac{\partial \phi}{\partial \nu}\right)_\tau = -G\Pi \tag{8.56}$$

and

$$\left(\frac{\partial \Theta}{\partial \nu}\right)_\tau = G\left(\Xi - L_0 \Theta\right). \tag{8.57}$$

In the SVEA, Eqs. 8.56 and 8.57 constitute a complete description of the time evolution of the amplitude and phase of an electromagnetic wave propagating through an ensemble of two-level quantum systems.

8.4   Solutions to the Arecchi-Bonifacio equations

The five equations 8.37 to 8.39, 8.56, and 8.57 are nonlinear, coupled, first-order differential equations. The dependent variables are Ξ, Π, Δ, ϕ, and Θ; the independent variables on which they depend are ν and τ. The first three variables are associated with the components of the electric polarization of the sample in quadrature and in phase with the driving E_1 wave, plus the population difference between the ground and excited states of the quantum systems of the ensemble, respectively. The latter, of course, is also a measure of the amount of energy absorbed by the sample from the light wave. The variables ϕ and Θ are associated with the driving field, E_1; ϕ is its phase, and Θ is proportional to its amplitude. The fixed parameters δ_0, g, G, and L_0 represent the difference between the frequency of the E_1 field and that of the quantum transitions, the ratio of transverse to longitudinal relaxation times for the components of the pseudopolarization vector, the spectroscopic gain coefficient (the equations were derived to describe propagation through an amplifier, with $D_e < 0$), and the broadband losses, respectively. They were first presented in the general form displayed here by Arecchi and Bonifacio.[2] The AB equations may also be described as a marriage between the Bloch equations 8.37 to 8.39, describing the atomic ensemble, and Maxwell's wave equations 8.56 and 8.57, describing the radiation field, in the SVEA.

Solutions to the AB equations can be found for several cases of special interest. The first of these will be the case of exact resonance between the atomic transitions and the radiation field,

$$\delta_0 = 0. \tag{8.58}$$

It should be assumed that the sample is initially at equilibrium with the heat bath, and that the initial wave front of amplitude Θ_0 crosses the entrance face of the sample ($z = 0$) at time $t = 0$. This leads to the following boundary conditions:

$$\Xi(\nu, 0) = 0, \tag{8.59}$$

$$\Pi(\nu, 0) = 0, \tag{8.60}$$

$$\Delta(\nu, 0) = 1, \tag{8.61}$$

$$\Theta(0, \tau) = \Theta_0, \tag{8.62}$$

and

$$\phi(0, \tau) = 0. \tag{8.63}$$

The initial behavior of the AB equations may be explored by replacing the derivatives that appear therein by finite differences:

$$\Xi(\nu, \Delta\tau) - \Xi(\nu, 0) = \left\{ -\Xi(\nu, 0) + \Theta(\nu, 0)\Delta(\nu, 0) \right.$$

$$\left. - \left[0 + \left(\frac{\partial\phi}{\partial\tau} \right)_\nu \right] \Pi(\nu, 0) \right\} \Delta\tau, \tag{8.64}$$

$$\Pi(\nu,\Delta\tau) - \Pi(\nu,0) = \left\{ -\Pi(\nu,0) + \left[0 + \left(\frac{\partial\phi}{\partial\tau}\right)_\nu \right] \Xi(\nu,0) \right\} \Delta\tau, \quad (8.65)$$

$$\Delta(\nu,\Delta\tau) - \Delta(\nu,0) = \left\{ -\Theta(\nu,0)\Xi(\nu,0) - g[\Delta(\nu,0) - 1] \right\} \Delta\tau, \quad (8.66)$$

$$\Theta(0,\tau)\left[\phi(\Delta\nu,\tau) - \phi(0,\tau) \right] = -G\Pi(0,\tau)\Delta\nu, \quad (8.67)$$

and

$$\Theta(\Delta\nu,\tau) - \Theta(0,\tau) = G\left[\Xi(0,\tau) - L_0\Theta(0,\tau) \right]\Delta\nu. \quad (8.68)$$

By means of the boundary conditions in Eqs. 8.59 to 8.63, Eqs. 8.64 to 8.68 can be solved to find

$$\Xi(\nu,\Delta\tau) = \Theta(\nu,0)\Delta\tau, \quad (8.69)$$

$$\Pi(\nu,\Delta\tau) = 0, \quad (8.70)$$

$$\Delta(\nu,\Delta\tau) = 1, \quad (8.71)$$

$$\phi(\Delta\nu,\tau) = 0, \quad (8.72)$$

and

$$\Theta(\Delta\nu,\tau) = \Theta_0(1 - GL_0\Delta\nu). \quad (8.73)$$

The purpose of this exercise is to show that, at exact resonance, Π and ϕ are "stuck" on 0 and cannot get off. The second round of iteration of the difference-differential equations will produce the same uninteresting result. If either Π or ϕ had any way of working its way off 0, it would soon (within one iteration) drag the other one off also, but this will never happen at exact resonance with a homogeneously broadened line. Therefore the solutions can be written immediately:

$$\Pi(\nu,\tau) = 0, \quad (8.74)$$

and

$$\phi(\nu,\tau) = 0. \quad (8.75)$$

This will leave only three equations,

$$\left(\frac{\partial\Xi}{\partial\tau}\right)_\nu = -\Xi + \Theta\Delta, \quad (8.76)$$

$$\left(\frac{\partial\Delta}{\partial\tau}\right)_\nu = -\Theta\Xi - g(\Delta - 1), \quad (8.77)$$

and

$$\left(\frac{\partial\Theta}{\partial\nu}\right)_{\tau} = G\,(\Xi - L_0\Theta). \tag{8.78}$$

Equations 8.76 to 8.78 were first discovered by WW.[1]

The next step is to solve Eqs. 8.76 to 8.78 on the boundaries $\tau=0$ and $\nu=0$. First at $\tau=0$:

$$\Xi(\nu,0)=0, \tag{8.79}$$

$$\Delta(\nu,0)=1, \tag{8.80}$$

and

$$\left[\frac{\partial\Theta(\nu,0)}{\partial\nu}\right]_0 = GL_0\Theta(\nu,0). \tag{8.81}$$

The solution to Eq. 8.81 is

$$\Theta(\nu,0)=\Theta(0,0)\exp(-GL_0\nu). \tag{8.82}$$

From the boundary condition on Θ in Eq. 8.62, Eq. 8.82 may be recast:

$$\Theta(\nu,0)=\Theta_0\exp(-GL_0\nu). \tag{8.83}$$

The reader may object that, at time $\tau=0$, the wave has not yet entered the sample and therefore cannot be damped as shown in Eq. 8.83. The paradox is resolved by remembering that τ is the local (retarded) time, not t itself. The amplitude described by $\Theta(\nu,0)$ moves through the sample at the velocity c. Equation 8.83 then describes a kind of "Beer's law fatigue" for the leading edge of the light pulse, shown graphically in Figure 8.3.

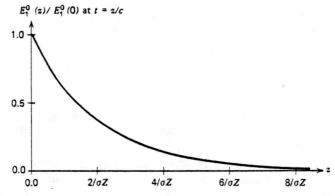

Figure 8.3.   Damping of the initial wave front by broad-band loss mechanisms. The characteristic length for this process is cT_2/GL_0, where $GL_0\equiv\sigma T_2/2\epsilon$ and Z, the impedance, is defined by $\epsilon c=1/Z$. The distance into the sample is z.

That there is any damping at all for the leading edge may also seem surprising, because presumably the quantum systems in the path of the beam do not have time to react to its passage. The presumption is correct, as may be seen from Eqs. 8.79 and 8.80, and the absence of p_E from the damping coefficient. All of the damping is produced by the σ term in Maxwell's equation 8.40, which is presumed to act instantaneously on the wave.

The results of this section can be summarized as follows. At exact resonance between a coherent electromagnetic wave and an ensemble of two-level quantum systems, the five AB equations reduce to the three WW equations. In this case the polarization wave will be exactly in quadrature with the driving field, and the reference phase of that field, ϕ, will be zero at all locations within the sample for all time. The leading edge of a light pulse will be attenuated exponentially in the medium, because of scattering, diffraction, and other broad-band loss mechanisms. The solutions to the AB equations at exact resonance will be discussed further in subsequent sections.

8.5 Optical analog to transient nutation

In this section, solutions to the AB equations at the entrance face of the sample ($\nu = 0$) will be discussed. If it is also assumed that there is an exact resonance between the atomic transitions and the light wave, the AB-WW equations reduce to

$$\left[\frac{\partial \Xi(0,\tau)}{\partial \tau} \right]_0 = \Theta_0 \Delta(0,\tau) - \iota \Xi(0,\tau), \tag{8.84}$$

$$\left[\frac{\partial \Delta(0,\tau)}{\partial \tau} \right]_0 = -\Theta_0 \Xi(0,\tau) - \iota g [\Delta(0,\tau) - 1], \tag{8.85}$$

and

$$\Theta(0,\tau) = \Theta_0. \tag{8.62}$$

The parameter ι in Eqs. 8.84 and 8.85 is of course equal to 1, but in order to identify the effect of damping on the solutions it is a very convenient label. For example, for times t that are very short in comparison with the relaxation time T_2, terms proportional to ι may be neglected. Equations 8.84 and 8.85 are then equivalent to Eqs. 6.189 and 6.190. The solutions are as follows:

$$\Delta(0,\tau) = \cos(\Theta_0 \tau) \tag{8.86}$$

and

$$\Xi(0,\tau) = \sin(\Theta_0\tau). \qquad (8.87)$$

Equations 8.86 and 8.87 are equivalent to Eqs. 6.203 and 6.204.

The population difference between the stationary states decreases in accordance with Eq. 8.86; an electric polarization wave grows in accordance with Eq. 8.87. As the difference Δ goes to zero, the envelope of the polarization wave Ξ reaches its maximum. If the exciting wave Θ_0 were terminated at this point, an optical $\pi/2$ pulse would result. Suppose, however, that the irradiation continues. As the elapsed time τ increases still further, Ξ diminishes to zero again and Δ approaches -1, indicating an inverted population of the energy levels in the quantum systems of the sample. Termination of Θ_0 at this point would mean that the sample had received an optical π pulse. If instead the excitation persists, Δ will increase to 0 and Ξ will become -1, indicating stimulated emission. If instead of shutting off the light now (producing an optical $3\pi/2$ pulse) it were allowed to continue, eventually the ensemble would return to its initial state $(\Delta = +1)$ and the polarization wave would disappear. If the irradiation ceased when this condition occurred, the result would be an optical 2π pulse. If instead the exciting wave persisted forever, the sample would alternately absorb and emit until relaxation set in. The resultant motions of the pseudopolarization vector constitute the optical analog to the nutation effect in magnetic resonance—the nmr effect was discussed in Chapter 6, and the optical one in Chapter 7 (see Eq. 7.35).

It is not necessary to restrict oneself to the limiting case of infinitely long relaxation times $(\iota = 0)$ in solving Eqs. 8.84 and 8.85—solutions may be found for arbitrary finite values of T_1 and T_2 $(\iota = 1)$. The algebra required is very tedious, however, and therefore has been relegated to Appendix A.3. The results are:

$$\Delta(0,\tau) = \frac{g + \Theta_0^2 e^{-\Gamma'\tau}[\cos\Gamma''\tau + (\Gamma'/\Gamma'')\sin\Gamma''\tau]}{g + \Theta_0^2} \qquad (8.88)$$

and

$$\Xi(0,\tau) = \frac{g\Theta_0\left(1 + e^{-\Gamma'\tau}\left\{-\cos(\Gamma''\tau) + \left[\Gamma'' + (\Theta_0^2 - \Gamma''^2)\Gamma'\right][\sin(\Gamma''\tau)]/g\right\}\right)}{g + \Theta_0^2}, \qquad (8.89)$$

where

$$\Gamma' = \frac{1+g}{2} \qquad (8.90)$$

and

$$\Gamma'' = \Theta_0^2 - \left(\frac{1-g}{2}\right)^2. \tag{8.91}$$

Equations 8.65 to 8.68 simplify considerably if $T_1 = T_2$ ($g = 1$), a case frequently encountered in practice. In Figure 8.4, Ξ is plotted versus τ for an ensemble satisfying the $g = 1$ condition. Formulas even more complicated than those presented in Eqs. 8.88 to 8.91 are possible if the atomic transitions are not in resonance with the exciting wave.

In summary, the situation in the layer of sample material just inside the entrance face of an optically thick sample is exactly the same as it would be throughout the body of an optically thin sample (e.g., in magnetic resonance). This is evident from Eqs. 8.62 and 8.63. The chromophores in this region are continually supplied with energy from the source. In contrast, quantum systems deep inside the sample see "used radiation"— the amplitude and phase of the associated wave may be modified substantially by passage through regions of the sample nearer to the light source. Solutions to the AB equations when such propagation effects are important will be discussed in the next section.

8.6 Self-induced transparency: the hyperbolic cosecant pulse

A final demonstration of the power of the AB equations will now be presented. A qualitative discussion of the self-induced transparency effect[4]

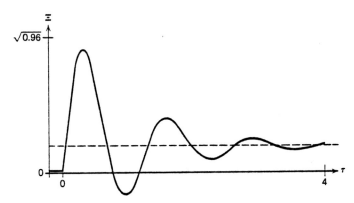

Figure 8.4 The transient nutation signal as a function of time, measured at the entrance face of the sample. The envelope of the polarization wave is Ξ; $P(0,t) = N' P_E \tanh(\hbar\omega_0/2k_0T)\,\Xi(0,t)\sin(\omega t - kz)$. If $g = T_2/T_1$ is set to 1, Eq. 8.89 of the text reduces to $\Xi(0,t) = [\Theta_0/(1+\Theta_0^2)][1 - e^{-\tau}\sec x\cos(x+\Theta_0\tau)]$ with $x \equiv \tan^{-1}\Theta_0$. The symbols τ and Θ_0 represent t/T_2, and $p_E E_1^\circ(0)T_2/\hbar$ at the entrance face. The curve displayed in this figure is based on Eq. 8.89 with $\Theta_0 = \sqrt{24}$.

was given in Chapter 7. Below it will be shown that a quantitative theoretical description of this phenomenon can be obtained by means of the AB formalism.

Exact resonance between the radiation field and the atomic transition will be assumed. For this reason, the starting point will be the WW equations 8.76 to 8.78. Broad-band losses, described by the parameter L_0 in Eq. 8.78, will be neglected, as will the relaxation terms $[-\Xi$ on the right-hand side of Eq. 8.76 and $-g(\Delta-1)$ on the right-hand side of Eq. 8.77] because the pulse is supposed to be of a duration much shorter than either T_1 or T_2:

$$\left(\frac{\partial \Xi}{\partial \tau}\right)_\nu = \Theta\Delta, \tag{8.92}$$

$$\left(\frac{\partial \Delta}{\partial \tau}\right)_\nu = -\Theta\Xi, \tag{8.93}$$

and

$$\left(\frac{\partial \Theta}{\partial \nu}\right)_\tau = G\Xi. \tag{8.94}$$

It can be shown that Δ and Ξ possess the properties of a vector of fixed length. Multiply Eq. 8.92 by Ξ and Eq. 8.93 by Δ, and add them to obtain

$$\left[\frac{\partial(\Xi^2)}{\partial \tau}\right]_\nu + \left[\frac{\partial(\Delta^2)}{\partial \tau}\right]_\nu = 2(\Xi\Theta\Delta - \Delta\Theta\Xi). \tag{8.95}$$

Therefore

$$\Xi^2 + \Delta^2 = f(\nu). \tag{8.96}$$

The boundary conditions in Eqs. 8.59 and 8.61 may be used to calculate $f(\nu)$, since Eq. 8.96 is true for all values of τ:

$$[\Xi(\nu,0)]^2 + [\Delta(\nu,0)]^2 = 1. \tag{8.97}$$

This means that f is truly constant in both space and time and numerically equal to 1. For that reason, Eq. 8.97 represents a version of the Pythagorean theorem for a conservative energy-spin space. Let

$$\Xi \equiv \sin U \tag{8.98}$$

and

$$\Delta \equiv \cos U. \tag{8.99}$$

To discover the value of U, Eqs. 8.98 and 8.99 may be substituted back into Eqs. 8.92 and 8.93:

$$\cos U \left(\frac{\partial U}{\partial \tau} \right)_\eta = \Theta \cos U \qquad (8.100)$$

and

$$-\sin U \left(\frac{\partial U}{\partial \tau} \right)_\eta = -\Theta \sin U. \qquad (8.101)$$

In either case, the result is

$$U(\nu,\tau) = U(\nu, -\infty) + \int_{-\infty}^{\tau} \Theta(\tau') d\tau'. \qquad (8.102)$$

It is easy to see from the boundary conditions in Eqs. 8.59 and 8.61, together with the definitions in Eqs. 8.98 and 8.99, that

$$U(\nu, -\infty) = 0. \qquad (8.103)$$

The next step is to calculate the velocity of the pulse. The total derivative of Θ is

$$d\Theta = \left(\frac{\partial \Theta}{\partial z} \right)_t dz + \left(\frac{\partial \Theta}{\partial t} \right)_z dt. \qquad (8.104)$$

If the pulse propagates at the velocity v, Θ ought to be constant on planes for which $z - vt$ is constant. Therefore, if

$$d(z - vt) = 0, \qquad (8.105)$$

then

$$d\Theta = 0. \qquad (8.106)$$

If Eqs. 8.104 and 8.106 are divided by dz, they will become

$$\left(\frac{\partial \Theta}{\partial z} \right)_t = -\left(\frac{\partial \Theta}{\partial t} \right)_z \left(\frac{dt}{dz} \right). \qquad (8.107)$$

Equation 8.107 will be correct, provided only that dt/dz satisfies Eq. 8.105. Therefore

$$\left(\frac{\partial \Theta}{\partial z} \right)_t = \frac{-(\partial \Theta / \partial t)_z}{v}. \qquad (8.108)$$

Equation 8.108 is called the "equation of continuity" for Θ; it says that any electric field produced from the dipoles in the neighborhood of $z \pm \Delta z$ during the time $t \pm \Delta t$ must flow out of that neighborhood at the velocity v, so that there will be no net buildup of electric field intensity. If both sides of Eq. 8.94 are divided by cT_2,

$$\frac{(\partial\Theta/\partial v)_\tau}{cT_2} = \left(\frac{\partial\Theta}{\partial z}\right)_t + \frac{(\partial\Theta/\partial t)_z}{c} = \frac{G\Xi}{cT_2}. \tag{8.109}$$

If Eq. 8.108 is substituted into 8.109,

$$\left(\frac{1}{c} - \frac{1}{v}\right)\left(\frac{\partial\Theta}{\partial t}\right)_z = \frac{G\Xi}{cT_2}. \tag{8.110}$$

A relationship between the pulse velocity and the parameter U can be found. It is known from Eqs. 8.100 and 8.101 that

$$\Theta = \left(\frac{\partial U}{\partial \tau}\right)_v = T_2\left(\frac{\partial U}{\partial t}\right)_z. \tag{8.111}$$

Therefore, Eqs. 8.111 and 8.98 may be used in Eq. 8.110 to find

$$\left(\frac{\partial^2 U}{\partial t^2}\right)_z = \frac{G\sin U}{T_2^2[1-(c/v)]}. \tag{8.112}$$

The parameter Υ may be defined by

$$\Upsilon = T_2\{[1-(c/v)]/G\}^{1/2}. \tag{8.113}$$

Note that Υ is real because T_2 is positive and both $1-(c/v)$ and G are negative for an absorbing medium. Note also that Υ has the units of time because $1-(c/v)$ and G are unitless. Therefore

$$\frac{\partial^2 U}{\partial t^2} = \frac{\sin U}{\Upsilon^2}. \tag{8.114}$$

To solve Eq. 8.114, it is convenient to make the substitution

$$\$ = \sin\left(\frac{U}{2}\right). \tag{8.115}$$

Then,

$$\Theta = \frac{2T_2\$}{\Upsilon} \tag{8.116}$$

is a solution to Eq. 8.115. This can be seen by substituting Eq. 8.116 into 8.110, and substituting Eq. 8.98 for Ξ:

$$\frac{2T_2\{\partial\,[\sin(U/2)]/\partial t\}}{\Upsilon} \stackrel{?}{=} \frac{T_2\sin U}{\Upsilon^2}. \tag{8.117}$$

From Eq. 8.117,

$$\left[\cos\left(\frac{U}{2}\right)\right]\left(\frac{\partial\Theta}{\partial t}\right) \stackrel{?}{=} \frac{\sin U}{\Upsilon}. \tag{8.118}$$

Again, using Eqs. 8.111 and 8.116,

$$\cos\left(\frac{U}{2}\right)\left[\frac{2\sin(U/2)}{\Upsilon}\right] \stackrel{?}{=} \frac{\sin U}{\Upsilon}. \tag{8.119}$$

Equation 8.119 is indeed satisfied, so that Eq. 8.116 is correct. Equation 8.117 therefore can be rewritten, using the above trigonometric identity on the right-hand side:

$$\frac{2(\partial\$/\partial t)}{\Upsilon} = \frac{2\sin(U/2)\cos(U/2)}{\Upsilon^2}. \tag{8.120}$$

From Eq. 8.115 and the Pythagorean theorem,

$$\frac{\partial\$}{\partial t} = \frac{\$\sqrt{1-\$^2}}{\Upsilon}. \tag{8.121}$$

Equation 8.121 can be written as

$$\frac{dt}{\Upsilon} = \frac{d\$}{\$\sqrt{1-\$^2}} = d\,(\mathrm{sech}^{-1}\$). \tag{8.122}$$

Equation 8.122 can be integrated:

$$\Theta = \frac{2T_2\{\mathrm{sech}[(t-t_0)/\Upsilon]\}}{\Upsilon}. \tag{8.123}$$

The parameter t_0 is a constant of integration, which may depend on z. It must be determined from the boundary conditions for the problem. It is easy to see that the important boundary condition is the one stating that Θ does not vary if $z - vt$ is constant (see Eq. 8.105). Therefore

$$t_0 = \frac{z}{v}. \tag{8.124}$$

This completes the derivation of the famous hyperbolic secant formula[4] for the self-induced transparency pulse:

$$\Theta(z,t) = 2T_2 \operatorname{sech}\left[\frac{t-(z/v)}{\Upsilon}\right]. \tag{8.125}$$

Equation 8.125 is presented graphically in Figure 8.5.

8.7   The $2n\pi$ condition: pulse duration and velocity

In the above derivation, Θ as given in Eq. 8.125 has been constrained to meet two conditions: (1) it will propagate at the velocity v without change of shape, and (2) it will satisfy the equation of continuity so that there will be no net buildup of Θ in any plane within the sample. However, several things have not yet been done. For example, the connection between the hyperbolic cosecant pulse and the $2n\pi$ condition expected from the vector model of the transition has not been shown. To do this, it will suffice to prove that

$$\Theta(v, \infty) \stackrel{?}{=} 2n\pi. \tag{8.126}$$

From Eqs. 8.102, 8.103, 8.125, and 8.126,

$$\frac{2T_2}{\Upsilon} \int_{-\infty}^{\infty} \operatorname{sech}\left[\frac{t-(z/v)}{\Upsilon}\right] d\tau \stackrel{?}{=} 2n\pi. \tag{8.127}$$

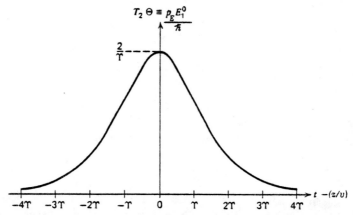

Figure 8.5.   The hyperbolic cosecant pulse. The electric field amplitude E_1° versus local (retarded) time for a pulse of coherent light satisfying the self-induced transparency condition—it rotates the psuedoelectric field vector through an angle of 360°. The characteristic time, Υ, is the half width between 0.64805 amplitude points, and v is the velocity of propagation.

Let

$$y_0 = \frac{t - (z/v)}{\Upsilon}. \tag{8.128}$$

Then Eq. 8.127 becomes

$$\int_{-\infty}^{\infty} \text{sech} \, y_0 \, dy_0 \overset{?}{=} n\pi. \tag{8.129}$$

From standard tables[5]

$$\int_{-\infty}^{\infty} \text{sech} \, y_0 \, dy_0 = \tan^{-1}(\sinh y_0) \Big|_{-\infty}^{\infty}$$

$$= \left(2n'\pi + \frac{\pi}{2}\right) - \left(2n''\pi - \frac{\pi}{2}\right)$$

$$= [2(n' - n'') + 1]\pi, \tag{8.130}$$

where n' and n'' are integers. Therefore the question posed in Eq. 8.129 has been answered in the affirmative, and the optical analog to a $2n\pi$ magnetic resonance pulse has indeed been found. The pulse is symmetrical in both space and time about the point

$$t - \frac{z}{v} = 0. \tag{8.131}$$

At the point of symmetry, the amplitude of the E_1 wave has a maximum value corresponding to

$$\Theta_{\text{max}} = \frac{2T_2}{\Upsilon}. \tag{8.132}$$

At the points

$$t - \frac{z}{v} = \pm \Upsilon, \tag{8.133}$$

the amplitude of the pulse is equal to its maximum value, multiplied by

$$\text{sech}(1) = 0.64805. \tag{8.134}$$

Since the electromagnetic energy density in the pulse is proportional to the square of the wave amplitude, the power at the points specified in Eq. 8.133 is equal to its maximum value, multiplied by

$$\text{sech}^2(1) = 0.41997. \tag{8.135}$$

For this reason, it is reasonable to call Υ the pulse duration (and $v\Upsilon$ the pulse length). In principle, Υ can be chosen arbitrarily by the experimenter (if his laser will cooperate!), subject only to the restriction that

$$\Upsilon \ll T_2 \leqslant T_1. \tag{8.136}$$

Once Υ has been chosen, everything else is determined. In particular, the maximum amplitude of the pulse must be given by Eq. 8.132 and the shape by 8.125. Also, in Eq. 8.113, it was shown that the pulse velocity was determined by the choice of Υ and by the gain coefficient, G. It was asserted earlier that the pulse velocity was related to the distribution of energy between the electromagnetic wave and the ensemble of quantum systems. It is now time to prove this.

The number density of photons in the radiation field, d_R, can be calculated from the irradiance J by means of Poynting's relation (see Eq. 1.18):

$$J_{rms} = c\, d_R \hbar \omega. \tag{8.137}$$

Also, from Eq. 1.7,

$$J_{rms} = \frac{\left(E_1^0\right)^2}{2Z}. \tag{8.138}$$

From Eqs. 8.19 and 8.32, together with 8.114 and 8.115,

$$d_R \hbar \omega = \frac{\epsilon \hbar^2 \Theta^2}{2 p_E^2 T_2^2}. \tag{8.139}$$

Equation 3.46 has been used to introduce the permittivity, ϵ. With the help of Eqs. 8.53 and 8.54, one can write

$$d_R = \left| \frac{D_e}{G} \right| \left(\frac{\Theta}{2} \right)^2. \tag{8.140}$$

To find the energy stored in the quantum systems, recall that the excess population of excited quantum systems per unit volume is $D_e \Delta$ (see Eq. 8.31), whereas at equilibrium the population will be only D_e. The difference between these two population densities is therefore proportional to the number of photons that have been absorbed from the light wave. In particular, each photon causes the difference to change by 2. Therefore, if the number of photons per unit volume absorbed by the matter is defined to be d_M,

$$d_M = \frac{|(\Delta - 1)D_e|}{2}. \tag{8.141}$$

Equation 8.141 may be divided by 8.140, and Δ and Θ may be substituted for by their equivalents in terms of U from Eqs. 8.99, 8.115, and 8.116;

$$\frac{d_M}{d_R} = |G|\left(\frac{\Upsilon}{T_2}\right)^2. \tag{8.142}$$

The quantity β_0 defined in Eq. 8.53 turns out to be the Beer's law absorption (or amplification) coefficient, in units of reciprocal distance (see Eq. 3.53). Therefore the dimensionless gain coefficient G defined in Eq. 8.54 may be interpreted as the ratio of two times. In the numerator is T_2, the transverse relaxation time to which all of the other times in the problem have been scaled. In the denominator is found

$$\frac{2}{|\beta_0|c} \equiv t_A, \tag{8.143}$$

which can be called the Beer's law absorption time. Physically, it is the time required for the electric field amplitude in a low-intensity incoherent light wave to damp to $1/e$ of its initial value, while traveling at the speed of light appropriate for the medium, c. From 8.142 and 8.143,

$$\Upsilon = \sqrt{t_A T_2}\left(\frac{d_M}{d_R}\right). \tag{8.144}$$

To state Eq. 8.144 in words, the pulse duration is equal to the geometric mean of T_2 with the Beer's law absorption time, multiplied by the ratio of the energy density in the matter to the energy density in the radiation field. The parameter Υ is shown as the dotted curve in Figure 8.6.
From Eqs. 8.113 and 8.142,

$$\left|\frac{1-(c/v)}{G}\right| = \frac{d_M/d_R}{|G|}. \tag{8.145}$$

Therefore,

$$v = \frac{cd_R}{d_M + d_R}. \tag{8.146}$$

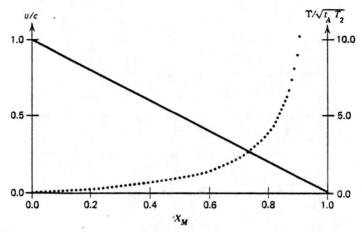

Figure 8.6. The dependence of the duration and velocity of a 2π pulse on the energy distribution. The fraction of the photons in the incident beam that are still in the radiation field is $1 - X_M$; the others have been temporarily absorbed by the quantum systems. The actual pulse velocity is v (solid curve), and c is the speed of light in the sample medium in the absence of the transition. The dotted curve represents Υ; the duration of the pulse (half width between half-amplitude points) is 1.317Υ, t_A is the Beer's law absorption time defined in the text, and T_2 is the transverse relaxation time.

Equation 8.146 says that the velocity of the disturbance through the sample is simply equal to the speed of light in the absence of the transition, times the instantaneous fraction of the energy of the disturbance that is in the form of photons. The parameter v is shown as the solid curve in Figure 8.6. Experimental results are presented in Figure 8.7.

McCall and Hahn[4], in their original treatment, also considered the problem of self-induced transparency associated with inhomogeneously broadened lines. The essential physics is the same; self-induced transparency does indeed occur in such a medium, and the pulse has a hyperbolic secant form.

8.8   Conclusion

In addition to the many other applications of the AB equations, a limited amount of progress has been made in solving the problem of a two-level system even when ... SVEA does not hold (as it would not, e.g., for extremely short pulses'). Whether or not the SVEA is employed, the fruit of the union of the Bloch and Maxwell equations is capable of describing an enormous number of optical phenomena. The passage of a coherent

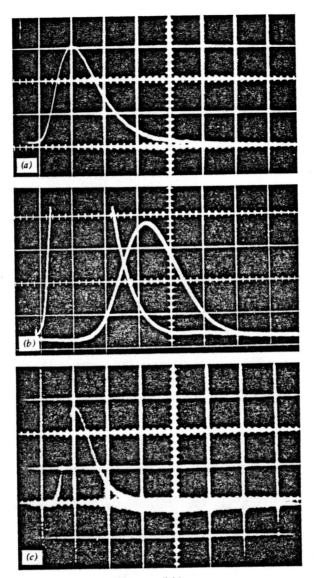

200 ns per division

Figure 8.7. Self-induced transparency of gaseous SF_6 to a coherent pulse of CO_2 laser radiation. Taken from *Phys. Rev. Lett.* **19**, 1019 (1967), Fig. 2, by Patel and Slusher. (*a*) Typical input pulse as measured through a 9.4-m absorption cell but without any SF_6. Horizontal scale, 200 ns per division. (*b*) Double exposure of input and output. Input same as in (*a*), but with the vertical scale expanded by 4. The delayed output pulse with 0.04 torr SF_6. (*c*) Output pulse with 0.04 torr SF_6 and 2 torr helium. Input intensity is adjusted to be just above the minimum to satisfy the 2π pulse condition for this mixture. Notice the nearly total absence of a delay and the *narrowing* of the output pulse as compared with the input. This occurs because the 2π pulse duration of $\mathcal{T}$ cannot exceed T_2, and T_2 has been shortened by the He.

312

electromagnetic wave through an ensemble of two-level quantum systems treated in this fashion provides a model for all spectroscopic processes.

In many cases the gyroscopic picture of the transition mechanism is not necessary. After all, a model based implicitly on the notion of Schrödinger quantum jumps (and the calculation of transition probabilities by means of time-dependent perturbation theory) has for years provided a satisfactory explanation for unsaturated slow-passage spectra of incoherently excited chromophores. In some cases, especially when the exciting radiation is weak, the gyroscopic picture is not sufficient and the fully quantum-mechanical treatment must be used.

In spite of these drawbacks, the fact remains that the gyroscopic model has an uncanny hold on human intuition. It is safe to say that no scientist ever devised a dramatic new transient coherent experiment without it. The situation in which both the Bloch equations and some competing theory give the same result is reminiscent of the competition between the model of planetary motion using elliptical paths about the sun and the model using epicycles. Both pictures lead to the same correct predictions of the positions of the planets, but no country today would describe the orbits of its artificial satellites by means of epicycles.

The cases in which the gyroscopic picture gives only an approximation to the correct answer are reminiscent of the situation in regard to the Eyring theory of rates of chemical reactions. Chemists now know that an exact treatment of this topic requires inelastic quantum-mechanical scattering theory. Because the approximate theory greatly facilitates visualization of the problem, however, it survives in competition with the rigorous description.

8.9 References

1. J. P. Wittke and P. J. Warter, "Pulse propagation in a laser amplifier," *J. Appl. Phys.* **35**, 1668 (1964).

2. F. T. Arecchi and R. Bonifacio, "Theory of optical maser amplifiers," *IEEE J. Quantum Electron.* QE-1, 169 (1965), and QE-2, 105 (1966).

3. J. A. Armstrong and E. Courtens, "Exact solution of a π-pulse problem," *IEEE J. Quantum Electron.* QE-4, 411 (1968); also, "Π-pulse propagation in the presence of host dispersion," *ibid.*, QE-5, 249 (1969).

4. S. L. McCall and E. L. Hahn, "Self-induced transparency by pulsed coherent light," *Phys. Rev. Lett.* **18**, 908 (1967).

5. Anonymous, *Handbook of Chemistry and Physics*, 38th ed., C. D. Hodgman, Ed. (Chemical Rubber Publishing Company, Cleveland, Ohio, 1956), p. 272 (I369).

8.10   Problems

8.1

a.   Show that, if $T_1 = T_2$, Eq. 8.89 reduces to

$$\Xi(0,\tau) = \frac{\Theta_0\left[1 + e^{-\tau}(\Theta_0 \sin \Theta_0 \tau - \cos \Theta_0 \tau)\right]}{1 + \Theta_0^2}.$$

b.   Prove that this reduces to the formula given in the legend to Figure 8.4.

8.2   Calculate d_R, the number density of photons in the radiation field, for a $\lambda = 10.6\ \mu m$ laser of irradiance $J_{rms} = 6.0 \times 10^4$ W m^{-2}. (Use Eq. 8.137; express the answer in meters^{-3}.)

8.3

a.   Calculate $|G|$, the "gain" coefficient, for a sample with $|\beta_0| = 1.0 \times 10^6$ m^{-1}, $c = c_0$, and $\tau = 1.0\ \mu s$. (Use Eq. 8.54.)

b.   Calculate t_A, the absorption time (seconds), for the same system.

8.4   Calculate, for a self-induced-transparency pulse of 100 ns duration:

a. d_M/d_R. (Use the results from Problem 8.3, plus Eq. 8.142.)

b. d_M. (Use the results from Problems 8.2 and 8.4a; express the answer in meters^{-3}.)

c.   The pulse velocity, v. (Use the results from Problems 8.2 and 8.4b, plus Eq. 8.146; express the answer in meters per second.)

Appendix

A.1 Transformation of the Arecchi-Bonifacio equations from dependence on z and t to dependence on ν and τ

To transform the derivatives on the right-hand sides of Eqs. 8.26 to 8.28 from the z, t to the ν, τ coordinate system, one must use the chain rule. For an arbitrary function, f,

$$\left(\frac{\partial f}{\partial \tau}\right)_\nu = \left(\frac{\partial f}{\partial z}\right)_t \left(\frac{\partial z}{\partial \tau}\right)_\nu + \left(\frac{\partial f}{\partial t}\right)_z \left(\frac{\partial t}{\partial \tau}\right)_\nu = \left(\frac{\partial f}{\partial t}\right)_z T_2. \tag{A.1}$$

Remembering that $k = \omega/c$, one finds that

$$\alpha = \delta_0 \tau - \omega_0 T_2 \nu + \phi. \tag{A.2}$$

Since

$$\left(\frac{\partial \alpha}{\partial \tau}\right)_\nu = \delta T_2, \tag{A.3}$$

it can be seen that

$$\delta T_2 = \delta_0 + \left(\frac{\partial \phi}{\partial \tau}\right)_\nu. \tag{A.4}$$

Equations 8.26 to 8.28 then become Eqs. 8.37 to 8.39.

The chain rule is also used to find an expression for $(\partial f / \partial \nu)$:

$$\left(\frac{\partial f}{\partial \nu}\right)_\tau = \left(\frac{\partial f}{\partial z}\right)_t \left(\frac{\partial z}{\partial \nu}\right)_\tau + \left(\frac{\partial f}{\partial t}\right)_z \left(\frac{\partial f}{\partial \nu}\right)_\tau$$

$$= \left[c\left(\frac{\partial f}{\partial z}\right)_t + \left(\frac{\partial f}{\partial t}\right)_z\right] T_2. \tag{A.5}$$

The expressions in parentheses on the left-hand sides of Eqs. 8.49 and 8.50 are of exactly the same form as the one on the right-hand side of Eq. A.5. Equations 8.51 and 8.52 follow.

A.2   Application of the slowly varying envelope approximation to the calculation of terms in the wave equation

Equation 8.43 may be differentiated once to yield

$$\left(\frac{\partial E_1}{\partial t}\right)_z = -\omega E_1^0 \sin(\alpha + \omega_0 t) + \left(\frac{\partial E_1^0}{\partial t}\right)_z \cos(\alpha + \omega_0 t)$$

$$-\left(\frac{\partial \phi}{\partial t}\right)_z E_1^0 \sin(\alpha + \omega_0 t). \tag{A.6}$$

Then

$$\left(\frac{\partial^2 E_1}{\partial t^2}\right)_z = -\omega^2 E_1^0 \cos(\alpha + \omega_0 t) - \left(\frac{\partial E_1^0}{\partial t}\right)_z \sin(\alpha + \omega_0 t)$$

$$-\omega\left(\frac{\partial \phi}{\partial t}\right)_z E_1^0 \cos(\alpha + \omega_0 t) - \omega\left(\frac{\partial E_1^0}{\partial t}\right)_z \sin(\alpha + \omega_0 t)$$

$$-\left(\frac{\partial E_1^0}{\partial t}\right)_z \left(\frac{\partial \phi}{\partial t}\right)_z \sin(\alpha + \omega_0 t) + \left(\frac{\partial^2 E_1^0}{\partial t^2}\right)_z \cos(\alpha + \omega_0 t)$$

$$-\left(\frac{\partial \phi}{\partial t}\right)_z \omega E_1^0 \cos(\alpha + \omega_0 t) - E_1^0 \left(\frac{\partial \phi}{\partial t}\right)_z^2 \cos(\alpha + \omega_0 t)$$

$$-\left(\frac{\partial \phi}{\partial t}\right)_z \left(\frac{\partial E_1^0}{\partial t}\right) \sin(\alpha + \omega_0 t) - \left(\frac{\partial^2 \phi}{\partial t^2}\right)_z E_1^0 \sin(\alpha + \omega_0 t). \tag{A.7}$$

Equation A.7 may now be carefully examined from the SVEA point of view, with confidence that nothing has been omitted inadvertently. The 10 terms on the right-hand side can be grouped into three categories, according to the sizes of the pair of rate terms (inversely proportional to the time) which are multiplied by the sine and cosine factors. The first one listed forms a category all by itself, since both of its rate factors are $\omega/2\pi \sim 10^{15}$ Hz. The second, third, fourth, and seventh constitute the second category. Each of these terms has one large rate factor ($\omega/2\pi \sim 10^{15}$ Hz) and one small one [either $(\partial \phi/\partial t)_z$ or $(\partial E_1^0/\partial t)_z$, depending on the term]. The third-category terms are the fifth, sixth, eighth, ninth, and tenth listed. Each term in this category has a rate factor that is either the product of two small rates or a single factor of the same order of magnitude as such a pair: $(\partial E_1^0/\partial t)_z (\partial \phi/\partial t)_z$, $(\partial^2 E_1^0/\partial t^2)_z$, $(\partial^2 \phi/\partial t^2)_z$, and $(\partial \phi/\partial t)_z^2$. It has already been stated that keeping just the first-category terms is not sufficient, but the third-category terms may be discarded safely. The resulting expression is given as Eq. 8.45.

A.3 General solution to the Bloch equations leading to the nutation effect with damping

Solutions for Eqs. 8.84 and 8.85 are assumed to be of the forms

$$\Xi(0,\tau) - \Xi(0,\infty) = A_1 e^{\Gamma\tau} + A_2 e^{-\Gamma\tau}, \tag{A.8}$$

and

$$\Delta(0,\tau) - \Delta(0,\infty) = B_1 e^{\Gamma\tau} + B_2 e^{-\Gamma\tau}. \tag{A.9}$$

Note that, if the real part of Γ is nonzero, only one of the two terms on the right-hand sides of Eqs. A.8 and A.9 can remain finite at $\tau = \infty$. Therefore, it will be assumed that

$$A_2 = B_2 = 0, \tag{A.10}$$

and the resulting equations will be differentiated:

$$\left(\frac{d\Delta}{d\tau}\right)_\nu = \Gamma\Delta \tag{A.11}$$

and

$$\left(\frac{d\Xi}{d\tau}\right)_\nu = \Gamma\Xi. \tag{A.12}$$

Since this discussion is restricted to $\nu = 0$, partial derivatives need not be used on the left-hand sides of Eqs. A.11 and A.12. If the latter expressions are substituted into Eqs. 8.84 and 8.85, one obtains

$$\Gamma A_1 e^{\Gamma\tau} = \Theta_0 \left[\Delta(0,\infty) + B_1 e^{\Gamma\tau}\right] - \left[\Xi(0,\infty) + A_1 e^{\Gamma\tau}\right] \tag{A.13}$$

and

$$\Gamma B_1 e^{\Gamma\tau} = -\Theta_0 \left[\Xi(0,\infty) + A_1 e^{\Gamma\tau}\right] - g\left[\Delta(0,\infty) + B_1 e^{\Gamma\tau} - 1\right]. \tag{A.14}$$

The terms in Eqs. A.13 and A.14 may be grouped as follows:

$$(\Gamma A_1 - \Theta_0 B_1 + 2A_1)e^{\Gamma\tau} + \left[-\Theta_0\Delta(0,\infty) + \iota\Xi(0,\infty)\right] = 0 \tag{A.15}$$

and

$$(\Gamma B_1 + \Theta_0 A_1 + 2gB_1)e^{\Gamma \tau} + [\Theta_0 \Xi(0,\infty) + \iota g\Delta(0,\infty)2g] = 0. \quad \text{(A.16)}$$

Equations A.15 and A.16 can be satisfied for all τ only if the terms in parentheses and the terms in brackets sum to zero individually. There are therefore four equations:

$$\Theta_0 B_1 = (\Gamma + \iota)A_1, \quad \text{(A.17)}$$

$$\iota\Xi(0,\infty) = \Theta_0\Delta(0,\infty), \quad \text{(A.18)}$$

$$-\Theta_0 A_1 = (\Gamma + \iota g)B_1, \quad \text{(A.19)}$$

and

$$-\Theta_0\Xi(0,\infty) = \iota g[\Delta(0,\infty) - 1]. \quad \text{(A.20)}$$

Equation A.18 may be substituted into A.20 to obtain

$$-\Theta_0^2\Delta(0,\infty) = \iota g[\Delta(0,\infty) - 1]. \quad \text{(A.21)}$$

Equation A.21 has the solution

$$\Delta(0,\infty) = \frac{\iota^2 g}{\iota^2 g + \Theta_0^2}. \quad \text{(A.22)}$$

From Eqs. A.17 and A.19,

$$\frac{-\Theta_0}{\Gamma + \iota g} = \frac{\Gamma + 1}{\Theta_0}. \quad \text{(A.23)}$$

The solution to Eq. A.23 is

$$\Gamma = -\Gamma' \pm i\Gamma'', \quad \text{(A.24)}$$

where Γ' is the average of the two relaxation rates, $1/T_1$ and $1/T_2$, suitably normalized:

$$\Gamma' = \frac{\iota(1+g)}{2} > 0, \quad \text{(A.25)}$$

and

$$\Gamma'' = \left\{ \Theta_0^2 - \left[\frac{\iota(1-g)}{2} \right]^2 \right\}^{1/2} > 0. \quad \text{(A.26)}$$

If $T_1 = T_2$ (a situation that occurs in nature rather frequently),

$$\Gamma' = \iota \qquad\qquad (A.27)$$

and

$$\Gamma'' = \Theta_0. \qquad\qquad (A.28)$$

Now, A_1 and B_1 must be determined. Remember that there were initially four constants rather than just two (see Eqs. A.8 and A.9), but two of them were set to zero (see Eq. A.10), so that the solutions would damp out at $\tau = \infty$. It is obvious from Eq. A.24 that terms of the form $e^{\Gamma \tau}$ has the required behavior at $\tau = \infty$, so that dropping C and D has the desired result. But this leaves an ambiguity in the algebraic sign of the imaginary part of Γ, which can also be seen from Eq. A.24. The ambiguity is resolved by noting that, if either choice of algebraic sign will satisfy Eq. A.14, the correct answer will be some linear combination of these choices. Equations A.8 and A.9 may be rewritten as follows:

$$\Delta(0,\tau) = \Delta(0,\infty) + e^{-\Gamma' \tau}(B_1' \cos \Gamma'' \tau + B_1'' \sin \Gamma'' \tau) \qquad (A.29)$$

and

$$\Xi(0,\tau) = \Xi(0,\infty) + e^{-\Gamma' \tau}(A_1' \cos \Gamma'' \tau + A_1'' \sin \Gamma'' \tau). \qquad (A.30)$$

One may very quickly determine A_1' and B_1' from the boundary conditions on Δ and Ξ in Eqs. 8.59 and 8.61:

$$1 = \Delta(0,\infty) + B_1' \qquad\qquad (A.31)$$

and

$$0 = \Xi(0,\infty) + A_1'. \qquad\qquad (A.32)$$

Next, Eqs. A.29 and A.30 may be substituted into either of the differential equations 8.84 and 8.85. Using the latter and equating coefficients of $\cos \Gamma \tau$ and $\sin \Gamma \tau$ separately, one can show that

$$-\Gamma' B_1' + \Gamma'' B_1'' = -\Theta_0 A_1' - \iota g B_1' \qquad (A.33)$$

and

$$-\Gamma' B_1' - \Gamma'' B_1' = -\Theta_0 A_1' - \iota g B_1''. \qquad (A.34)$$

Equations A.33 and A.34 can be solved for A_1'' and B_1'' in terms of A_1' and B_1':

$$B_1'' = \frac{(\Gamma' - \iota g)B_1' - \Theta_0 A_1'}{\Gamma''} \qquad (A.35)$$

and

$$A_1'' = \frac{\left[(\Gamma' - \iota g)^2 + (\Gamma'')^2\right] B_1' - (\Gamma' - \iota g)\Theta_0 A_1'}{\Theta \Gamma''}. \tag{A.36}$$

Finally, the definition of Γ'' and Γ' from Eqs. A.25 and A.26, together with the solution of A.31 and A.32 for A_1' and B_1', may be used to obtain

$$B_1' = 1 - \Delta(0, \infty), \tag{A.37}$$

$$A_1' = -\Xi(0, \infty), \tag{A.38}$$

$$B_1'' = \frac{\iota[(1-g)/2][1 - \Delta(0, \infty)] + \Theta_0 \Xi(0, \infty)}{\Gamma''}, \tag{A.39}$$

and

$$A_1'' = \frac{\Theta_0[1 - \Delta(0, \infty)] + \iota[(1-g)/2]\Xi(0, \infty)}{\Gamma''}. \tag{A.40}$$

To show the physical significance of these rather complicated results, the aforementioned assumption $T_1 = T_2$ (see Eqs. A.27 and A.28) will be introduced. Equations A.39 and A.40 become

$$B_1'' = \Xi(0, \infty) \tag{A.41}$$

and

$$A_1'' = 1 - \Delta(0, \infty). \tag{A.42}$$

Equations A.37, A.38, A.41, and A.42 may then be substituted into Eqs. A.29 and A.30:

$$\Delta(0, \tau) = \Delta(0, \infty) + e^{-\iota\tau}\left\{[1 - \Delta(0, \infty)]\cos(\Theta_0\tau) + \Xi(0, \infty)\sin(\Theta_0\tau)\right\}, \tag{A.43}$$

and

$$\Xi(0, \tau) = \Xi(0, \infty) + e^{-\iota\tau}\left\{-\Xi(0, \infty)\cos(\Theta_0\tau) + [1 - \Delta(0, \infty)]\sin(\Theta_0\tau)\right\}. \tag{A.44}$$

Equation A.22 already contains an expression for $\Delta(0, \infty)$. That result may be substituted into Eq. A.20 to yield

$$\Xi(0, \infty) = \frac{\iota g \Theta_0}{\iota^2 g + \Theta_0^2} .$$ (A.45)

If the original differential equations 8.84 and 8.85 are now inspected, it can be seen that, for times very short in comparison with T_2, the appropriate limiting form of the equations may be achieved by allowing $\iota \to 0$. This will cause $\Delta(0, \infty)$, $\Xi(0, \infty) \to 0$, and Eqs. A.43 and A.44 will reduce to Eqs. 8.86 and 8.87. Equations 8.86 and 8.87 may be compared with Eqs. 6.203 and 6.204, derived in Chapter 6 under similar assumptions for the magnetic resonance transient nutations. What has been done here is much more general than was done before, however. Using Eqs. A.22, A.25, A.26, A.29, A.30, A.37 to A.40, and A.45 with $\iota = 1$, one may obtain Eqs. 8.88 and 8.89.

Index

1-MONTH